D1587323

/271

NURSERY NURSING

A Handbook of Child Care

FIG. 1   Open air activity with friends.

Nursery Nursing
A HANDBOOK OF CHILD CARE

A. B. MEERING
S.R.N., S.C.M., Health Visitor Cert., M.R.S.H.
Council Member, National Association of Nursery Matrons;
Hon. Member, National Association of Certificated Nursery Nurses.
Formerly Examiner, Royal Society of Health Diploma;
Examiner, National Nursery Examination Board;
and Tutor, Wellgarth Nursery Training College

and

G. E. M. STACEY
S.R.N.
Senior Health Lecturer, Nursery Nurses Training Course,
College of Food and Domestic Arts, Birmingham

Foreword by Dr Ursula Shelley M.D. F.R.C.P.
Physician to the Children's Department Royal Free Hospital,
Queen Elizabeth Hospital for Children, and Princess Louise (Kensington)
Hospital for Children

Fifth Edition

BAILLIÈRE TINDALL · LONDON

© 1971 Baillière Tindall & Cassell Ltd
7 & 8 Henrietta Street London WC2

HANDBOOK FOR NURSERY NURSES

First edition 1947
Reprinted 1949
Second edition 1953
Third edition 1959
Fourth edition 1964

NURSERY NURSING

Fifth edition 1971
Reprinted 1972
Reprinted 1974

ISBN 0 7020 0361   1

Published in The United States by
the Williams and Wilkins Company, Baltimore

PRINTED IN GREAT BRITAIN BY
ROBERT MACLEHOSE AND CO LTD
THE UNIVERSITY PRESS, GLASGOW

Foreword

It is obvious to everybody who takes an interest in the welfare of children of all ages that their care in the early years is of paramount importance. Those girls who train as nursery nurses will have an enormous advantage when their turn comes to raise a family, and this book could remain their reference library for many years after they have passed their final examination or gained a diploma. They may choose to train as a sick children's nurse or to work in a maternity hospital rather than continue to work in a day or residential nursery; in all these differing types of work with children *Nursery Nursing* will remain a valuable friend.

Mrs Meering has had many years of experience in training nursery nurses and in examining them. She knows precisely how to give them the theoretical information which makes their practical training and experience come to life.

That this book is now entering a fifth edition indicates how valuable it has become in the past twenty-three years. The present day awareness of the need for the continuing study of early growth and development is to be found in the increased importance given to this subject in the new edition. Variations of the normal must be understood before abnormality is suspected. Simple disorders must be recognised lest they become more important or dangerous. The framework of the body and its physiology must be understood in simple terms rather than in overmuch detail, while more importance is given to understanding the growth of mental development and maturation.

I believe that this handbook will continue to retain a valuable position on the bookshelf of every student who uses it and everybody who opens its pages will benefit from a study of some part or all of it.

January 1971   URSULA SHELLEY

Preface

The aim of this book is to give student nursery nurses a good basic background of theoretical knowledge, with emphasis on the practical application of both the physical and intellectual aspects of nursery work. Although the book is presented in sections to assist in theoretical and practical teaching, the aim is to ensure that the student realises how closely emotional, intellectual, social and physical growth are dependent on each other. The text covers the syllabus for the National Nursery Nursing Examination Board examination, and also that of the Royal Society of Health Nursery Nursing examination. Nurses may take both qualifications, providing they have had residential experience in the care of children.

It is hoped that this book will also be of value to the many others concerned with the care of children, particularly to the hospital nurse during her time in the paediatric ward and for the young nurse training to serve the community as a health visitor or district nurse.

Since the fourth edition of this book was published it is evident that there have been many changes of thought especially concerning children deprived of a normal home background. In caring for these children there is now a new emphasis and urgency which will be given further impetus when the legislation arising from the Seebohm Report has been implemented.

I invited Mrs G. E. M. Stacey, Senior Health Lecturer of the Nursery Nurses' Department at Birmingham to join me in writing the new edition. With the scope of child care widening all the time her experience has been invaluable in revising the book to meet the needs of students in training today and of parents caring for their own children.

We are most grateful to Dr Ursula Shelley for her continued interest and guidance, and for her kindness in writing the foreword for this new edition. Our thanks must also go to Miss Gardner and the staff of the Chiltern Nursery Training College for their help and kindness when the photographs were taken for this new edition, and to the photographer Mr Grugeon. To the publishers and their staff our grateful thanks for their guidance and help which we have greatly appreciated.

January 1971   A. B. MEERING

Contents

Part Eight

SOCIAL AND WELFARE SERVICES

The Role of the Nursery Nurse

Each child is an individual, and whether he is in a residential nursery, day nursery, nursery at an infant school, with foster parents or at home, he still needs the essentials of a good home background to ensure his complete happiness. To provide this in a nursery is not always easy, but with skill, observation and knowledge, it is possible for a nursery nurse to help the child in achieving a happy and contented attitude to life, which will help him to become a stable and happy adult.

Nursery nursing is a profession, and a well trained nursery nurse is an expert in the care of the normal child under seven years, and consequently she has a wide variety of work open to her. She is also a suitable person to care for handicapped children, enabling them to overcome difficulties, and to grow up into independent individuals. Nursery nurses can become members of the staff of maternity hospitals and children's hospitals and their knowledge of normal babies and young children is a great asset in the care of children in hospital. They are also employed in the infant and handicapped schools to assist the teacher, being responsible under her guidance for the care of the children, their day to day needs and the problems that may occur.

The essential qualities which a good nursery nurse should possess are patience and a happy nature, combined with sympathetic understanding. She must be intelligent, calm and quick to observe and appreciate the needs of children in all sorts of different circumstances and it is always necessary to work in close cooperation with parents. The work, although interesting, is very exacting, and demands a good deal of physical and mental effort; therefore good health is essential for the nursery nurse.

The educational background of the student is important, and the student with the General Certificate of Education or with a good grading in the Certificate of Secondary Education will find the theoretical part of her training reasonably easy. Frequently the girl who has not achieved such a good standard of education is very good on the practical side of the work, but may need to give more time to understanding the theory. Attention to detail in all practical work is most important and supervision is essential.

The period of training can be valuable if the student really enjoys working with children. At the same time as she acquires knowledge she should gain confidence and develop her own personality, and through this be able to give much more to the child.

Class discussions during training are most valuable in developing self expression and confidence. Joint discussions with health and education tutors are essential as the mental and physical aspects are so interwoven. Written questions are also important, and throughout the training the student must be given experience in answering written questions in preparation for her final examinations.

Throughout her training, the art of observing the individual child and groups of children must be practised. The student should write up her observations of the children, and note the various stages of their development. In this way she will realise that each child is an individual, with his own particular abilities and temperament. These observations may be asked for by examiners and inspectors of the National Nursery Nursing Examinations Board.

PART ONE
Growth and Development

CHAPTER 1

The Child and his Parents

Children are born as the result of the love of a man and a woman and they will develop most naturally and best in an atmosphere of love. The child who grows up in a happy home will have tremendous advantages over his less fortunate friends which no amount of money nor the resources of the Welfare State can entirely counterbalance. Where love and the warmth that goes with it is missing, there is bound to be some degree of deprivation to the children concerned.

There are many reasons for this type of deprivation and some may be beyond the parents' control, so not only the child but the whole family should be looked at sympathetically.

Many children come into the world unplanned and unwanted. Their parents may not have mastered the techniques of birth control, or simply are not able to foresee the results of their actions or look beyond the present moment. As a result their families go on increasing; the father's income, in spite of family allowances, does not stretch far enough; and the mother becomes less and less able to cope with her family, so the children suffer. The parents could probably have managed quite well with one or two children, but more than this makes life impossible for them.

Bad housing conditions are another cause of deprivation to the children. Many families are forced to live in one room with inadequate facilities and intolerably cramped conditions, and however hard they try it is often impossible for the parents to surmount their difficulties and provide a reasonable atmosphere for the children to grow up in.

The children of unmarried mothers are frequently at a disadvantage. In many cases they were not wanted, and even with the best will in the world it is very hard for a mother to bring up her child with all the love and attention he needs when she also has to work to earn enough to keep them both.

Then there are the children of broken homes. The tensions and unhappiness between the husband and wife are bound to be felt to some degree by the children, and the tearing apart of their home has a tremendous effect on them. An unhappy marriage that does not in fact break up can be just as disastrous to the children for it is bound to create a background that is just the opposite to the calm and relaxed atmosphere of a happy home.

The illness of one or other of the parents or of a child can so disrupt a home that the children do not know whether they are coming or going, and if a child is handicapped in any way, this too can have very serious consequences not only on the child in question but on the whole family.

If the parents have problems to worry about such as finances or changes of work their preoccupations may affect the children, who could come to feel that their place in the centre of the family had been destroyed.

These are just some of the causes of deprivation and the reasons why some children have problems and why some of them may end up in homes or under local authority care. The great majority of children grow up in happy homes with adequate love and care and are able to develop deep relationships of love and trust within their families and later within the community as a whole.

The first relationship that any child develops is with his mother. During the first weeks of his life she supplies him with all his needs, and at this stage these are simply food and warmth and comfort. Gradually his horizons expand and he begins to notice his father and the other members of his family. He will enjoy watching people and smiling at them and their response to him will lead him on to other interests and exertions. The child who knows he is loved feels secure and will be much more adventurous in trying out new things and responding to new faces.

By the time he is two or three he will be coming into contact with a wide circle of acquaintances outside his own family; the people he meets when he goes shopping with his mother, children of his own age who come to play or whom he may meet at nursery school, and many others, and he is much more likely to be warm and friendly if home is a secure and happy background. If he cannot always be sure of the reactions of his parents he is going to be much more cautious about making contact with other people, however encouraging they may be. The same holds good when he reaches school; he will be in a far better position to make the most of all the new opportunities that are offered to him there if life at home presents no serious problems.

It is not only childhood that is affected by the home; the whole of a person's life can be moulded by his early years, and the disadvantages to someone who for any reason has felt insecure in childhood can be very great, even though they may not be apparent until quite late in life. There are very few people who are not faced with some problem or difficulty at some stage in their life and the way we approach such problems will depend to a considerable extent on how we learnt to deal with them in childhood. Prolonged illness, poverty, separation from family and friends, are bound to cause some distress to almost any one, but the person whose life has been built on a secure childhood will probably be able to come to terms with these things in a more satisfactory way.

One of the hardest things that parents have to learn is how to let go their attachments to their children, how to untie the apron strings when the right time comes. From the moment they enter school children begin to need independence but they still also need strong home ties. Gradually their interests become more and more tied up with their friends, and their home, though still of great importance, begins to play a less obvious part in their lives. Then by the time they reach puberty they have a real need to assert their independence and this is the stage at which so many hitherto happy family relationships begin to run into difficulties. It is impossible to be dogmatic about how such problems should be overcome, but once again we are thrown back to the fact that the child whose relationship with his parents has been from the start reliable and secure, and of equal importance the parent whose own childhood was similarly secure, will be able to manage this stage quite well, and emerge from it still happily linked with each other but in a new and more mature way.

Perhaps the most important thing of all that a happy childhood brings, is the effect it has on the establishment of really firm and lasting relationships in adult life. When two people fall in love, if their love is to last they need to be able to trust each other completely in every way and under any conditions and if they can do this they are in a very good position to begin the whole cycle again and start a family of their own.

The foregoing may suggest that the child whose home is inadequate or nonexistent has a poor chance of ever becoming a mature and satisfactory member of the community. Although his disadvantages should never be underestimated, they can be compensated for by adults who really understand the problems. If for any reason a baby cannot be with his mother during his earliest weeks, then the next best thing is that he should have another adult who is fully responsible for him and to whom he can become attached. He will suffer most if he is endlessly handled by different people and if there is no-one whom he can really feel is his own. The same is true to almost the same extent as he grows older, though as in the case of a normal family there will gradually be room in his life for more people to play a part, providing there is always one stable person to whom he can turn. This is the chief reason why children who for one reason or another come under local authority care are placed in foster homes whenever possible, rather than in residential nurseries, and why within the nurseries, the children are split up into family groups and have their own nurses and their own territory as far as possible. The first aim of any one who has the care of babies and young children should be to see that their lives approximate as far as possible to those of children in a normal home. If this is always kept in mind the children will have every chance to grow up happily and become responsible and independent adults capable of full and lasting relationships and of coming to terms with any situation in which they may find themselves.

CHAPTER 2

The Baby Before Birth

The female reproductive organs

In order to understand the way in which the baby develops in the uterus before birth it is important to have some knowledge of the reproductive organs and how they work. Situated in the lower part of the abdominal cavity, these organs are, internally, the vagina, uterus (womb), two Fallopian tubes, and two ovaries (see Fig. 2); and externally, the vulva.

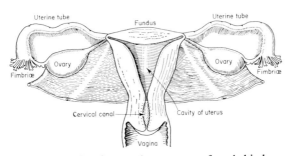

FIG. 2. The female reproductive organs from behind.

Vagina. The vagina is a passage from the uterus to the external skin, its exit is just behind the urethra, it is approximately four inches (10 cm) long, and its walls are made of muscle and fibrous tissue which are capable of very considerable stretching. The walls are normally touching one another, so that it is really only a potential passage which can open when necessary.

Uterus. The uterus is a muscular pear-shaped organ, 3 inches (8 cm) long, 2 inches (5 cm) wide and 1 inch (2.5 cm) thick. It lies behind the bladder and in front of the rectum, and is held in position

by ligaments. The muscular wall of the body of the uterus is constructed to allow the enlargement necessary when it contains the
growing foetus, and also to contract powerfully to push out the baby
at birth. The lower part of the uterus is called the *cervix*; this is
made of muscle and fibrous tissue around a narrow canal leading to
the vagina and capable of stretching when the baby is born.

Fallopian tubes. These are narrow tubes about 4 to 5 inches (10 to
12 cm) long which open into the uterus at one end and into the
abdominal cavity at the other, close to the ovaries. They provide a
passage way from the ovaries to the uterus along which the ova and
the sperm pass in opposite directions. They are lined with cells
bearing cilia, which are hair-like processes which wave rhythmically
helping to push the ova along. The ends near the ovaries are fim-
briated, that is fringed rather like a sea anemone, and these fingers
help to waft the ova into the tube.

Ovaries. The ovaries are small glands situated on either side of the
uterus in the abdominal cavity. They are roughly almond-shaped
and are $1\frac{1}{2}$ inches (4 cm) long. Their function is to produce the ova
or female egg cells, and also to produce the female hormones oestrogen
and progesterone. Oestrogen is responsible for a woman's female
characteristics and causes the bodily changes of puberty, and it is
also responsible for the growth of the uterus and other female organs
of reproduction. Progesterone is needed during pregnancy to produce
substances from the lining of the uterus which nourish the fertilized
ovum. It is also concerned with the development of the breasts in
pregnancy.

The breasts. The breasts are present in an undeveloped state in
both sexes at birth, but develop at puberty only in the female. They
are glands consisting of minute tubules leading to the external surface
in the nipple. The functions of the breast are only associated with
pregnancy and these are brought about through the action of
progesterone. The breasts begin to enlarge during the second month
of pregnancy, and by the end of the fourth month a minute amount
of colostrum is being excreted through the many tiny openings in
the nipple. *Colostrum* is a yellow fluid, similar to but weaker than
breast milk. When the baby is born and begins to suck the breast the
flow of colostrum is stimulated and after two or three days it changes
to milk. In this way the baby's digestive organs are brought into
action. The secretion of milk stops when breast feeding comes to an
end and the breasts gradually return to their normal size.

The menstrual cycle. During the reproductive period of a woman's life, that is the years from puberty to the menopause, an ovum is released from one ovary every 28 days and travels along the Fallopian tube to the uterus. This usually occurs about 14 days before the next menstruation. The ovum cannot move itself but is pushed along by the cilia which line the tubes. The tubes themselves contract and relax and this too helps to propel the ovum on its way. During the first fourteen days of the menstrual cycle, before the ovum has reached the uterus, the wall of the uterus is thickened with spongy tissues through the action of the hormone oestrogen, and this is to provide a bed for the fertilised ovum, should this be required. Once the ovum has been fertilised no more ova will be developed or expelled from either ovary until after the baby has been born. If fertilisation does not occur the ovum disintegrates, as does the lining of the uterus, which contains a very large blood supply, and these are discharged through the vagina forming the menstrual flow. Menstruation generally lasts from three to six days, and when it has stopped and the old lining of the uterus has been shed a new one begins to form. At the same time a new ovum begins to ripen in the ovary so that the whole cycle can begin again.

The male reproductive organs

These organs consist of the scrotum, the testicles and the penis. The *scrotum* is a sac-like fold of skin situated in front of the rectum and behind the penis. Within it lie the *testicles*; these are two glands whose function is to produce the *spermatozoa*. The spermatozoa are microscopically small, each with a minute head and relatively long tail, rather like an elongated tadpole, and they are capable of propelling themselves. They are in a liquid secretion called *semen* and floating in this they leave the testicles through a fine tube, which with blood vessels forms the *spermatic cord*. This passes over the front of the bladder to two small sacs where the semen is stored, and from there it is passed on through the prostate gland into the *urethra*, the passage in the penis. The *penis* is composed of a spongy type of tissue, called erectile tissue which becomes rigid during intercourse and is capable of ejecting the spermatozoa into the vagina. The *foreskin* is a loose fold of skin covering the end of the penis; in some babies it may be too tight, and may have to be stretched or cut away by circumcision.

Fertilisation

While the female produces only one ovum at a time the male

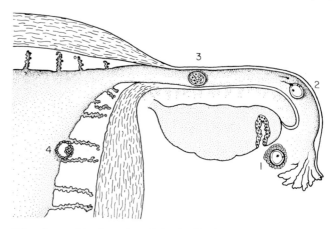

FIG. 3. Migration and implantation of the fertilised ovum. 1, ovum released from the ripe follicle; 2, fertilisation; 3, migration of fertilised ovum (morula) along the uterine canal; 4, implantation of fertilised ovum in the uterus lining.

produces millions of spermatozoa. Once in the vagina they are capable of propelling themselves and swim up it, through the cervix into the body of the uterus and through into the Fallopian tubes. If a sperm meets the ovum, which it does at the outer end of the Fallopian tube, it will penetrate it and thus fertilise it. Although millions of spermatozoa are ejected into the vagina each time intercourse takes place only one will reach the ovum and penetrate it, and even this will only happen if the timing is right. The sperm can only survive for two or three days and the ovum can only survive for a similar length of time after leaving the ovary, so fertilisation can only take place during two or three days in every cycle.

The development of the foetus

From the moment the sperm penetrates the ovum a new life begins. It is known as the moment of conception though it is never possible to tell exactly when it occurred in a particular person.

The ovum is a round cell about the size of a pin head with a central nucleus, while the microscopically small sperm also contains a nucleus. These nuclei contain the *chromosomes* of the mother and father, and these determine the physical characteristics and sex of the child. A chromosome is made up of *genes* and each gene carries one parental characteristic to the child, but there are many combinations of the genes and these are different for each child born in a family. In the case of *identical twins* there is an exception to this rule.

They develop from a single ovum which splits in half after fertilisation and so the genes they inherit are identical. *Non-identical twins* develop when two ova are fertilised at the same time by different sperms; then the resulting children are no more alike than an ordinary brother and sister.

Once the ovum has been fertilised it is pushed along the tube by the action of the cilia and reaches the uterus in three or four days' time. By the end of the first week the united cells have divided many times to form about a hundred cells, and this collection of cells which is rather like a minute raspberry is known as a *morula* (see Fig. 3). Once in the uterus it becomes embedded in the lining which has been prepared for it. When this has happened menstruation ceases to recur and the female hormones now act on the uterine lining to produce the very special type of lining needed for pregnancy known as the *decidua*. It is rather like a nest for the baby to develop in.

The cells continue to divide and to take on special characteristics. Some form the placenta (which later becomes the afterbirth), some become the brain and nervous system, others become the bones, blood vessels, muscles, skin and ultimately every part of the body is formed. By the end of the first month the *embryo* as it is now called is recognisably human, but it still is only ½ inch (14 mm) long. It has a very large head with small folds that will become the ears and eyes and mouth, a heart which beats and a system of blood vessels quite separate from its mother's. It also has a digestive system, kidneys and a liver. The embryo lies in a sac known as the *amnion* and this is full of fluid to protect it and act as a shock absorber until the baby is born (see Fig. 4).

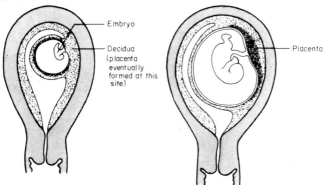

FIG. 4. Foetus and placenta in uterus, early and late stages.

During the second month the embryo comes to look much more like a miniature baby and by eight weeks will be completely formed and will measure about $1\frac{1}{4}$ inches (30 mm). It is attached to the placenta by a stalk that will become the umbilical cord. The placenta is the source of all the baby's needs at this time; it supplies it with oxygen and also carries out the functions of the internal organs such as the liver, kidneys and intestines. It does this by acting on various substances obtained from the mother's blood stream to provide nourishment for the baby, and by disposing of the baby's waste products. At this stage the rapidly growing organs are very vulnerable to outside influences and this is the time when damage can be done by the german measles virus or by the drug thalidomide. From eight weeks the embryo is termed the *foetus*.

In the third month the foetus grows to 3 inches (70 mm) and it begins to move its limbs, but it is still so small that these movements cannot be felt by the mother. The nails appear on the fingers and toes and the eyelids develop, and the nose, ears and mouth take on a much more definite shape. At this stage also the genital organs develop.

By the fourth month the baby will be about 6 inches (140 mm) and should weigh approximately 4 oz (115 g) and during the fifth month he will double this length and become three times as heavy so that he weighs 1 lb (454 g). By now his muscles have become much stronger and the mother may begin to feel his movements. The baby's heartbeat may now be strong enough for a doctor to hear it through a stethoscope. At this stage the hair and eyebrows and lashes are beginning to appear. In the sixth month the baby goes up to $1\frac{1}{2}$ lb (680 g) and will measure about 14 inches (340 mm). His permanent teeth are beginning to form behind his milk teeth, and his skin becomes coated with a thick white cream to protect it from the fluid in the amniotic sac.

During the last three months before he is born the baby is getting ready for life in the outside world. He puts on a great deal more weight chiefly to keep him warm and this means that he is no longer able to move about so freely. By the time he is ready to be born he will probably weigh about $7\frac{1}{2}$ lb (approx. 3.5 kg) and be 20 inches (50 cm) long. During the last few weeks he will receive through the placenta some of his mother's antibodies. These will give him some immunity against various diseases that his mother has had, and should serve to protect him until he has built up his own antibodies.

The baby usually stops growing a week or so before he is born, and the lower part of the baby, normally the head, sinks down into the pelvis.

Throughout the pregnancy the placenta has produced hormones which help to maintain the right conditions for the development of the baby but at the end of 40 weeks its functions are largely over and it begins to degenerate, and this may account for the onset of labour, though this has not been finally proved.

The baby's birth

When the baby is ready to be born the mother goes into labour. It is now the function of the uterus to push the baby out into the world, and as we have already seen its walls are made of muscles with very strong powers of contraction and retraction which enable it to do this. When the muscle fibres have contracted they do not return to their previous shape but retract, that is become shorter and fatter so that gradually the cavity of the uterus becomes smaller and smaller forcing the baby out. In order for the baby to get out of the uterus, its narrow neck, the cervix, has to stretch open. While the upper part is thickening the lower part is thinning out and the hole dilating so that there is a continuous passage for the baby through into the vagina and out (see Fig. 5). It is usually at this stage that the bag surrounding the baby bursts (the rupture of the membranes) as there is no longer anything to support it.

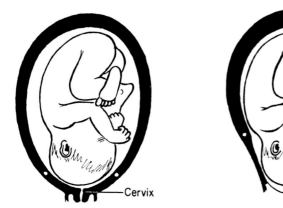

FIG. 5. Changing shape of the uterus and dilatation of the cervix in labour with the baby forced into the birth canal.

Labour

The duration of labour varies considerably and it is impossible to

state an accurate length of time. The average duration for a first baby
is 16 hours but there are wide degrees of variation on either side of
this. For subsequent births the time is usually shorter.

Labour is divided into three stages. The first stage is when the
uterine muscles are contracting up until the time when the cervix
is fully dilated. The mother has no control over this stage of the
proceedings but the second stage involves the actual birth of the baby
when the mother has to combine her own physical efforts at pushing
the baby out with the uterine contractions now known as 'bearing
down pains' which are doing the same thing. Once the baby's head
has been born there is little more effort required as the rest of the
body usually slips out quite easily. The third and final stage of labour
is the expulsion of the placenta; its function is now over for as soon
as the baby is born it starts to breath with its own lungs and is

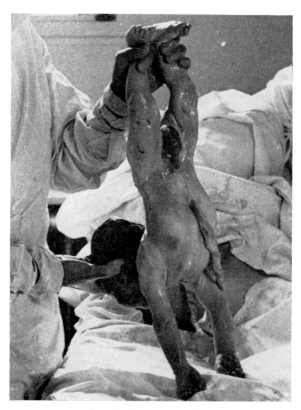

FIG. 6. A new born baby.

capable of taking its own nourishment as soon as it needs it. The cord that joined the baby to the placenta is cut as soon as the baby is born and a small contraction pushes out the placenta shortly afterwards. Fig. 6 shows a new born baby before the cord has been cut.

The new born baby

It is incredible how quickly the baby accustoms himself to his new surroundings. Usually the sudden contact with the air makes him cry and this helps to fill his lungs with oxygen and he begins to breathe. He can and usually does move his arms and legs, and if put to the breast will know exactly what to do.

This account of the ante-natal life of the baby should help to throw some light on the best way in which to deal with very young babies. It is important to remember the tremendous contrast between life in the womb and life in the world, and to realise that the sudden change from the one to the other, however natural it is, must have a profound effect on the baby. He has left behind a place where the temperature was always constant, where he had a confined and secure place, where there were no sudden loud noises, no changes from light to darkness and perhaps most important of all, where he had no needs that were not met with the moment they arose. Mothers and nurses looking after new born babies have to remember all this and do their best to make the baby's arrival in the world as comfortable and secure as possible.

CHAPTER 3

Physical Growth

A healthy, well-nourished and happy mother is likely to have a normal and happy baby. Throughout her pregnancy it is important that she should have good ante-natal care, to ensure a normal confinement and thus give the best possible advantage to the coming child.

The baby at birth is a very helpless creature, being entirely dependent on the adult. Up to this time he has led a sheltered life within his mother, but on entering the world he becomes a separate individual, and must make some effort for himself. These changed circumstances give rise to many and varied experiences, which although taken for granted by the adult, who has forgotten her own sensations at this early age, are real and strange to the baby. After birth the various processes of respiration, digestion, elimination and heat regulation are brought into action, which means that the baby has to learn by degrees to adjust himself. Although he cannot express his needs, he is extremely sensitive to his experiences and surroundings. The baby is quick to sense good handling and affection, and this is important in aiding and in maintaining good growth. He very quickly learns to appreciate gentle but firm handling, the difference between a kind or an angry tone of voice.

Compared with other animals, the human infant is the most helpless and his growth is very slow.

Warmth. There is a violent change of conditions for the baby at birth making it vital that great care is taken to provide adequate warmth for the baby. The child's relatively large surface area in proportion to his weight makes him more susceptible to chills than the adult, and on top of this risk, he has not yet learned to withstand changes of temperature. Warmth with the maximum amount of fresh air is essential, but draughts must always be avoided. Garments of fine wool will allow ventilation while at the same time giving warmth without weight.

Food. The right quality is provided by the mother, and no other humanised milk mixture is as good as nature's food, either from a physical or psychological aspect. The baby can suck well (see Chapter 12) almost as soon as he is born.

Good Hygiene. This is extremely important to the development of the infant, as he has little resistance to infection and any illness will interfere with his normal growth (see page 31).

Types of growth

There are four main types of growth which make up the physical development of the child, and these can be classed under the following headings:

        (*a*) skeletal growth
        (*b*) neural growth
        (*c*) lymphoid growth
        (*d*) genital growth

(*a*) Skeletal Growth

This refers to the development of the whole skeleton, and to the general muscular system. This type of growth is registered by charts

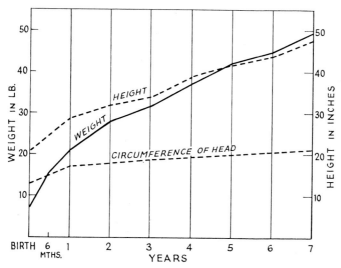

FIG. 7. Chart showing the average height and weight of the child and the circumference of head to seven years.

illustrating the height and weight of the child (see Fig. 7). It must be remembered, however, that babies may vary quite considerably in their rate of growth, and yet be quite normal. Illness and malnutrition affect and impede the formation of healthy bones, muscles and teeth.

(b) Neural Growth

Neural growth is the development of the brain, spinal cord, the eyes, the ears and the skull. At birth these organs are well developed and they continue to grow very quickly until about two years of age, when 60 per cent of complete development has taken place. By seven years they have almost reached the size of the normal adult. See Figs. 7 and 8.

(c) Lymphoid Growth

Lymphoid growth is associated chiefly with the lymphatic glands and the tonsils. This type of development is rapid in the early years; for example, note the relatively large tonsils of young children compared with those of adults. Growth slows down after seven years until puberty is reached. Late in adolescence there is a marked decrease in lymphatic tissue.

(d) Genital Growth

Genital growth, as the name implies, refers to the genital or sex organs. These grow very slowly until about ten years of age, then before puberty and throughout adolescence they develop rapidly. This rapid growth begins rather earlier in girls than in boys (see p. 20).

Weight

The average weight at birth is approximately seven and a half pounds (3.4 kg). The baby doubles his weight between five and six months, and trebles it at one year. By two years he is usually approximately four times his birth weight, at five years about six times his birth weight, and at six to seven years he may be seven times his birth weight. It is valuable to keep a weight chart, which will show the increase over a period rather than only from one week to another. During the first six months the normal weekly gain should be approximately five ounces, and about three ounces from six months to one year (see Fig. 7).

Height

At birth the average length of a baby is approximately twenty inches (50 cm), and by one year is usually about twenty-eight inches (70 cm), showing that the greatest increase in any one year is found in the first twelve months of the baby's life. Throughout certain periods in childhood, for example, from three to four years and from five to seven years, the increase in height is more marked, and these

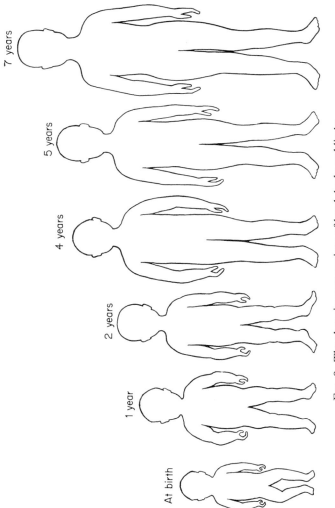

FIG. 8. The changing proportions of head, body and limbs.

times are referred to as springing up periods. Parents often worry at these times because the child appears to be so much thinner on account of the quick growth of the limbs (see Fig. 8).

Size of Head

The size of the head is relatively large in proportion to the body of the child at birth – about thirteen to fourteen inches (33 cm – 35 cm) in circumference, which increases to approximately eighteen inches (45 cm) at one year and about twenty inches (50 cm) by seven years (see Fig. 7).

Fontanelles

There are two fontanelles (see Fig. 9), the anterior and the posterior. The anterior is situated on top of the head. It is a diamond shaped space between the bones of the skull. It is covered with membrane, through which the pulsation of the brain can be felt. This fontanelle gradually closes up as the bones of the skull grow together, which will be at about eighteen months to two years. The posterior fontanelle is triangular in shape and very small. In a healthy infant it closes in six to seven weeks. Late closing of the fontanelles is a sign of poor bone growth and could be an early sign of rickets.

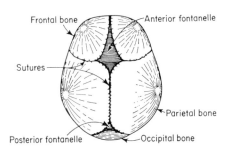

FIG. 9. An infant's head at birth showing the fontanelles.

Proportions of the Baby

It is often stated that the baby is a miniature of the adult, but this is quite untrue. At birth the head is almost one quarter of the infant's whole length, the face is small, the body is large and the limbs short. As the infant grows, there is a marked lengthening of the limbs in proportion to the size of the trunk and the head. Up to seven years of age the growth of both sexes is alike, but towards puberty the girl usually develops rather earlier than the boy.

Teeth

The baby is born with the foundations of both sets of teeth, the first set having developed early in pregnancy, and the second set in the later months. The first teeth are known as 'temporary' or 'milk' teeth and they usually start to erupt at about six months. By twelve months about eight teeth are cut and the complete set of twenty by two years. The usual order of eruption is the two lower central incisors, then the two upper ones, followed by the two upper and the two lower lateral incisors, then the four first molars, the four canines

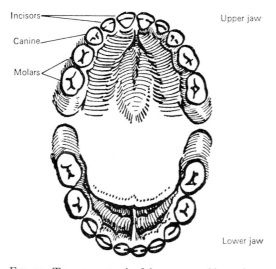

FIG. 10. Temporary teeth of the upper and lower jaw.

and lastly the four second molars (see Fig. 10). Teething is a natural process in the child's development and although it may cause discomfort and feverishness in some children, it is certainly not responsible for all ailments in the first two years of life.

The permanent teeth take the place of the first set which are shed from about six years. At this period there is a marked lengthening and broadening of the lower part of the face, which frequently begins to show a resemblance to some member of the child's family.

The second set consists of thirty-two teeth; four incisors, two canines, four premolars and six molars in each jaw. The first molars are usually the first of the second set to be cut, and the third molars, termed the 'wisdom' teeth are the last to be cut, usually at about eighteen years of age.

As the temporary and the permanent teeth start to develop before birth it is important that the mother has a good diet throughout her pregnancy, and her own teeth must receive special care.

Tooth formation

The crown is the visible part of the tooth, the neck is where the tooth meets the gum, the root or fang is the part embedded in a socket within the jaw bones under the gum. Teeth consist of a very hard substance known as dentine, and in the crown of the tooth there is an outer layer of enamel (which is the hardest substance in the body). The dentine in the root is covered with a hard layer of cement. Each tooth has a small cavity containing nerves and blood vessels, which provide for sensation and nourishment. If the crown is damaged, nerves may become exposed and this will cause pain (see Fig. 11).

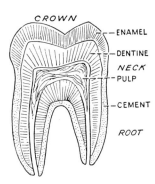

FIG. 11. Section of a tooth showing the structure.

Types of teeth

The incisors have a chisel-shaped crown for biting. The canines have a slightly pointed crown, the premolars or bicuspids have two cusps, or projections, for chewing. The molars are larger with four or five cusps for mastication. The bones of the jaws become more developed from six to seven years, when the second set of teeth begin to erupt (see page 21). It is at this age the first permanent molars appear and these must not be confused with the temporary teeth.

Salivary glands

There are six salivary glands which secrete saliva into the mouth.

This action is stimulated by the sight of attractive food and by the presence of any solids in the mouth. Saliva secreted from glands in the mouth moistens the food and starts the first stage of digestion. The food is passed to the back of the mouth and into the pharynx which, by muscular action, passes it into the oesophagus and on its way to begin digestion in the stomach (see Chapter 8).

Stools

After birth the infant has a few very dark green and rather slimy stools, which are known as meconium. In a few days the normal stool of the baby is pale yellow and of a creamy consistency with a slight odour. The breast-fed baby is often found to have less frequent or smaller stools than the artificially fed infant, due to the more complete absorption of breast milk. The number of stools vary from two to four each day for the infant up to two months, and afterwards one or two stools daily. Gradually the stools become deeper in colour and more solid; by one year they are brown and more formed, with a slight odour. The character of the stools can be altered by the diet, by infections or by some medicines; for example, excess sugar may cause a green stool and iron which occurs in large quantities in spinach and blackcurrants, a black stool.

Urine

Normal urine is a pale, clear, straw-coloured fluid. Any deposits, offensive odours or other marked changes are abnormal. The bladder is small in the infant, with little muscular control and the urine is passed frequently and in small quantities. To pot the baby at regular intervals may sometimes save a wet or dirty napkin, but this is not really training. From about fifteen to eighteen months he begins to know when he wants to pass urine, but if he is busy playing with a new toy, it is usually far simpler to wet his pants than to go and find his pot. By gentle adult encouragement he will gradually learn that it is better and more comfortable to use the pot, but exasperation and annoyance on the adults part usually makes matters worse. Gradually he will learn to control his bladder and bowel action, and by two years he begins to be able to understand and he should be praised, which helps enormously.

At home or in a nursery the child should be taken to the lavatory approximately every $2\frac{1}{2}$ hours. The child in a residential nursery should be encouraged to pass urine about 10 p.m., or if at home before his parents go to bed. The amount of urine passed daily will vary considerably in individuals. This is influenced by the amount of fluid intake, and by the action of the skin, particularly in very hot weather. An infant of six months may pass approximately 8 to 16 ounces, and a child of five years may pass 20 ounces or more. Any abnormal conditions should be reported to the doctor.

Temperature

The normal temperature of the body is 98.4° F (37° C). In the very young baby there may be a slight rise to 99.0° F (37.3° C) which is quite normal. The child's temperature is easily affected and any rise of temperature must be carefully noted (see Chapter 23) and his condition closely observed.

Pulse Rate

To record the pulse accurately it is important that the child should be quiet. In young children it is often found easier to take it at the temporal artery on the side of the forehead without disturbing the infant. For older children the pulse can be taken at the wrist or wherever an artery is near the surface of the skin.

The average rate at birth is	130 to 140 per minute
The average rate at 3 months is	120 to 130 per minute
The average rate at 6 months is	110 to 120 per minute
The average rate at 1 to 2 years is	100 to 110 per minute
The average rate at 3 to 5 years is	90 to 100 per minute
The average rate at 5 to 7 years is	80 to 90 per minute

Respiration

The rate of respiration in the normal healthy infant is approximately 40 per minute, and this is gradually reduced to 24 to 30 per minute at two years of age, and about 24 to 26 per minute by seven years. In some very young babies the respiration may be slightly irregular under quite normal conditions and this must not be overlooked.

The normal adult rate is about 18 per minute. In deep sleep the rate may be slightly reduced, strenuous exercise will increase the rate, and in illness it may become seriously affected (see Chapter 23).

The appearance of the baby at birth

The average healthy child should have bright, clear eyes, glossy hair, straight limbs, firm flesh, good colour and a clear skin. He sleeps well. He is happy and contented, has a good appetite, and breathes through his nose. Interest and intelligence is shown in his expression.

Normal Stages of Development in the First Seven Years

1 month Sucking is usually well established. The baby's wants are made known by crying, his only way of communication. He can turn his head and appear to gaze at a brightly coloured object or a light, but he cannot focus, and so cannot see clearly. As yet he has little muscle tone and his limbs feel soft to the touch. He moves his arms rather more than his legs but with no coordination. If a finger is placed in the palm of his hand he may grip it without using his fingers, then he will quickly let go. The infant can recognise his mother or her substitute by her voice and her handling. He normally will enjoy the freedom of his bath and close contact with his mother. He may cry if handled by an unknown person which is why a baby should be cared for by as few people as possible when he is in a nursery.

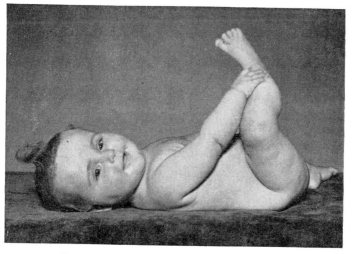

FIG. 12. A well developed three month old baby.

3 months The baby cannot lift his head but there is stronger movement in his arms and legs, which is very noticeable in his bath. He will often show signs of enjoying his bath. He reaches out to try to touch brightly coloured objects or lights, with no idea of distance. He will enjoy the freedom of lying on a rug to exercise his limbs, and he may turn his head. Although he still gets the essential safety and affection from his mother, his interests are now extending to his immediate family. He responds to them by smiling or laughing and sometimes making gurgling sounds when they talk to him or play with him. But he still does not see the features of the face in any detail (see Fig. 12).

4½ months There is marked lengthening of the limbs, the muscles are much firmer, the movements are more definite and quite often these are associated with excitement or pleasure. The infant still grasps with the palm of his hand, but he has a firmer hold, and loves a rattle or a toy which makes a noise. By now he will often turn his head in the direction of a light or sound, such as music or singing, which he seems to like. Loud unexpected noises may frighten him. When lying on his

FIG. 13. An active six month old baby.

back he has become more aware of his feet and enjoys kicking and playing with them, and he makes an attempt to lift his head. He shows an interest in the spoon when being fed and tries to grasp it, thus showing the very early signs of the desire to be independent.

6 months   The proportions of head, body and limbs have completely changed. His legs, arms and body have become longer. The posterior fontanelle should have closed. The child is more active and enjoys being propped up for short periods in his cot or pram; he can roll over on to his abdomen and should be allowed perfect freedom on a rug for short periods or in a play pen (see Fig. 13). His smaller muscles are beginning to develop and he is trying to use his fingers and thumbs. He reaches out to grip things, with little conception of distance, but he cannot as yet coordinate the movements of his two hands, although he tries to clap his hands. He is interested in his surroundings and shows intelligence. By now he gurgles, laughs and makes definite sounds such as 'ma, ma', or 'da, da' which, as yet, have no specialised meaning to the baby. He will be happy and contented in his pram or cot, or exercising on a rug. Teething has started and this may cause him to be fretful at times. He will be having mixed feeding (see Chapter 11). He will smile at members of his family when they talk to him.

9 months   At this stage his interests are increasing rapidly, if the opportunity to explore is provided. He will crawl as soon as his muscles are strong enough, and each child uses his own particular method. Facilities must be provided for the child to exercise at regular times, as part of his daily routine. Suitable play material will stimulate his activity and interests. Exercising with bare feet on a safe flat surface will stimulate his attempts to stand. In the home a play pen can be very useful at this time as this allows the mother to leave her baby in safety. The play pen must be stable and secure ideally with a raised base and with bars not more than $3\frac{3}{4}$ inches apart. Speech may be slowly developing in the form of single words, through copying the adult who should speak to the child when attending to him. He is interested in using a spoon and attempts to feed himself though without much success (see Chapter 12).

1 year   The anterior fontanelle is much smaller and he now has about eight teeth. The normal child can usually stand by himself or pull himself up and may be able to walk with some help at one year. To encourage the baby's confidence, a smooth, plain surfaced floor is

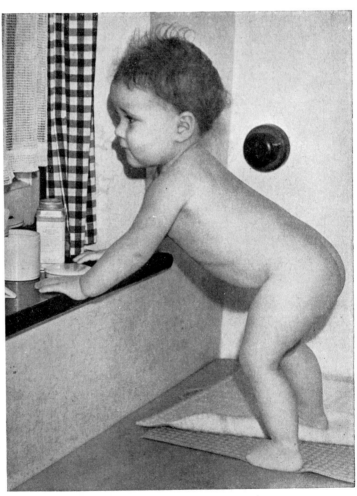

FIG. 14. A well developed one year old child
showing interest in his surroundings.

easy to cope with, and he will manage to grip the floor better if he is barefooted. But care must be taken to ensure there are no dangerous articles about. By now the child is really active in mind and body and should be given suitable play material to encourage activity. Words are developing quickly, his vocabulary is increasing and he chatters quite happily by himself or to a toy. He still has little or no control of bladder or bowel. Control of his eye muscles is developing, although he may squint at near objects. He is eating and sleeping well. He enjoys going out in his pram and may smile if talked to by strangers (see Fig. 14).

15 months Walking should be established and this is always in a forward direction, but he frequently loses his balance. He walks with a wide gait and appears rather flat-footed due to his feet still being short and fat, and his arch muscles are not yet very strong. His interests are varied and he shows definite desires to touch everything or to get things. Speech is progressing, and he is beginning to make his wants known by one or two words, which may mean a whole sentence or a demand. He will begin to understand the meaning of the many words the adult uses when speaking slowly to him.

18 months The anterior fontanelle may have closed and he has about sixteen teeth. By now the child is capable of trotting about and has a definite mind of his own. He should be able to use a spoon and drink from a cup. If given the right environment he should be chattering quite freely in his own way. He may be learning to use a pot in the day time, but life at this stage is so full of fascinating distractions that he may often forget or remember only when it is too late.

2 years At this age he may have his first set of 20 teeth and the anterior fontanelle will be closed. His muscles are firmer and he is capable of running quite quickly, and he also has better control over his smaller muscles such as those in his fingers. He is happy and very active exploring his ever enlarging world. Clean habits are gradually becoming established, and he is eager to do things for himself. As yet he has little idea of any social behaviour and when with other children is usually only concerned about his own affairs. His vocabulary is increasing and his speech is clearer and he will derive great pleasure out of communicating with other members of his family.

2–5 years Although the general physical growth is less rapid than in the first two years of life, this is still a fast growing period. The child is now more active and interested; he is slowly becoming more independent and is gradually learning to play with one or more children. Between three and five years there is a marked growth of limbs which makes him seem thinner although he will have put on weight. Finer muscular development is also progressing during this period which can be seen as the child becomes more adept in difficult movements such as using a paintbrush or a pair of scissors, and in managing buttons or tying up his laces.

FIG. 15. Physical activities.

FIG. 16. Physical activities.

He is beginning to ask a whole series of questions about life in general some of which require answers far too complicated for him to understand. He can benefit from attending a nursery school, if only for a few hours daily, and his father can encourage him by playing games with him and by being a real companion to him at home. He will enjoy going out for walks with his family (see Figs. 15 and 16).

5–7 years Within this age range children vary very much in their stature. After the springing up period at about three years anatomical growth slows down until five years of age, when another springing up period occurs. At about six to seven years the child's jaw will be increasing in size in preparation for his second set of teeth, which will be beginning to erupt. The feet are more muscular and the arches are stronger and more pronounced. Good environment with suitable activities are as important as ever at this stage. In providing these things not only must the child's age be considered but also the development of his brain (his mental age). With the start of school usually a new maturity and independence becomes apparent. Hand and eye coordination progress so that the child can throw or kick a ball roughly in the right direction, and usually manage to catch it. It is now evident that he

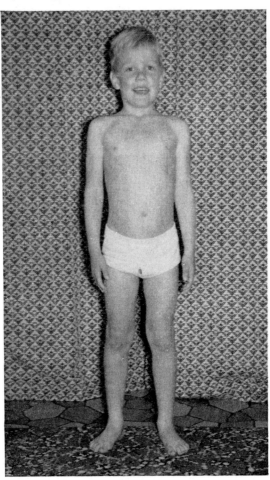

FIG. 17. An active and healthy seven year old with
poise and confidence.

uses a pencil in a more adult fashion and requires large sheets of paper. At this stage too he learns to take part in games with other children (see Fig. 17).

Posture

Posture is a term used to describe the manner in which the child walks, stands, sits and his general carriage. Much will depend on his general health and particularly on the tone of his muscles. The child should stand erect, his head up, the chest out, the shoulders back and with firm muscles holding his abdomen in position. The curves of the back develop gradually in the first few years, but if any exaggerated condition of the spine is present, then a doctor must be consulted. Well-shaped and comfortable footwear will help tremendously in promoting good posture. The sitting position is influenced by the relative size of the chair and the table which the child uses and a slouching position must be discouraged, as this is extremely bad for chest development. It is more comfortable and better for the child to sit with his feet easily reaching the floor, rather than having his legs dangling.

To stand, walk and sit correctly means that the muscles are supporting the whole body without unduly straining any particular set of muscles. In this way the muscles do their real work, and fatigue due to strain is prevented, thus encouraging good health.

If the child has made steady, normal progress in all types of growth, including mental development, he will be happy, and secure. These feelings, combined with the joy of life, all tend to help him to develop a graceful carriage, good poise and confidence.

General requirements for growth

Good nutrition, fresh air and sunlight, exercise with adequate rest and sleep, are all important factors in relation to growth. These combined with good environment, freedom and affection must all work in harmony to achieve the best results. Any lack of good conditions will hamper both the physical and the mental progress of the child. Naturally the detailed needs of each individual child will vary according to the age and personal requirements. From the very early days the adult, whether mother or nurse, must carefully observe the infant and then provide whatever is necessary for his development. This need not involve expensive and elaborate equipment, but rather the simple type of materials used in any good home, combined with good care and affection.

Illness may arrest the growth and may impair or even handicap the child for life. Therefore it is important to take all precautions to prevent illness of any kind affecting the child. Young children should never be taken into crowded and badly ventilated halls, such as cinemas, as there could be a great risk of infection in such conditions. The maximum of fresh air and sunlight is essential to maintain health and to prevent disease.

Routine

For children of any age a regular routine is of very great value in promoting a happy and secure childhood. It is good for the physical and mental needs of the child. Through the application of a good routine which, however, should be flexible, the whole body benefits. Good feeding habits enable the digestive system to function well, which in turn helps the excretory system and so the good effect goes on through the whole body.

When planning a routine for any young child, it is essential to consider the child's basic needs, for example, food, activity and sleep, and at the same time not to forget the other members of the family and their requirements, as the young child is a member of the family and not a separate individual. Meal times can be the chief focus when planning the routine. These must be suitably spaced throughout the day to ensure that the child will be hungry, so that he will accept food willingly and thus enjoy it. Meals under these circumstances will become happy times to which he will look forward.

Activities will occupy a fairly large part of the morning and the afternoon; consequently a young toddler will need a rest or sleep before the midday meal to avoid over-tiredness, with a short rest in the afternoon. The older child will only require a short rest in the afternoon. Following this there should be time allocated for play in the open air, weather permitting, before the third meal of the day. This should be followed by a quick period in preparation for bed at a reasonable time. This is important, as it allows the parents and other members of the family to relax and enjoy each other's company in the evening, and to be free to enjoy visitors. In principle, this also applies to the staff of residential nurseries.

At the same time the child learns the routine of the day and gradually he can understand and cooperate with the adult.

Suggested routine for the baby up to 6 months:

It is not imperative that a baby should be fed at 6 a.m., but it is essential for him to be fed at regular intervals or when he is hungry. Gradually by the end of the first month, he usually wants food at regular intervals. Variations in infants is quite normal. Some mothers find it convenient to start the day at about 6.30 a.m. or 7 a.m., and adjust feeding times accordingly.

6.30 a.m. approximately		Change napkin and wash hands and feed baby. Change napkin again if necessary.
8.0 a.m.	,,	Mother's breakfast.
9.15 a.m.	,,	Prepare for bathing; strip cot. Allow baby to exercise on rug or play pen or on knee. Bath baby. Feed baby and get his wind up. Settle baby in pram out of doors, if possible. Change napkin when necessary.
1.0 p.m.	,,	Mother's lunch.
1.40 p.m.	,,	Change napkin and feed baby, gradual introduction of solids. Allow exercise. Settle baby in pram or cot.
2.0 p.m.	,,	Mother should rest, if possible.
3.0 p.m.	,,	Take baby for walk in pram, and allow freedom on rug at home.
4.0 p.m.	,,	Return – attend to any needs of the baby.
4.30 p.m.	,,	Mother's tea.
5.15 p.m.	,,	Mother prepares for baby's evening toilet. Baby has exercise. Face and hands washed – attention to buttocks. Feed and settle in cot for night.
10.0 p.m.	,,	Change napkin – feed if necessary.

It is necessary to change the baby's napkin between the specified times, when he is wet or soiled. Opportunity must be given for adequate exercise according to his age and the development of the baby.

Never attempt to settle a baby in his cot after a feed until he has got his wind up. (See Chapter 9.) A baby fed by demand feeding methods usually follows a similar routine to that suggested above after the first few weeks. It is important to remember that the baby's routine has to be fitted into the normal routine of the home. Some young mothers are dismayed by the amount of time their first baby seems to consume, and often need reassuring that it will soon be much easier than at first.

Suggested routine for a child of 9 months to 2 years:

7.30 a.m. approximately		Drink of fruit juice on waking. Morning toilet.
8.15 a.m.	„	Breakfast with mother or family. Has a crust to chew, placed in high chair with support. Sits on pot, hands and face washed. Dressed.
9.0 a.m.	„	Period of exercise and play – in the open air, when possible.
10.0 a.m. – 11.0 a.m.		Rest or sleep – in open air if possible.
11.45 a.m.	„	Exercise and preparation for dinner.
12.15 p.m.	„	Midday dinner with mother.
12.45 p.m.	„	Uses pot, hands and face washed.
1.0 p.m. – 2.0 p.m.		Rest and sleep.
2.0 p.m. – 4.0 p.m.		Periods of exercise and play, with opportunities to lie down or sit down when necessary – preferably in the open air. An outing in the pram is valuable contact with everyday life. Prepare for tea.
4.15 p.m. approximately		Tea. Pot; hands and face washed.
5.0 p.m.	„	Mothering – quiet play – bathing, bath play and preparation for bed.
10.0 p.m.	„	Sit on pot (most children scarcely wake up and their night's rest is not disturbed). Feed if necessary.

Extra visits to the lavatory and changing may be necessary.

Suggested routine for child of 2–5 years:

7.0 a.m. – 7.30 a.m.	Drink of fruit juice or piece of apple or piece of orange. Play with toys in bed. Toilet, hand washing, face and teeth. Dressing.
8.15 a.m. – 8.45 a.m.	Breakfast with family.
8.45 a.m. – 9.15 a.m.	Toilet and hand washing.
9.15 a.m. – 11.45 a.m.	Freedom for play – out of doors when weather permits; otherwise periods with variety of play materials available, such as stories, modelling, painting, looking after living and growing things, music, sing-

	ing, dancing, etc., or games in small groups.
	Helping mother about the house or with the shopping. Drink of milk or orange at some stage.
11.45 a.m. – 12.15 p.m.	Toilet and preparation for dinner. Helping to prepare the dinner table.
12.15 p.m. – 12.45 p.m.	Dinner.
12.45 p.m. – 1.15 p.m.	Toilet and hand washing.
1.15 p.m. – 2.15 p.m.	Rest in open air, if weather is suitable.
2.15 p.m. – 4.30 p.m.	Occupations should vary from those of the morning. Most mothers get their housework done during the morning and are freer to do specific things with their children in the afternoon such as a walk or a trip to the play ground.
4.30 p.m. – 4.45 p.m.	Preparation for tea.
4.45 p.m. – 5.15 p.m.	Tea.
5.15 p.m. – 5.45 p.m.	Story telling or quiet reading.
5.45 p.m. – 6.30 p.m.	Bath. A drink of milk with a biscuit, etc. Teeth cleaning.
10.0 p.m.	Pot or lavatory if necessary.

Arrangements should be made for the child who needs to pass urine during the night. An older child will be capable of going to the lavatory himself, and a small light should be left on to prevent him bumping himself or falling down on the way.

The suggested programmes have been planned to fit into residential nurseries, day nurseries, nursery schools, as well as the ordinary home. It will be noticed that the meal times are regular, and the programme for the day revolves round these times. Other important factors are the provision of good open air exercise, without causing any undue fatigue, rest and sleep, and a free choice of suitable occupations which will help the development of the child.

It is essential for all children under five years to have a period of rest some time during the day. This, when convenient, can be taken in the open air. The stretcher bed should be a few inches off the ground and be equipped with two blankets, one to lie on and the other for a cover. Naturally in hot weather he will not need the top blanket, but if he goes to sleep and the sun goes in, as it often does in our climate, it is safer to cover him to avoid chilling.

In cold or damp weather it is safer to have the child under cover, or inside the nursery, which should be well-ventilated.

Throughout the day children are very active and can become tired without realising it, therefore small chairs and settees should be provided to encourage them to sit down and look at books and do other restful things. Although a child will often sit on the floor if he has an interesting thing to play with, he should get into the habit of using a chair as well.

FIG. 18. Children at play in the open air.

Open air exercise is valuable and should be encouraged, provided the child is clothed suitably for the weather. A wide variety of equipment to give the children a choice between something new or an old favourite makes this much more fun (see Fig. 18).

For the young child just beginning to walk, a toy pushcart that gives him a little support will help him to develop confidence, and make brave excursions on his own. The ground should be fairly level for such exercise. Pull-along toys at a slightly later date will be an incentive to a great deal of running around.

Most children will vary their activities, automatically taking a quieter exercise after a strenuous game, which is what nature intended them to do. Set physical exercises are quite unnecessary for normal children, and may even do more harm than good.

From five to seven years there is a very marked growth of the limbs, which gives the child a more elegant and mature stature. During this period the jaws make rapid growth, in preparation for the increased number of teeth in the second set. In these two years the rather chubby child develops into a confident happy individual.

The activities also take a more mature form, according to their sex.

For the child to get most from his play he must be suitably clothed. Activity requires freedom, therefore garments must be well cut, of the right shape and size and washable, and must provide the necessary warmth and comfort.

The following play equipment will encourage valuable exercise and interests for all children, without much cost.

Wooden planks – to make see-saws, bridges, etc. A pair of steps and a plank can be used as a slide.

Tree trunk and a plank can be used as a see-saw.

Strong wooden boxes, either with or without wheels.

Spades and buckets or old enamel bowls.

Balls, bats or rackets.

Bicycle or tricycle.

Sand pit.

Bath with water.

Rubber tyres.

Tent.

Dressing-up clothes.

Equipment for domestic play, cups, etc., table, tea-party equipment.

Dolls, pram.

All play grounds, whether at home or in a nursery or nursery school, must have all play equipment inspected regularly to avoid accidents. Cleanliness is important to avoid infection. All gates must be securely fastened to prevent any child from straying on to the road.

The adult responsible for the child should explain and show him how to cross the road. The Royal Society for the Prevention of Accidents will demonstrate this to children in a nursery.

CHAPTER 4

Intellectual Growth

Mental development is classed under three main groups, namely,
intellectual, emotional and social. Although they are discussed
separately, each is dependent on the others and good health is
essential to all.

The importance of mental growth cannot be over-estimated.

As stated in Chapter 2, exercise is necessary for good physical
growth. In the same way, the brain must be used and facilities must
be provided to ensure that the child is given the opportunity, encouragement and guidance he requires. The well-developed child is
much more likely to be a happy child, who will in the future, become
a good citizen, because he is capable of adjusting himself to his
surroundings and to other people.

Intellectual Development

Intelligence is necessary to enable children to learn:

(*a*) to control and direct muscular activity;

(*b*) to adapt behaviour to particular and varied situations, in
which they find themselves.

(*c*) to conform to certain accepted standards of social and emotional
behaviour.

The development of intelligence is influenced by health, environment and inheritance.

The growth of intelligence is influenced by a healthy brain, which
is relatively large in the new born baby and continues to make rapid
growth up to seven years, when it is almost as large as that of the
adult. This, however, does not mean that the intelligence of the child
is fully developed in any way in comparison with the mature adult.

At birth, the senses of the baby, being well-developed, help to make all his experiences valuable to him from his actual birth, and every thing that happens to him will have some effect on the growth of his intelligence. In his early weeks he is most sensitive to his only real needs, good handling, feeding, warmth and comfort. All of them convey affection and give him great pleasure. As the baby's physical growth progresses, gradually his activities will be associated with his experiences.

A healthy baby born into a good home will have a very good start in life (see Chapter 1). The child handicapped by poor health, poor vision or blindness, defective hearing, or by deformed limbs or internal organs, will, because of his handicap, have limited experiences. Such a child even with a well developed brain cannot learn and make as speedy progress as a normal child. Neglect in early diagnosis of defective hearing or sight, for example, could lead a child to be wrongly classed as mentally subnormal. In most cases of physical deformity he will grow up though he may be backward because of his difficulties in learning. The mentally handicapped child on the other hand, can seldom become intellectually fully mature, though great strides forward in some types of mental illness in children are being made, and the outlook is much more hopeful than it used to be.

At birth the baby is helpless and incapable of any coordinated movements, or of maintaining himself. Within the short span of seven years he becomes an independent little boy or girl with a personality of his own.

The newborn baby is faced with a tremendous task, that of bringing the complicated structure of his whole being into action. Some infants cry as soon as their head is born, showing a good healthy response to changed circumstances. Others may be slower in getting going, possibly due to influences during birth. Much of his behaviour immediately after birth will depend on the functioning of the nervous system. The young infant can swallow, vomit, cough, yawn, suck, grasp, cry, pass urine, pass meconium or faeces and move his limbs in an aimless manner. All these actions are movements which take place independently of the will, and are a response to a stimulus from a receptor, such as a sense organ. They are known as reflex actions. These activities are valuable in helping to stimulate the brain, which grows very quickly in the first year, and this encourages the development of intelligence.

Sensitivity

Although the baby is extremely helpless in his early weeks he is most sensitive and will quickly know his mother or her substitute by her handling and her voice, and because of this be contented and happy. He is very aware of his needs, and will soon make his wants known by crying. This behaviour should not be mistaken for naughtiness, as it is the only way that the infant can make his wants known. By careful observation the adult quickly learns the cause of his crying. As one would expect, the hunger cry is the most demanding one, often accompanied by sucking of fists. Food must be given in response to such behaviour, otherwise the baby will feel frustrated and angry and may refuse food when it is offered later. The periods between the demands for food will vary considerably, when the baby is very young. The pleasure he derives from sucking is important to him at this time, and this emotion quickly turns to love when his need is satisfied. Discomfort is a common cause of crying and some babies feel this very acutely, but as soon as attention is given they settle quite quickly.

Another important cause of crying is loneliness, and a child crying for this reason is often mistakenly thought to be spoilt. If the baby is awake and cannot hear anyone about he will think he is alone and may cry until he is reassured. For this reason it is always kind to speak to him when passing the cot. Failure to appreciate this need could be responsible for difficult behaviour later, or the cause of problems in adolescence and in later life.

The first impulsive movements of the baby are constantly repeated and he gains much satisfaction in this way. The activity gives rise to sensory experience, which is most valuable to him in the growth of his intelligence. At first his mouth is the most developed sense organ; every thing is carried to it and hands are only accessories. By sucking and chewing and feeling objects, small babies gradually come to terms with different textures, shapes and sizes. The child soon becomes aware of his limbs and takes great delight in managing to get his toes in his mouth long before he is able to sit up.

By about two to three months the baby's intelligence is increasing very rapidly and he is beginning really to use his hands. With the help of suitable toys such as a rattle with a thin handle, which he can grasp comfortably or a small colourful brick, he is learning various movements. As his sight becomes clearer he is attracted by bright colours and often takes notice of a shining object such as his mothers glasses.

Awareness of other people

The very young baby's interests are centred entirely on his mother or her substitute. She is the only person who matters to him because she satisfies all his needs, and he recognises her handling and knows her voice. Very gradually, however, he becomes more aware of his father, who should as far as possible take an active part in the baby's life. The baby will come to know his father's voice and will respond by smiling or laughing when he talks or plays with him. Soon he becomes aware of the other members of the family, and quickly accepts them and will respond to any attention they give him. In this way the baby learns the art of making friends, thus enabling him to form good relationships in adult life.

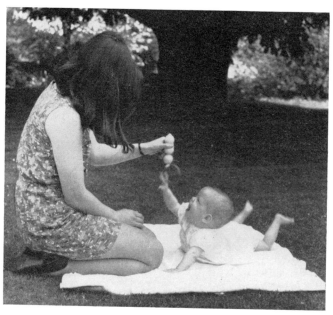

FIG. 19. The child's interests are awakening.

Later, through more contacts with the outside world, his interests expand beyond his own family circle. The average baby will enjoy admiration from a stranger when out in his pram with his mother, and he will be interested in his surroundings, but even if the child is intelligent and friendly, it is important not to overtax him with too much excitement at an early age.

As the child's contacts with other people increase and his interests develop, the mother must accept this as the beginning of a new stage in his development, in which he will want to be more independent of her. Nevertheless he still wants to know that she is at hand to help him when he meets a situation which is new to him, and for this he needs her affection and understanding as much as ever. It is often at this stage that the mother resents the child growing up and away from her, because she thinks she is losing his affection and she may react by over mothering him. In this way she may be creating much unhappiness for herself and the child, as by limiting his experiences and forcing him to remain dependent on adults he is unable to develop as he should.

Sight

At birth the eyes are open and there is a reflex action to a bright light, shown by closing the eyelids. In the beginning the baby appears to look but cannot make his eyes focus. Gradually he begins to notice bright colours and may move his eyes trying to follow them but he probably does not see a clear outline of the object. By about three months he will turn his head when he is talked to, thus following the direction of the sound, but is doubtful whether he sees any details of the face. Following this stage he will sometimes notice if his mother is wearing glasses, and may try to reach for them though with no idea of distance. By about six months he begins to focus properly but tends to squint at nearby objects, as he has not yet learnt to control both eyes at the same time. From now on he makes rapid progress and at 9 to 10 months he is capable of seeing quite small objects, for example a pin on the floor. Sometimes he can manage to pick it up, but tends to drop it again. Apparent lack of interest when shown light coloured toys, may be due to defective vision rather than to low intelligence, or may simply show a preference for brightly coloured things. Careful observation should reveal the cause so that treatment can be prescribed if necessary.

Defective vision can also retard the child's general intelligence and development. Abnormalities in vision, for example very long or very short sight, can usually be noticed by close observation.

Hearing

At birth the baby responds to sudden and loud noises by blinking or jerking his head. From the second month he can recognise a well-known voice, for example his mother, and gradually begins to recognise familiar sounds associated with his own personal attention. At six months the baby will look in the direction of sound and usually shows pleasure on hearing a known voice, or he may respond to music or singing. This interpretation of appreciation of sound develops quickly in the first year, and plays a large part in promoting good intellectual growth. It must be remembered that unusual and very loud noises can give rise to fear, and cause crying. Defective hearing will be apparent through a lack of response to the adult, defective speech or poor intellectual development, and any such indications must be investigated.

Smell

Smell is thought by some people to be undeveloped at birth but this is very difficult to assess in the infant. Quite young children use the action of smelling, but because their experience and intelligence are limited, it is difficult for a child under three years to express what he smells, or to distinguish various odours. Quite often the young child will try to copy the action of the adult, for example smelling a flower but how much he actually smells is questionable.

Taste

Taste is certainly appreciated at a very early age; a young baby will often accept sweetened water and refuse plain, and very soon after the start of mixed feeding some babies show marked preferences for certain flavours. In some cases, though, it may be the texture rather than the flavour that is objected to.

Some children can be difficult about trying out new foods possibly because of their different colour or general appearance, and it is usually best not to force them but to try again at a later stage.

Learning to move about

The child's movements help to develop his interests, and the reverse is true, as an interest in things will encourage him to start moving. Providing he is given freedom to exercise, this continued practice will lead to the beginning of coordination between his muscular and nervous systems. Children vary very much in the type of movements they use; for example, one child will start to crawl in his own particular way and in time by his method and be capable of quite speedy movements, whilst another child will not succeed in crawling but may find it easier to achieve the ability to balance and thus stand earlier than the other. It is therefore obvious that normal babies pass through the various stages at different rates. By one year of age the average child can usually stand, or even take a few steps if he has had opportunities to use his body, developing confidence and skill. A little encouragement and assurance from the adult, but without real interference, will help to promote further efforts. As he cannot concentrate for more than a few minutes, the young child is constantly changing his interests from one toy to another, or to anything which happens to attract him. After walking is established there is a whole new field of movements to master, such as running, jumping, climbing, riding a tricycle or toy, sliding, hopping and dancing. Gradually good coordination makes his movements become almost automatic.

Slow development of movement may be due to many causes, quite apart from illness. The child may lack confidence because he has never been allowed to make any effort for himself and thus starved of opportunity, will be slow in action though his intelligence may be good. Fear which may be the result of lack of affection, or bad conditions at home might retard development for a time, and too many diversions can have the same result.

From the very beginning the adult should encourage or create an incentive for good movement. She should allow the child to make an effort to reach for something he wants rather than simply handing it to him, and encourage him to go one step further before taking his hand, because achieving things on his own is both thrilling and satisfying for him.

Using hands and fingers

At birth the thumbs and fingers are not under the baby's control. After a few weeks the fingers are used for feeling, for example, the infant can often be seen touching one hand with the other, and he can be seen examining his legs and feet. It is essential for him to learn about himself and he should be free to do this. He sometimes tries to bite or chew his toes. Gradually he learns to grasp and later to let go. From about six months onwards he will be seen to pick up and hold things, such as a spoon or a small brick, and by nine months he reaches out for anything which may attract him. Throughout his first year he is constantly feeling and handling materials such as rattles, spoons, cups, small bricks, clothing, his cot, or his mother's person. In this way he is constantly learning about things in common use, and gaining experience.

His intellectual development progresses as he is given the opportunity to compare one thing with another. After repeated trial and error he finds out that a small tin will go into a big one, but that the big one will not go into the smaller one. Exploring the things around him stimulates his curiosity and helps to make him more adventurous

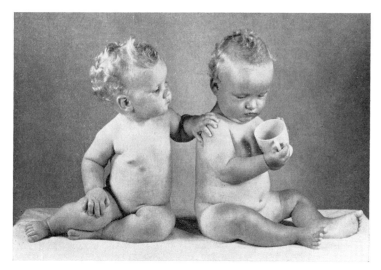

FIG. 20. Whatever is it?

in experimenting with his toys, thus developing his powers of observation, concentration and reasoning. During this period his powers of concentration are still very limited and he is still very dependent on adults, but he must be allowed the opportunity and freedom to use his experience. From about nine months onwards he can bang with a spoon and show great delight in his achievement. His small muscles are now coming into action. This process carries right on into maturity and even after, according to each individual's capabilities and training.

Development of speech

From birth the infant will make all sorts of vocal sounds, and can within a few weeks indicate his wants by his cry, which will gradually become more descriptive of his feelings.

Through speech the child can acquire knowledge, make social contacts, make demands, or express his needs, his loves and hates. He learns to relate experiences or to tell an imaginary story and gradually he will present ideas and simple reasoning. Speaking is a complicated muscular action, which forces air through the vocal cords and thus produces sounds.

The young infant gurgles and coos in the early months and the vowel sounds, such as 'a' and 'o' are usually the first to be used

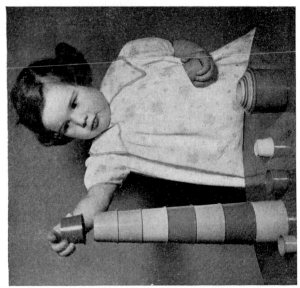

FIG. 22.   Age two and a half years – showing good muscular coordination.

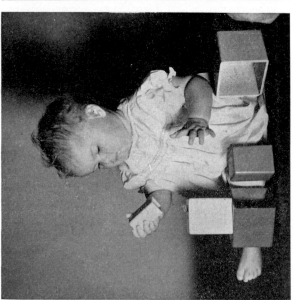

FIG. 21.   Age fifteen months – 'Where shall I put it?'

because they are easy to master. Next, the consonants with the vowel, for example 'Ma, ma, da, da' which is universal. Each parent is always delighted to hear such chatter, although to the child it has little meaning in the sense of real speech. The infant should be talked to as much as possible so that he becomes interested in speech and by seven to eight months is trying to imitate and to make definite sounds. The adult can be a great help at this stage by linking objects with their names so that the child begins to associate the word with its object and points to it before he can say it properly himself. By a year he can usually say single words and pronounce and use them intelligibly. When one word is achieved it is repeated many many times until it is distinct and intelligible.

After this, the child will begin to use two words together and gradually he starts to use short phrases or sentences. By eighteen months chattering is usually established, and the child will talk away to toys, or perhaps to an adult, although he does not really expect an answer. His vocabulary is still very restricted, but the child understands many more words than he actually uses himself, as is the case with most grown ups. At this age children have the most fascinating pronunciation for words, but this should not be encouraged or ridiculed. The adult should not use baby talk when chatting to the child, as it is of no advantage to the child to learn that a horse is a gee-gee and then later have to forget gee-gee and learn the word horse.

Some children find difficulty in pronouncing certain consonants, for example 's', 'th' or 'f'. This in some instances may be due to lack of effort on the child's part or to the fact that he hears careless speech. Anyone speaking to a child or speaking in his hearing must speak clearly and simply, as the child learns to speak only by copying what he hears. This also applies to grammar and the correct formation of a sentence. The child should be familiar with the sound of correct speech right from the start. Some children are extremely late in talking, three years old or even later, but when they do start they usually make very good headway, often using sentences from the beginning.

Intelligence and speech are closely related and dependent on each other. Speech usually develops more quickly in a home where there are older children, as the younger child will benefit from hearing and joining in the talk of the other members of the family. The companionship, for example in a nursery or nursery school, is helpful to speech development. The greater the opportunities to use and understand speech the wider the knowledge the child will gain. Intelligent conversation with the child encourages a more fluent vocabulary.

Good, well-chosen picture books, nursery rhymes, and story telling are of great value in promoting the command of speech.

Slow development of speech may be due to lack of opportunity to hear and copy speech, or lack of incentive to ask because the child's every need is anticipated. Often the mother or nurse does not realise that it is her responsibility to provide a pattern. Anxious parents by trying too hard or too soon may also hinder the development of speech. It is important to remember that persistant mispronunciation by the child may be caused by low or high pitched deafness or by some degree of deafness. Very careful observation is necessary sometimes to detect speech defects. The mentally retarded child is invariably slow to develop speech. If the adult is in any doubt about the child's ability to hear, expert advice must be obtained to prevent any unnecessary retardation (see Chapter 19).

Stuttering may frequently be caused by excessively proud parents who want to show their child off to their friends. He then becomes self-conscious, fearing ridicule, hating it when people laugh at him and worried that he will be unable to reach his parents' standards. The vocabulary even of an intelligent child is very limited and his mind may race on far beyond his vocabulary making him stammer in an attempt to say what he wants to. Shock from an accident, illness or an unhappy home can all cause this nervous condition, but with good care it can usually be overcome. When in doubt it is wise to have an expert's opinion.

During his first year while the baby is still totally dependent on the adult his mind does not appear to develop as fast as it does at a slightly later stage, when he can move about by himself and make use of the experience he is acquiring all the time. When he begins to talk there is further stimulation to intellectual ability and one stage in this development is when he begins to relate past experience to present circumstances. The power to do this varies in different children and it is impossible to state any definite age by which a child will have reached an exact stage of development, although most children follow a similar pattern at slightly different rates. Throughout the growth of intelligence the child's personality begins to show and at this stage certain hereditary traits of character may begin to manifest themselves. Occasionally great skill and understanding are necessary to guide these into channels which help rather than hamper the child.

The child's intellectual growth and behaviour depend to a large extent on the provision of suitable play things, on a good environment and on his contacts with the grown up world.

FIG. 24. Persistence – succeeding and achieving.

FIG. 23. Persistence – using hands and feet (1 year).

C

Learning to think and learning muscular control

Learning to think can be a very complicated process. In the beginning the child knows something is there only if he can see it and will forget about it only if it is out of sight. Gradually he learns that the article can still be there even if it is covered up. Adults when playing with a child will often hide a toy for a minute. The child's expression shows that he thinks it has gone, and when it reappears he shows surprise and great delight. In time he learns that a toy might be hidden and he will try to find it.

By about eighteen months he can usually run around quite quickly but he will frequently sit down to investigate something he has noticed. He can only concentrate for a very limited time, and his attention changes with astonishing rapidity.

FIG. 25. Care is needed but independence should be encouraged.

In the latter half of his second year his leg muscles gradually come under his control, and he can walk and run quite quickly with a closer gait. All the time he is investigating new things. He will resent interference from another child when he is playing. Up to now his interest in other children is simply one of curiosity rather than companionship. He will play with his mother or father or other members of the family for short periods. This family play is the early beginning of a really good relationship, and this is most essential for true happiness in life.

FIG. 26. Becoming independent.

Until they are two years old children tend to play alone, but gradually they will begin to show interest in what other children are doing and will join in with them. They often use simple play materials with great ingenuity; a cardboard box becomes a boat one minute and a cooking stove the next, while a strip of wood alternates between a race track for small cars and a sword. It is very seldom that the happy child will really lack adequate exercise, and his abilities quickly increase. Water is utterly fascinating to him and offers endless scope for sinking things, floating things, pouring and splashing.

Independence is gradually developing and shows in the child's attempts to do things for himself, such as dressing and doing his hair and washing his hands (see Fig. 26). He should be encouraged in this and in anything else he can learn to do. Imitation of other children spurs him on to acquire new skills; the art of jumping off a step without falling over, of riding a tricycle and making it go at least roughly in the right direction, of pouring water from one container into another and actually getting some of it in, and countless other games and activities.

These early years are the most impressionable of a child's life and it is no exaggeration to say that the whole shape of his future life may depend on them. This places an enormous responsibility on those who care for him to provide the best possible relationships and environment.

From three to five years through the carefully planned routine of his home, nursery or nursery school, he learns to live both as an individual and as a member of the society in which he finds himself. He becomes more independent and able to do far more things for himself. This is also a time of great social development as his world gradually opens up.

It is of great importance that as he grows up he should be given toys suitable to his age. He needs things to play with that will stretch his imagination and lead him on to use his mind and his muscles as extensively as possible. This is not to say that old toys should be discarded but the new ones should be introduced alongside the old to encourage him to move on. Toys that teach him to work things out for himself are especially valuable at this stage; how to fit one piece of wood into another, how to post the right brick through the right hole, how to link the trailer to its lorry and so on. All these things will give him a sense of balance, weight, proportions and many other things which will be of great importance to him in the future. As regards colour, it is the bright colours that are appreciated first and more easily distinguished, and then later the more delicate tones. Another noticeable development at this stage is that the child's constructions gradually become more skilled and realistic. The pile of bricks which formerly bore little resemblance to the house or castle it was claimed to be, really begins to look like its name. Hands are used with greater precision in painting and modelling too and indeed by the time the child is five he has his whole body under quite reasonable control.

From five years of age the child's interests become much more varied, and he is now capable of taking part with other children in games that have simple rules. School influences begin to work side by side with those of home and his school life enlarges his whole outlook, though his adjustment to the new regime will depend very much on his temperament and past experiences. The understanding teacher will play a very important part in the child's life at this time, but he will still need the security and affection of his family, if he is to take full advantage of all the new opportunities open to him.

Slow growth of intelligence may be due to many causes. Over-indulgent or anxious parents can hinder this growth by too much protection, thus preventing the child from making any effort. The wrong type of play materials and lack of opportunity to explore will also hinder development (see Chapter 7).

Reasoning

The child reasons in exactly the same way as the adult, but the adult has the great advantage of a much larger store of experience. The chief factor in intellectual activities is the ability to use and relate past experience to present circumstances. This situation can be very difficult for a child with limited experience. Suitable play materials will encourage him to make simple decisions through a process of trial and error. The rate at which the child gains ability to do this varies very much in normal children. With unobstructive guidance from the adult he will be stimulated to reason and to make a suitable decision.

Learning Good Habits

It is the wish of all parents that children should develop good habits which will unconsciously be maintained throughout their life. It may guide the adult if she can look at the circumstances through the eyes of the child and realise that what she is expecting him to do is complicated and possibly involves the use of very detailed muscular action. Training a child in good habits can only be achieved when his body, brain and nervous system are sufficiently developed for what-ever we wish him to learn, otherwise any attempt will produce a failure. He learns quite naturally by copying, by listening, by trial and error, and even by suggestion. Pleasure-giving experiences are far more likely to be repeated and to become habits.

Learning good sleep and relaxation habits

Such habits, learnt in childhood can continue throughout adult life. The ability to sleep soundly and to relax are of the greatest value in promoting good physical and mental health. The placid child is more likely to sleep soundly than the excitable or nervous child.

Sleep is essential for the well-being of everyone, and in the early weeks of life is closely associated with food. The baby feeds, sleeps and is awakened by hunger. As he develops and becomes more active, he learns to keep awake for longer periods and he then usually takes more time to relax into sleep. Some children are good sleepers, others are restless and are very light sleepers. Sleep can be affected by digestive upsets, strange environments, wet napkins or discomfort, fear or any emotional tension and excitement.

The average child should sleep quite well in his home, without any restriction having to be made for television, or any music or social life of the family. If there are any unusual noises or very loud sounds, then a careful watch must be kept in case the baby wakes and is startled by the unusual happenings. A gentle word from someone whose voice is known to him will reassure him, and in this way the development of such fears can be avoided. In time the infant begins to recognise the various voices and whether the tone is harsh or endearing.

Sleep is considered to be of a rhythmic nature, working in close harmony with the child's mental and physical needs. Thus in sleep all the systems of the body are slowed down, including the brain. Some children need much more sleep than others. By careful observation of the individual child, his needs will be known and tiredness and too much excitement avoided. Bed time should be a happy time for the child and it is essential for him to be put to bed by a well-known adult. Then feeling secure and happy, he will quickly form good sleep habits.

Rest, meaning 'relaxation', is just as essential to the child as sleep. With his instinctive desire to know about everything he is constantly using his brain. Some children, after a period of physical activities, will automatically sit down and quite unknowingly take a rest.

Other children may go on and get very tired and therefore irritable without realising that they are tired, and for these firm help is often needed to get them to rest.

Learning feeding habits

Feeding habits are relatively simple to learn, primarily because feeding times are usually happy and satisfying times for the baby at a stage when he has so many other things to learn about. From about four months or in some cases even earlier, new tastes and textures are introduced, some of which the baby will like and accept, while others may be refused. He will also have to learn to take food from a spoon and may resist this method of feeding to begin with. But gradually he should learn to accept the new procedure and as his abilities develop he may try to grasp the spoon and attempt to feed himself. However incapable he may appear to his mother to be, these attempts should never be discouraged. He will still gain satisfaction from sucking at this stage and the close contact with his mother will still be of great value to him.

As more interest is shown in food he will gradually be content to give up sucking, and begin to use chewing movements, and it is not long before his efforts at feeding himself begin to be fairly effective. At first he will find difficulty in manipulating a spoon and will quickly tire; he will feed his eyes, his ears and his hair with a great sense of achievement and at this stage help rather than exasperation will lead him on to better things. Anything that diverts his attention will cause him to forget what he is supposed to be doing, so that he will learn much more quickly if he can have his meals in peace with only his mother or nurse.

By about two years of age he should have mastered the basic techniques of eating, and then it is much better for him to have meals with the family, so that he can see and copy the way other people eat. There are problems however, as bad habits are always much more fun to copy than good ones, so there is a burden of responsibility on all the other members of the family. The inevitable distractions may make him terribly slow, and there is also the danger of his deciding not to like something just to be like his brothers or sisters. But with common sense and a sense of humour these things can generally be overcome so that by the time they are seven, most children should have reasonable table manners, and be able to make conversation during their meals.

Learning bowel and bladder control

Nature demands that the body must function in rhythm concerning the intake of food and the excretion of waste matter from the body. This process is primarily of a physical nature in the young baby. He has no control of his excretions and he cannot be trained in clean habits until he is able to understand what is expected of him. This may occur at any time from one year to two and a half or even later. Observation will often show that a young baby will pass a stool very soon after he has taken a feed. In these circumstances there is no harm in supporting him carefully and comfortably on a small pot on the knees of an adult. If a stool is passed then a dirty napkin is saved, but this must never be confused with true habit training. The adult must accept wet or dirty napkins as a normal procedure, without showing displeasure or anxiety for the child will very easily sense disapproval. As urine is passed more often, and as a wet napkin seldom seems to cause discomfort to a child even at a later stage it is often difficult to persuade him to go in search of a pot. Bowel control on the other hand is usually achieved more easily. There are generally definite warning feelings that are easy to recognise and the discomfort caused by a dirty nappy can be quite acute even in small babies.

In the first seven years of life rapid intellectual growth has enabled the normal baby to develop into an active and independent child, capable in many ways of attending to his personal needs. If he has had a good environment he can converse and reason with adults; his actions are performed in a capable manner showing that his brain and whole muscular system are working in harmony, and his degree of intelligence enables him to be observant of all that is going on around him, thus forming a sound foundation on which to build his future life.

CHAPTER 5

Emotional and Social Development

Babies from birth are extremely sensitive to their surroundings and although they have not learned to express their feelings and desires verbally, they are nevertheless affected by the adults' attitude to them.

Good emotional development is just as essential to mental and physical well-being as food. There can be no contentment and real happiness for the person who is not emotionally stable, nor can he be a useful member of society. Any immaturity of the emotions affects the character of the individual, making him shrink from life or become aggressive and discontented. The intellectual being is usually very sensitive and feels very acutely the joys and sorrows around him. Although pain may be caused by such intense feelings it makes for a much fuller and happier life, provided the individual is capable of controlling his emotions, and adjusting his reactions to his social needs and conditions. Failure to control these emotional impulses will lead to much unhappiness, both in childhood and in adult life. Suppressed emotions will also result in many difficulties and much misunderstanding, perhaps jealousy, aggressiveness, lack of confidence or even ill-health. It is frequently found that the maladjusted person aims at notoriety through his actions, and in some instances he will go to any length, even to committing crimes in order to be noticed. Therefore it is important that the young child should be guided and encouraged to express his feelings in a manner suitable to each particular occasion.

The first responses

The first intensive feelings shown by the baby are associated with sucking, and any dissatisfaction at feeding time may make him very angry. This he shows by crying or kicking or both, as these are the only ways he knows, but as soon as he can suck and obtain food his anger turns into love and satisfaction. At this age the emotions are not specialised, but gradually they become specific as the child develops. Because of the pleasant experience of sucking and the warmth and comfort of his mother the infant is content and feels secure.

In the early stages a baby is quite unable to control his feelings and he requires very careful handling to help him come to terms with them. He needs to be encouraged to use and to express his needs in a balanced way, thus laying down the basis for good emotional growth. This is made much easier for him if the adult is consistent in her response.

The baby with a placid nature will express his feelings quite plainly, but in a quieter manner than a more boisterous child who makes his demands in no uncertain tones. This sort of behaviour should never be interpreted as being naughty or bad tempered for at this stage all the infant's needs are urgent and should be satisfied.

The baby must have enough food and adequate satisfaction through sucking, and at times he may seem very demanding. In the past great stress has been put on regular feeding times, known as 'feeding by the clock'. Anyone with experience of babies knows that they are individuals with very varying needs. There are different schools of thought about feeding on demand or about feeding at three hourly or four hourly intervals, but it is obvious that the baby will take some time to adjust himself to a separate existence, and the essential factor is to supply his needs. Observations have proved that hunger is felt very acutely from his earliest days, and that the baby cries to announce his hunger and the comfort he derives from sucking. If his needs are not met quickly he reacts by showing anger, which in some instances may cause him to refuse food when it is offered.

After a few weeks the baby will have formed his own rhythm, which becomes a fairly regular one. After his immediate hunger is satisfied the baby will often respond to his mother with a smile and show signs of recognising her voice. By breast feeding the mother is giving love to the baby which he accepts with real affection. The pleasure of sucking is very intense and anything which he is given will probably go straight to his mouth.

During the first few months the baby accepts his mother as the giver of all good things, and his world is focused round her as she gives him the pleasant feelings of satisfaction and security. Any incident to upset these enjoyable times is met with strong disapproval by crying, banging or kicking or even refusing the feed. Gradually other reasons for crying arise, the discomfort of a dirty napkin, handling by an unfamiliar person, or pain, or a feeling of loneliness; some babies appear to hate their everyday routine; they cry furiously while they are being dressed or undressed or having their napkin changed, but they gradually learn to accept these procedures. Bathing with a good firm hand is usually just tolerated at first, but quite soon it should become a great source of pleasure.

Gradually the baby begins to recognise voices and he will respond by smiling when his father or someone else he knows speaks. Then as his happy experiences increase he may show real joy and even try to touch the person concerned. He enjoys seeing his family and smiles at them. Satisfaction through sucking is still a necessity to him, and many babies suck their thumb or a toy or rag, particularly when going to sleep.

From two to four months mixed feeding is introduced and this requires careful management because of the new method of feeding and the unusual tastes and textures of solid food. Success can only be achieved if the baby is willing to accept the new foods. For this reason it is important to reduce the sucking periods very gradually, so that there is no sudden contrast between one way of feeding and the other.

From six months to one year the baby is more active in his cot or playpen and when he finds a new toy will often show it to the adult with great delight. This is partly a sign that he still needs someone there to reassure him, as he is often uncertain or even afraid. Gradually confidence grows and he will begin to show a desire for independence, but he still needs to know that someone is there to help him sort out his bewildering experiences and emotions. At times when an unknown adult speaks to him he may quickly close his eyes pretending to be shy, or he may even think that by doing this he can no longer be seen.

From one to two years the child starts to express his desires, and if carefully guided will begin to learn to control his emotions. This is a difficult period for the child, because while he is trying to learn independence he still feels the need of his mother's love and presence. If he gets the impression that his mother does not love him through her angry words or her lack of response to his demands, he will find life doubly trying as he still needs her love and does not want to lose it. This creates a problem for the child that he finds very difficult to tackle, and he will often cry or lie on the floor, kicking and screaming, as this is his only way of expressing his feelings. The wise mother or nurse will understand and give him the assurance he needs by showing

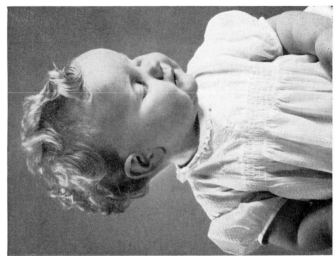

FIG. 28. I'm very shy.

FIG. 27. Life is grand.

affection and guidance rather than disapproval of his behaviour. This will give him the security he needs and he will feel free to try out more new ideas.

When he can walk by himself he will constantly find new experiences through his play and his every day routine. There may be surprises which are pleasant and exciting, when he will laugh and enjoy them and attempt to make them happen again. Unfortunately the child has to learn about the opposite side of life too; he may feel afraid of some strange article, or an unusual sound and his first impulse will be to run away, or to hit the offending article. In running away he is losing ground and letting fear be his master, but by wise guidance he can be helped even to laugh at the incident and in this way get the better of his fears.

The young toddler has a strong desire to become independent and to dominate, which could set up many emotions, the chief of these being anger, jealousy and obstinacy. When he is with another equally determined child there will probably be a good deal of quarrelling, but nevertheless companions are essential to help him come to terms with other people. Children at this stage will often resent the adult's authority and can become extremely difficult if not handled with understanding.

Adult authority

Some children when not well guided may come to enjoy bad behaviour, such as crying, shouting and tantrums. It will be essential to teach the child that such behaviour is not tolerated. At times a child may behave badly simply to show off and attract attention. Such behaviour should be ignored, for in this way the child's whole aim is lost and he is unlikely to go on with a game that does not bring forth the response he had hoped for.

The mother in showing her affection, should not carry this to extremes, as the child must be encouraged to become emotionally independent, although love is still vital to him. The child is naturally affectionate, but this should not be endlessly encouraged by excessive fondling by his mother, but rather by sharing pleasant experiences with him, and by helping when his emotions get out of hand. A young child may even show that he is jealous when he sees his father or mother showing signs of affection to each other, since he regards himself as the sole rightful recipient of such attentions.

Play with such materials as sand and water, clay and paint, are of great value to the young child as these can be bent to his will, thus providing outlets for aggression without hurting any one, and helping him to learn to control his emotions.

Social life from two years old

Between two and five years the impulses of the child are very strong, and because of this it is better for him to know a larger circle of

Fig. 29. The four year old child offers
help to the two year old.

adults rather than just his parents, and to have plenty of company and
companions. In this way he is more likely to gain a true perspective
of his relationship to other children and adults. Quite frequently a
child may become difficult at home by not eating, or by refusing to
do what he is asked, but when he is in a nursery or nursery school he
behaves very well and takes his food without any fuss. This may be
due to the fact that the child having been emotionally dependent on
his mother, now wants to fight the emotional tie between them in an
effort to become independent. Some children naturally turn to
fantasy play and work out their problems through games with dolls
and animals, or imaginary friends whom they can dominate and
control to their heart's content.

At this stage a day nursery or nursery school can provide opportunities for widening the child's horizons which are not available at
home. At first the child may well be apprehensive about the new
environment and will want his mother to stay with him. If she is
able to do this to begin with it may be of great help to him. The child
from a small family may not be used to playing with so many other

children, and to begin with may keep close to the teacher or nurse rather than daring to join in with the others. Most children will quite quickly make a move to join in once they have overcome their preliminary shyness, though within the group they may prefer to

FIG. 30. The two year old asserts his independence.

play on their own. Older children often enjoy playing with younger ones, and can be a great help in encouraging them to integrate in the group (see Fig. 29 to 32).

A first child, taken unawares by the birth of a new baby, is bound to feel jealous of the new arrival, whom he sees as having usurped his place in his mother's affection. This situation can be avoided by wise parents, who prepare the child beforehand, encouraging him to look ahead as they are to the new baby, who will be his as well as theirs (see Fig. 31).

If he is allowed to feel jealousy the child will probably resort to baby behaviour in an attempt to regain the affection he thinks he has lost.

Keeping pets is a useful way of helping the child to take responsibility and to express his tender feelings. In this way he learns to be considerate and kind to every one, and he is given the chance to gain

FIG. 31. Mother and child enjoy the new baby.

experience which will enable him to meet some of the demands made on him socially when he gets to school.

The five year old child eagerly anticipates his going to school. He feels he is at last really grown up. When he attends school he will meet many unexpected circumstances and may find difficulty in coping with them. These may cause him to try and hide his emotions in the presence of his playmates, for fear of their teasing him. An understanding teacher can help him, but it is equally important for his parents to be interested in their child's school life. In this way any pent up emotions can be released, and the child's confidence restored, so that he will be able to manage the completely new school environment. By seven years of age he should have learnt how to deal with most of his relationships with teachers and with other children.

Fear is experienced by every one at some time. It is not an emotion to be ashamed of owning, as it is perfectly normal and is really a measure of defence. The person who is never afraid is probably one who is not very receptive to possibilities and conditions; in fact he may be rather dull and insensitive. The presence of strangers, large animals, unusual surroundings, darkness or sudden noises such as thunder or a dog barking may all cause a child to experience fear through a feeling of insecurity. In any unusual circumstances where the child appears to be rather timid, it is wise for the adult to reassure him by simply holding his hand and chatting to him, until he realises that all is well and that he is quite safe.

The particular type of fear varies with the stage of development of the child, and many of these fears if mismanaged in childhood can last right on into maturity.

FIG. 32. Children should get the opportunity
to play with other children.

It is cruel and almost criminal to suggest that 'the policeman will take you away' or 'a bogey man will catch you if you go out there'. If the child is afraid of a certain thing, it is wise to find out if possible the cause and explain this away, but a child should never be forced to do any thing of which he is really afraid. For example he should never be made to go out in the dark, or into a dark room alone if he is frightened, but should be taken by an adult who is sympathetic and

FIG. 33. The four year old can help her young sister.

FIG. 34. Tender feelings shown by a six year
old, but doubt by the younger child.

understanding. When it is found that all is well they can both laugh about it, which will relieve the strain and give the matter quite a different perspective.

Laughter should be a normal part of everyday life for everyone. It is essential for the child's happiness that he should gradually learn to master fear, and as he does so both his courage and his character will be built up. Latent fears can cause a child to be very aggressive and may hinder him from fitting in to normal social conditions.

FIG. 35. At seven years he is working happily with his sister.

Guided in the right way the child can learn to use suitable responses and in time may develop a real sense of humour which will be most valuable to his well being.

Fears of things with which the child is quite familiar may appear to develop suddenly without any apparent cause, but there could easily have been anxiety in the child's mind although no one had ever noticed it. Here again the adult must show understanding rather than coercion to help him grow out of his fear.

FIG. 36. A seven year old boy happily explaining
pictures to his two year old sister.

During the child's experiences he has spontaneous impulses of great variety, and in the beginning he is at a loss to know how to manage them. At first his response may produce behaviour which is quite unsuitable to the occasion, and it is at these times that he needs help, to enable him to learn to deal with different situations. Such ability will prove to be of great value to him throughout life, helping him to face unexpected conditions and problems calmly and well. Good emotional development combined with good health, will go a long way towards helping the child to fit into his environment and to lead a normal happy life.

Self discipline

The young child thrives on the love of his parents, but to prepare him for real happiness in adult life, it is most essential that he should learn to control his emotions and gradually develop self discipline. Even the one year old child shows a desire to be independent and to have freedom to explore, although he still both consciously and unconsciously needs the safety and protection of the adult. It is no good expecting obedience at this stage of growth, because the child cannot control his emotions and will openly show rebellion. During his early years the child must be free to respond to his inner impulses, and having this freedom he will be more willing to accept that there are certain rules of behaviour to which every one must conform and that he is no exception to the rule. Discipline must never be an arrangement of rules and restrictions, but should be unobtrusively exercised through example and guidance. Requests rather than de-

FIG. 37. Sucking can be a comfort.

mands can be made to the child, but there are times however, when a direct command is essential, for example when the child is advancing towards an electric plug or a boiling kettle. From about four years old a child will probably enjoy being asked to help with small tasks, but it is not until nearer five or six years that he is really ready and willing to accept direction.

Very rigid discipline and a demand for unquestioning obedience in childhood may cause various reactions which will continue through life. It may produce a person who is unable to think for himself, or one who shows open rebellion and who is constantly struggling against authority, or a third type who will give apparent obedience, but underneath is resisting and resenting and developing a bitter attitude to life.

Through self discipline the child will be learning to fit in happily and willingly, so that as he grows up he will have no desire to drop out of society. The so-called difficult child is usually the result of mismanagement in the home or nursery. If the child has the freedom to use his energies in a way that satisfies him he is seldom really naughty.

Personality

The growth of personality continues from infancy to maturity; and some people continue to develop their personalities throughout their lives, because they never lose the art of learning from their experiences.

It is interesting when observing a baby, to notice the response shown to an adult who talks to him and perhaps holds his hand. This pleasure in life is the beginning of the development of personality, and this happy response, given so naturally, gradually develops during the early months as the child's abilities and experiences increase. Although the personality pattern is almost certainly partially inherited from the parents, its actual development will be strongly influenced by emotions and experiences within the home.

The behaviour of adults around a child will naturally form a basis for his own way of living. From the start, if the adult explains what she is doing and why, the child will much more readily understand what is expected of him. Praise means a great deal to children and is one of the best boosts to their self-confidence, and all children do something that is worth praising, even if it is not the most obvious of skills or achievements. Children should never be made to feel odd or different, but if and when special talents or interests develop, they should be encouraged to pursue them as far as they can.

CHAPTER 6

Routine Care of the Child

The child's day should be planned to fulfil his all round needs. Although essentially the same throughout childhood, it will differ in details according to his age, development and environment. It is important to remember that all his growing needs, physical, emotional, social and intellectual must be provided for in the daily routine. The child's need should come first even if it means the home or nursery does not look as clean and tidy as it might, or that the staff are unable to do things in exactly the order they had wished.

Cleanliness is essential to health, and if this fact is presented to children in the right way it will give many opportunities for learning from the very earliest days. Organised routine with flexibility is necessary for all children as it helps them to accept and understand the adult's programme, but to be really successful the adult must also consider the child's point of view.

The infant is extremely sensitive to his mother's touch so that bathing and changing on her knee is far more satisfying to him than if these things are done on a bed or table. Any lack of confidence when handling the child may create a nervous tension which will react on the child and make him nervous. The baby appreciates firm but gentle handling and he will enjoy being talked to, sung to, and smiled at. Hurried or impatient movements will give him a feeling of insecurity, and if this persists it may have a far reaching effect on his mental development. Throughout the day the baby must be changed and made comfortable and in each handling love should be conveyed. Fondling and talking to him at these times is very important.

Changing the napkin

As a safeguard against infection, it is best to change the baby in the bathroom. Before lifting the baby prepare all the necessary equipment, which should include a bowl of warm water, soap, buttock flannel, buttock towel, clean napkins and clothing if necessary, bucket with lid, powder and cream, and a low chair. Put on a 'changing' apron. If baby is asleep wake him gently by talking to him.

With the baby on the knee, take off the dirty napkin, taking care to fold the napkin over any faeces, and immediately place it in the bucket and replace the lid. Place the towel under the buttocks and wash and dry them carefully with warm water and a patting movement, whether wet or dirty. Apply a little cream or lotion if necessary, and put on the napkin arranging the clothing comfortably. Return the child to his cot or place him on a rug or in a play pen for exercise. Clear up the equipment, remove the apron and wash the hands.

Bathing the baby

In the first week of life daily bathing is not essential, because too much bathing removes the natural oils and leaves the skin more open to infection.

At bath time the baby gets direct contact with his mother or nurse. The attention and love then given to him will give him a very real feeling of security and help a great deal in his general development. It should be a happy time for the mother and baby and it is much more likely to be so if there is a carefully planned and regular method of procedure.

The young baby is bathed usually in the morning before the 10 a.m. feed. Later when he reaches the crawling stage the most convenient time will probably be in the evening before he goes to bed.

Equipment for bathing a young baby

Bath. Approximately 36×18 inches (1000 cm $\times$ 500 cm) usually made of polythene, and sometimes with a stand though this is not essential. It can also be a fixed baby bath or an ordinary sink or hand basin.

Pail made of polythene or some other type of plastic material, for used napkins. Dirty napkins should be soaked in cold water until they are sluiced.

Pail or enamel bowl for the infant's dirty clothes.

Low chair without arms which enables the mother to handle the baby with ease and comfort.

Plastic apron which can be disinfected if it becomes dirty.

Apron, made from soft Turkish towelling, with a bib. This can be boiled and is comfortable for the child.

Bath towel, fairly large and made of soft towelling.

Face towel.

Face cloth of fine, soft cotton material.

Body cloth. If used, this should be soft and should have a distinguishing mark on it.

Soap. This should be a good quality of super-fatted soap, which may also be used for the hair although a special baby shampoo should replace this later.

Baby basket or box, with a loose washable lining and a cover. This is useful to keep the soft hair brush, comb, safety pins, orange sticks, round pointed scissors, a jar with a screw top for small cotton wool swabs, and any other necessary articles.

Small bowl for boiled water.

Receiver for dirty swabs.

Powder is not necessary as a routine measure.

Petroleum jelly and *zinc and castor oil cream* if necessary for buttocks

Preparation of the room

The *temperature* of the room should be about 65°–70° F (18°–21° C). A small screen is useful to prevent draughts. If bathing near a fire, either sit directly in front of the fire, or with baby's feet towards it. Some people prefer to stand and to bath the baby on a table – if so, the table should be covered with a waterproof sheet and a large, soft bath towel, and the equipment would be the same as previously described, but this method is not advised. Rain water is soft and if boiled to avoid any risk of contamination, is ideal for the bath. Boiling very hard water for a few minutes will help to soften it. When preparing the bath, pour some cold water in first, and then add the hot water. The temperature of the bath should be 100° F (38° C) when baby is put into it. After the first few months the temperature can be gradually reduced to 90° F (32° C) for the average child of about one year. The bath thermometer must be read with the mercury bulb in the water, but the water can be satisfactorily tested by using the elbow, which is more sensitive to heat than the hand. The water should feel just warm. There should be a change of clothing warming on a clothes horse near at hand, placed in the order required.

Bathing technique. During the whole procedure the adult must talk to the baby and thus convey love and security to him. Both the knee and table methods are used in this country, but the knee method will be described, as in this the infant has the maximum contact with the adult. Having made all the necessary preparations and arranged everything within reach, take off any dangerous jewellery, as babies are always attracted by a glittering object, wash the hands and then pick up the baby. Gentle but firm handling is essential. If the baby is asleep talk to him and rouse him slowly, letting him wake up thoroughly before starting to undress him. Strip and air the cot. Young babies must lie comfortably on the mother's

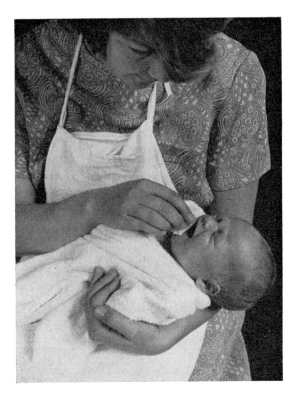

FIG. 38. Washing the baby's face before bathing.

lap, the head supported on her thigh. *Never sit a young baby upright.* When undressing the baby undo all fastenings and ease the garments from under the infant, then slip the sleeves off, and finally take the garment over the head. Take off the top garments, leaving only the vest and napkin or undress the baby completely and wrap him in a towel until the head toilet is completed. *It is unnecessary to bathe the eyes.* Any discharge from the eyes is abnormal and dangerous and should be reported to a doctor. Massage each nostril very gently and with a small piece of moist cotton wool clean the lower part of the nose. The inside of the mouth should not be touched, but the baby will frequently open his mouth, when its appearance should be noted, so that anything abnormal can be reported and treated in the early stages. Wrap the bath towel round the baby, if not already done, securing his hands, and with the face cloth or cotton wool swab and water, wash the face and surface of the ears (Fig. 38). Soap can be used if the face has become smutty. Dry thoroughly with the face towel. With the left hand supporting the spine, the left wrist supporting the head, and the bath towel covering the baby, hold the head over the bath, far enough to avoid water running into the eyes. Keep the infant's feet well over to the left side to avoid any risk of the child jumping or slipping out of the grasp. First wet the hair with the face cloth, then on alternate days, soap the palm of the hand and apply the lather with gentle massage to the scalp including the anterior fontanelle. *Rinse very thoroughly* and dry the head and ears with the child on the knee. After six months the head can be washed about twice a week. Now wash and dry the baby's hands. Next remove the napkin and place it in a receptacle, if soiled clean up the area of the skin with a little cotton wool and baby lotion or water and wash hands in a small bowl of water. Take off the vest carefully preventing it rubbing over the face, and wrap the baby in the bath towel.

Soap the arms from the wrists to the shoulders, the lower limbs from the feet to the thighs, the trunk from the neck downwards, then rolling the baby slightly towards the nurse, soap the back, finishing with a circular movement on the buttocks. Rinse the soap from the hands and gently lift the baby into the bath, with the left hand firmly gripping the left shoulder, and wrist supporting the head, and the right hand under the buttocks and gripping the left thigh. Support the infant in the bath and rinse off the soap with the other hand. Never allow the child to slip and feel insecure, as this may lead to a permanent dislike of the bath. As the child develops and becomes stronger, he can be turned over in the bath and given more time for kicking and playing with a toy, but remember to avoid any risk of chilling. With the bath towel on the knee, and using the same grip as before, lift the baby on to the towel placing him on his back and cover immediately with the towel. Alternatively the baby can be removed from the bath and placed on his tummy, drying his back first. Always turn the baby towards you. *Dry very thoroughly and gently*, as the skin is very easily damaged by rubbing, being especially careful with folds of skin at the neck, armpits, groin, buttocks, knees and also between the fingers and toes. Roll the infant over on to his abdomen and lay him on a dry apron or a blanket, removing the bath towel, then finish drying the back. Powder is unnecessary for the average child, as it is liable to clog the pores of the skin. If it is used it should be sprinkled on the palm of the hand, and then smeared over the skin; too much powder should not be used. Slip on the vest and turn the baby on to his back, always remembering to roll the baby towards the adult.

It is advisable with a male child, as a matter of routine, to push back the foreskin very gently, about once a week. Later it need not be done so frequently. Any sign of a discharge from the vagina of a female child should be immediately reported to the doctor.

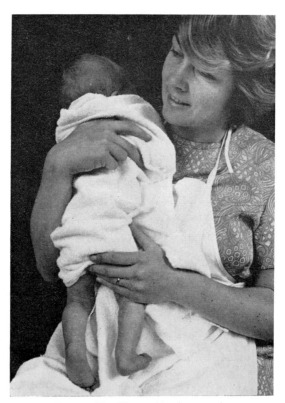

FIG. 39. Fondling and having exercise.

Babies of all ages enjoy a little fondling after the bath and their mental development benefits by it (Fig. 39). Clad only in a vest the infant can enjoy a little exercise with more freedom. By exposing the skin to the air for brief periods at first, the body learns to cope successfully with changes of temperature.

Napkins can be applied in several ways. *The pilch method* has much to recommend it, as there is no risk of pulling it up too tightly between the legs or of restricting the leg movements. It is comfortable and gives adequate protection. To apply a 36-inch (1 m) Harrington square as a pilch, fold the napkin lengthways and then double it again to form an 18-inch (50 cm) square. Place the napkin under the buttocks and bring the remainder up between the legs. Pin the back edge on to the front edge of the napkin at each side, with the safety-pin lying across the abdomen for comfort, at the same time securing the vest to avoid a gap between the napkin and

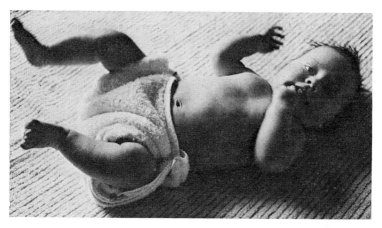

FIG. 40. Napkin should be comfortable and allow freedom for movement.

the vest. A piece of cotton sewn on to the lower edge of the vest at each side, will prevent the safety-pin tearing the vest. An 18-inch or 20-inch (50 cm or 55 cm) towelling napkin can also be used as a pilch napkin (see Fig. 41).

To apply a triangular napkin, fold the 24-inch (60 cm) square of towelling into a triangle, placing the longest edge under the buttocks and bring the middle points up between the legs. For a baby girl, the inner layer of the napkin can be doubled back under the buttocks and only one layer brought up between the legs. Place the centre point on the strengthened part of the vest, and bring over the left and right sides of the napkin. Pin all together with one curved safety-pin. Care must be taken to avoid pulling up the napkin too tightly between the limbs. This method is not comfortable for a big baby.

The kite method gives good protection. It fits snugly round the thighs with no tightness between the legs and is extremely comfortable for the baby.

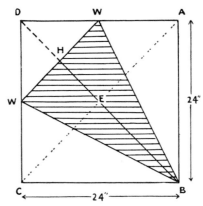

FIG. 41. Napkin folded for 'kite' method.

Fold the edge A–B to the diagonal line D–B, so that A meets H. Now fold the C–B edge in a similar manner so that C and A points meet at H. Fold the narrow point B over to the centre of the square at E and fold the D corner a few inches over the B point. Now the napkin is folded, place the wide edge W–W under the baby's buttocks, bringing the narrow edge between the legs, and secure with a safety-pin at each side, as in the pilch method.

To give extra protection after fixing the napkin, a Turkish towelling square can be wrapped round the buttocks as a skirt and the lower edge left perfectly free.

Continue the dressing, remembering that the clothes must be comfortably arranged, if the baby is to be contented and happy. Any unnecessary turning should be avoided as one turn should be sufficient. Brush the hair in varying directions with a soft brush, and if necessary clean the nails with an orange stick. Use blunt ended scissors to cut the nails the shape of the fingers. Lay the baby in a safe place to kick, and clear away the bathing equipment. All towels and flannels should be dried after use and washed and dried regularly.

Infant's cot

There are many types of cots on the market, such as a basket cot, or a treasure cot type, which are only suitable for use up to approximately 4 months as they would then be unsafe on account of the child's ability to move about. Ideally a baby should have two cots, a small one or carry cot to begin with and then a larger dropside cot to last until he is ready to change to a bed. Whatever type is chosen, it should be washable and allow good ventilation. Cots can be improvised in emergency by using a washing basket, a drawer or a carry cot, which is useful for travelling. The child should lie in a cot at a fairly high level to enable him to have the maximum amount of fresh air without draughts.

The *enveloping blanket* method of making up a young baby's cot is simple, comfortable and free from draughts. First place the blanket, 72 in. × 48 in. (180 cm × 120 cm) lengthways across the cot, allowing the sides and foot to hang over the cot. Next place a firm hair, flock or chaff mattress, with a washable cover, in the cot on top of the blanket. If desired a half-filled pillow case can be placed on top of the firm mattress, then a waterproof sheet 24 in. × 14 in. (60 cm × 35 cm), and this may be covered either with a sheet or a large piece of cotton. Never use a long draw sheet as it is not hygienic. A pillow is not necessary but if desired a small, flat, Dunlopillo pillow is advisable in preference to a down or feather one, as with these there is a danger of suffocation if the baby rolls over. After feeding and changing wrap the baby snugly in a shawl. This gives a comfortable and secure feeling, which encourages contentment and sleep. Accustom the child to lie on his left and right side alternately, but in the first weeks he should be placed in a semi-side position, as his muscles are not strong enough to prevent him rolling over onto his face and possibly smothering himself. Very young children should not be placed on their backs in case they are sick and choke. After the baby is placed in the cot he is covered with a cot sheet, the one side of the blanket is brought over and tucked in; the other side is then placed over the first layer and tucked in, and the foot is fixed neatly under the mattress and the top of the sheet is arranged over the blankets, which must not impair the free passage of air to the baby or restrict his movements. Place the cot out of draughts but allow the maximum amount of fresh air. In the daytime the baby can sleep out of doors in his pram whenever the weather is suitable.

After four months the infant should use a *full-size cot*, with the bars not more than three inches apart, a drop side with a strong safety catch and a good firm mattress of hair, flock or Dunlopillo. This cot is made up in the usual manner with a waterproof sheet under blanket, sheet, top sheet and blankets as required and it should last until the child can use a small single bed at about three years. The use of pillows varies; some people prefer no pillow whilst others like a flat pillow. As young children often kick and wriggle in their sleep, it is necessary to have a fair amount of sheet and blanket to tuck in, but this must not mean the slightest restriction to the child. A waterproof sheet will be necessary until the child is well established in clean habits, but it must be discarded as soon as possible. A well ventilated eiderdown is useful in very cold weather, but it should not be covered as this will hold the air and prevent ventilation. A counterpane can be attractive in the daytime and it keeps the dust off the blankets, but it is quite unnecessary at night.

Cots must be completely stripped each morning and the mattress should be well aired. The mattress must be given adequate protection. Blankets should be shaken out of doors if possible and washed at regular intervals or whenever necessary. The framework of the cot must be dusted daily and washed or polished regularly.

A *screen* is useful in preventing a draught reaching the baby. Quite a good one can be made by covering a clothes horse with a gaily coloured print. Pockets can be arranged on the screen to take the child's personal toilet things.

Prams, like cots, must answer to the rules of hygiene. Very deep prams are to be avoided, because the air is likely to become stagnant. The same equipment is necessary for the pram as for the cot. The pram hood should be adjustable and only be used fully up in wet weather, as it prevents the free circulation of air round the baby. In cold, windy weather the hood can be slightly raised to protect the infant from the oncoming wind. Waterproof covers are unhealthy things and should only be used in actual rain. In hot, sunny weather a canopy with a green lining fixed on the pram is useful, as it allows all the fresh air to reach the child and protects him from the glare of the sun. An improvised canopy can be made with four rods approximately 24 inches long (60 cm), one securely fastened to each corner of the pram or cot. These can support a large bath towel or similar material lined with brown paper. The pram should be carefully watched to make sure that as the sun moves round the canopy is still effective.

When a pram is being chosen many factors have to be considered. It should be well made, have good springs and a reliable and strong foot-brake. The handle is adjusted to the height of the mother or nurse. A pram of medium height is usually the most satisfactory. It must be long enough to allow the young child to lie down comfortably but the choice of size may be influenced by the space available for storage and by the cost.

Fig. 42. The baby in his pram with the safety strap fastened.

The pram must be dusted regularly and the inside cleaned once a week. The hood and framework should be polished once a week and the wheels and brake should be oiled regularly and kept dry. The hood should be kept fully up, when not in use.

Safety straps of the harness variety must be used for any active child and although they secure the child, should allow perfect freedom for the limbs (see Fig. 42).

Push chairs. These are useful when the child can walk only a short

D

distance and is too heavy to be carried, particularly if the mother is shopping or going by bus. They are most unsuitable for the child if he falls asleep because there is no support to his spine and there is little protection for him in bad weather.

Hot water bottles are needed at times, but whenever possible it is wiser to warm the bed or pram before putting the child in it. If one is used, care must be taken to fix the cap very securely after having allowed all steam to escape, so as to eliminate the risk of burning the child. A thick cover must envelop the entire bottle including the screw top.

Morning Toilet (6 months to 2 years)

The routine care of this age group in the morning will vary very much according to the stage of development. The younger child may require similar care to that already described for the baby, but gradually he will progress to that suggested for older children.

The crawler's bath time

To the child who is beginning to crawl, life is one long exciting adventure. This learning is essential to the child's mental and physical development and the adult must be patient and kind, in her handling of the child. The busy mother or nurse should avoid any suggestion of rush. As soon as he shows any desire to try to take off or to put on his shoes he should be encouraged (Fig. 44).

Bath time for the crawler is more difficult to manage than in the early months because the child is active, and usually very interested in the things around him. At this stage, it is more practical to give the bath about 5.30 p.m., just before his evening drink and bedtime.

The actual bathing equipment is much the same as for the baby, except that it is now necessary to use the big bath as it provides better scope for fun and exercise. Bath toys can be provided but the water itself is the best possible play thing.

General technique

Everything should be prepared before undressing the child, until he reaches the age of wanting to help and do more for himself and then this should be encouraged. If the child is to be potted he should be left for only a short time on the pot and his mother or nurse should remain with him all the time. The pot should be placed on a plastic mat which can easily be washed if there is a spill. Prepare the

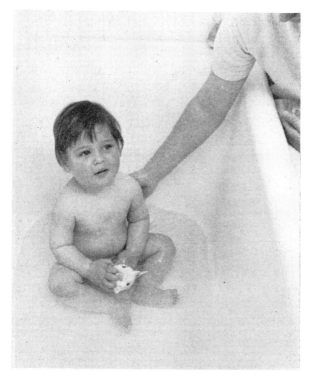

FIG. 43. Using the big bath at home.

bath water which should be about 98° F or 100° F (37° C or 38° C).
When the big bath is first used, care must be taken to keep the bath
fairly shallow to avoid fear of the unusually large quantity of water.
Undress the child on the knee, except for the vest, or if a dressing
gown is available, this could be used instead of the vest. Cover the
shoulders with the bath towel, wash the face and ears with the face
cloth, and dry very thoroughly with the face towel. The ears require
careful washing but *cotton wool is unnecessary and extravagant.* Any
sign of a discharge must be reported to a doctor. The nose should be
gently cleaned with cotton wool swabs or nasal tissues. This may
cause the child to sneeze which helps to clear the nasal passages and
the nose can then be wiped. The hair is washed about twice a week
when the infant is under one year. This is done after the face, and in
the same way as the young baby's head. After 12 months the hair
need only be washed once a week, when it is better to do it in the

day-time and quite apart from the bath. After the head toilet, slip off the remaining garments and for the child under one year soap all over on the knee, then lift him into the bath, but the older child can be soaped and washed in the bath, standing the child in the water to wash his buttocks and groin. If a cloth is used to wash the body, good hygiene demands that it is kept apart from the face cloth and these should both be frequently boiled. A small nail brush should be used for the hands and nails. A healthy child can have a cold shower

FIG. 44. I have to learn to do this.

after his warm bath, followed by a brisk rub down, but if he shows any unfavourable reaction such as shivering after this, then it should be discontinued. *Cold showers* are valuable in toning up the action of the skin. At this age the child is usually rather plump and it is important to see that all the creases in the skin are thoroughly dry before dressing him. Brush and comb the hair. The finger and toe nails must be inspected after the bath, kept cut straight and short, and any dirt removed with an orange stick.

After the bath it is usual to give a drink of milk and the teeth should be cleaned before getting into bed at 6.30 p.m. He will be tired after his activities, and if he knows the person attending to him, he will be quite happy and content to settle down to sleep possibly with a favourite cuddly toy. It will be necessary to lift the child at about 10 p.m. to make him comfortable for the night.

Toilet training

To most adults cleanliness is important and has become so much a part of life that it is difficult to remember how hard it was to learn. A baby does not understand about being clean and at first the emptying of the bowel and of the bladder is a reflex action which occurs automatically. In the early days a baby has little or no control in coordinating his muscular action and if he responds when sitting on a pot it is more by luck than anything else. It is pointless to try and train a child until the muscles of his bladder and bowel have grown strong, and the part of the brain controlling these functions has developed.

There are also the baby's own feelings in the matter. He does not feel any disgust when he dirties his nappy, it may even give him a certain amount of pleasure. In time he will learn to be clean because he knows his mother wants it, but he should never be made to feel disgusted when he dirties a nappy until he is properly trained. It can do great harm to make a child feel guilty about something he cannot help. Once he has been trained and is really capable of controlling his bowel and bladder then is the time to show disapproval when he does not do so.

When then is the right age to begin training a child? Usually between twelve and fourteen months, but many children are not ready then and it does no good to force them to sit on a pot if they do not understand why they are there. Training should never begin before a child can sit comfortably on his pot without fear of overbalancing; the feet should reach the floor and the baby should be able to sit up alone. Most children pass a motion at a regular time each day, so if the child is put on his pot at this time he will probably use it. Sometimes a child may indicate a desire to use a pot by becoming silent and going red in the face. He cannot wait when once he feels the urge, but if he is put on the pot quickly he will probably respond and use it. If his achievement is recognised with a smile he will be anxious to please again the next time. The mother or nurse should never scold or be distressed if there are lapses but should learn to accept them calmly, as they are bound to occur. The child is best helped by an adult who will cooperate with him, and too great an insistence on cleanliness may make the child rebel against using the pot and then the whole process will take much longer.

By the time the child is 18 months he will probably remain dry for about two hours at a time during the day. If he is taken to his pot at two hourly intervals and helped to sit on it, he will gradually learn that this is more comfortable than being wet. He should not be left for more than three or four minutes or be made to feel that he must use the pot. With patience and cheerful encouragement on the adult's part most children will have achieved clean habits by the time they are three years old.

One danger of too rigid toilet training is that it may instil in the child a fear of all things dirty so that he is afraid to play with such things as sand and water and clay and thus misses out on some of the most valuable play experiences.

Bed wetting

This is a fairly common condition among older children and usually has some sort of nervous origin. As with infants patience on the part of the adult is essential as any form of scolding will almost certainly aggravate the condition. Bed wetting should never be discussed in the child's presence, though after a dry night a word of praise is helpful. It is often helpful to have the advice of the family doctor who may refer the case to a psychologist if it seems necessary.

Toddler's Hygiene (2 to 5 years)

By two years of age the child is gradually developing a desire to be independent, to grow up and be like mummy or daddy. These are signs of normal mental development and the child must be given every opportunity and encouragement to become an independent, self-respecting individual. Good hygiene is essential to health and good habits formed in early years lay the fundamental principles on which the child will eventually live in adult life.

Morning toilet

The active child is normally very alert and keen to get out of bed in the morning. In his dressing gown he can go to the lavatory and then to the bathroom to clean his teeth, blow his nose, and wash his hands and face, though this routine should be done under supervision. Dressing follows and attention to the hair. Although he may be slow, it is wise to encourage independence, but it will be necessary to arrange the getting-up time to enable him to be ready for breakfast without having to be rushed.

Bath

Bathing must be a combined operation between the adult and the child and efforts made by the child should be appreciated, even if they don't get him any cleaner. A routine method is necessary, so that the toddler has some idea what he is expected to do, and by his repeated efforts he will eventually achieve efficiency. The adult must not expect an adult's standard, but one which is in relation to the age of the child.

The toddler's bath, therefore, is not simply a daily procedure to get the dirt off the skin, but a very valuable educational part of the daily routine, which provides scope and opportunities and experiences, combined with training in good hygienic habits.

Equipment necessary for bathing is as follows:

Bath towel and face towel.
Body cloth and face cloth.
Bath mat and chair.
Good super-fatted soap.
Shampoo as required.
Nail brush.
Brush and comb.
Tooth brush and mug.
Dressing gown and slippers (if possible).
Bath apron, orange stick and scissors.

Technique of bathing

Everything should be placed in readiness before beginning with the child. The toddler must first be encouraged to use the lavatory or chamber, while the adult prepares the bath water which should be about 95° F–100° F (35° C–38° C). Then the child can sit on the bath mat providing it is dry, or on a chair, and try to take off his shoes and socks; gradually by continual efforts and encouragement he will undress himself, which is much easier to him than the actual dressing.

The *routine* to adopt would be for him to undress as far as his vest. In the home, this would possibly be done in the bedroom, when a dressing gown and bedroom slippers would then be used to go to the bathroom. Good nasal and dental hygiene should be encouraged before bathing. Keen observation on the part of the adult is extremely important, to detect any discharges, rashes, or any signs of oncoming illness, in fact, any signs which might be unusual to the particular child.

The child should then attempt to wash his face and hands with the face cloth (Fig. 45), the adult supervising the ears, neck and general procedure. The face towel should be kept only for the face.

After the head toilet is completed the remaining garment is removed and the toddler climbs into the bath or tries to do so. Naturally the mother or nurse will have to wash the child, but he should be given the opportunity to soap his body cloth, and to use it. The buttocks and groins should be washed with the child standing up in the bath. A young nervous toddler should be allowed to hold on to something in case of slipping. All the soap must be well rinsed off followed by a cold shower, if suitable for the child. Drying is extremely important and powder is unnecessary. The child should now try to put on his pyjamas. The type of garment and the fastening must be chosen with this end in view. Sufficient help must be given to avoid any chilling or discouragement on the part of the child. After his bath he will enjoy a warm drink before going to bed.

The toddler's *nails* require a good deal of attention, both in the bath and out of the bath. From the early months a tiny manicure

FIG. 45. Washing his face before the bath.

set for the child will frequently establish a pride in the care of the nails, and indirectly prevent any tendency to nail biting later on.

The *hair* must be well brushed and combed at intervals during the day, and washed once a week or when necessary. A small mirror at the toddler's level is a great joy and encouragement when he tries to brush or comb his hair, also to see how he cleans his teeth. The child should be taught to tidy up his belongings after using them.

Nasal hygiene. The child should be encouraged to clear his nasal passages first thing in the morning, before meals, and at bedtime. With the handkerchief, as a personal possession, he will gradually learn the art of blowing his nose by copying the adult, but it is not until after three years of age that he is capable of using the handkerchief by himself.

In the nursery soft paper handkerchiefs are provided, and after use placed in a receptacle for the purpose. These must be burnt and the receiver should be disinfected each day and kept out of the child's reach.

Using the lavatory

The toddler will very quickly learn to use the lavatory provided it is a suitable shape and size. In nurseries and nursery schools small lavatories are part of the equipment and fittings. The position of the child on the lavatory is very important. Both feet should be flat on the floor and the knees should be slightly higher than the hip joint. For the toddler to achieve this position, the lavatory requires to be very low, not more than 9 inches in height. In the home, where there is no special provision for the toddler, it is better to use a pot. To accommodate an adult's lavatory to the toddler, it is possible to fit a foot step round the lavatory pedestal or to place a removable, smaller, plastic child's seat onto the adult seat. This is most helpful to the child. Sometimes a young toddler seated on an adult lavatory dislikes it because he feels insecure, and this, combined with a bad position for bowel action, will hinder the establishment of regular habits. In these cases a pot should be used but as the child gets older the step around the lavatory or the child's seat will help. Many instances of constipation could be avoided if the toddler was seated in the correct position on the lavatory; a certain amount of privacy too may help the sensitive or shy child. A toddler's small lavatory is usually provided with a low chain which he can pull himself, and although he should be encouraged to attend to himself and to pull the chain, it is essential for the adult to see the *type of stool* which has been passed, to ensure that any abnormal stool is reported and treated. This can be done in a quiet way which will not arouse the special attention of the toddler. Suitably designed garments with easy fastenings, help the toddler to become independent.

Hand washing must form part of the routine of the toilet hygiene, both for the child and for the adult who has assisted him. In nurseries, wash hand basins are arranged at convenient heights for the child to reach, but in the home a stool will be necessary for him if he is to reach the wash hand basin and try to wash himself. Where hot water is provided, which is likely to be very hot, then adequate supervision is required to avoid accidents. The child can be taught always to put some cold water in the basin, before using the hot water. To bar completely the use of the hot tap will only lead to curiosity, and the desire to turn it on. Gradually the child can be taught to use soap economically, and to use his towel only when his hands are clean. Facilities should be available for the child to replace his towel after use and to drain away the washing water.

Preparation for meals must include nasal and toilet hygiene, hand washing and attention to the hair. To enjoy a meal, it is important that the child can breathe freely through the nose and to do so the air passages must be clean. Therefore, the child should learn to blow his nose, use the toilet if necessary, wash his hands and attend to his hair in preparation for a meal. Children vary tremendously in the help they require during this process, but patience and guidance on the part of the adult will help children eventually to become very capable.

Care of the teeth

Ideally the teeth should be cleaned after every meal, but this is not always practical and if they are cleaned really well twice a day, at bedtime so that there is no risk to the teeth due to the formation of acids during the long night interval, and in the morning when it is refreshing to include dental hygiene in the routine morning toilet. For children in day nurseries it is essential to give a lesson in cleaning teeth after one meal during the day, and this might also be done in the home. By one year old the child should possess a soft tooth brush, with which the adult cleans the teeth. After two years the child can be taught to help, but care must be taken to ensure that the brush is not used as a toy. At first only water is necessary; later on common salt, bicarbonate of soda or tooth paste may be used. Children get a thrill out of possessing their own tooth paste (see Fig. 46).

A routine method of brushing the teeth should be taught. Place the teeth together and say 'E' and in this position put the bristles of the brush sideways against the gum of the upper jaw, and brush

FIG. 46. I like cleaning my teeth.

with a slight turning and downward movement over the teeth, repeating the process until all the upper teeth are cleaned. Clean the lower teeth in the same way. After this, open the mouth – say 'AH' and repeat the method described on the inner side of the teeth and finish by brushing over the crowns of the teeth. Then rinse the mouth with a little water from the tooth mug.

As soon as the child is old enough to understand, he should be encouraged to gargle, after cleaning his teeth. This is an excellent habit and proves of great value in cases of illness. The tooth brush should be rinsed after use and allowed to dry in a rack covered by the tooth mug to protect it from dust.

Regular dental inspection. Regular visits to the dentist for inspection should be paid from about two years, for in this way decay can be checked and extractions of the first teeth prevented.

To some children a visit to the dentist is almost a nightmare which lives in the child's mind from one visit to another; in fact it can be so upsetting to the child that the parents may even cancel the next visit. The cause of such a condition must be investigated and removed. The child should have had no fear before his first visit unless given some idea about the procedure by his parents or nurse. It often happens that an adult, in talking about the visit tells the child that the dentist won't hurt him and it will all be better soon. In this way the suggestion of pain and hurting is given to the child and he immediately starts to worry a good deal about the unknown, which it is said 'does not hurt'. Then when he actually goes to the dentist, and finds a man looking at his teeth and using shining instruments, he still wonders when the pain is coming and if he can really trust this kind man in the white coat. Even if the first visit proves a success it makes it very difficult for the dentist to gain the child's confidence, as the fear is there and it must take some time to be eradicated.

The adult must be honest with the child and should tell him he is going to see the dentist, who will examine his teeth, because it is necessary for him to have good teeth. The dentist, who knows if he is likely to have to hurt the child, will tell him just what is going to happen. By this method the dentist gains the child's trust, and any future visits will be exciting rather than worrying expeditions. If a visit must be paid to a dentist or doctor, it is a very bad policy to take the child under false pretences. This will shake his faith in his mother or nurse, on whom he is dependent, and may be the cause of difficult behaviour later on, whilst at the same time it makes the medical adviser's task an extremely difficult one.

Hair washing

This can be a most unpleasant ordeal for the toddler but it can also be fun, especially if there is a mirror for him to see his soapy hair in. He should never be put to bed with wet hair.

General technique. Take off the outer garment and any others which may be necessary to leave the child's neck free. If a plastic cape is available, tie this in position and then wrap the bath towel round the neck as well. Brush and comb the hair, preferably with the child seated. Then arrange the child comfortably either kneeling or standing on a chair or stool sufficiently high to enable him to lean the head well over the wash hand basin. Give the child a small towel to hold over the eyes to protect them. Prepare some water about 100° F (38° C) and wet the hair all over, then apply a little shampoo or soap the hands and rub up a lather. Massage the scalp gently with the fingers and wash the hair thoroughly. If very dirty apply more shampoo or soapy lather and wash again. Rinse in three waters, finishing with cool water. Wring the hair and wrap in the bath towel. Rub it well, then gently brush and comb it. Replace the outer garments. If the weather is warm and sunny, dry the hair in the open air, otherwise aid the drying by frequently rubbing and keep the child in a warm room.

Maintaining a clean head can only be done by routine washing and small tooth combing of the hair, at least once a week. Children are often found with their heads together in play, and in this way a clean child may easily become infected by a child with head lice (see Chapter 22).

The child usually scratches his head when there is any trace of vermin present. Many methods of cleaning dirty heads have been used in the past. These were unpleasant for the child and if carelessly applied may be a danger to the eyes. In treating dirty heads one should remember that the child has not done anything wrong, and the approach must be sympathetic and understanding. The child is sensitive and a compress labels him to his playmates. Although dirty heads can be treated at the cleansing station (see Chapter 31), it is much kinder if a known person cleans the head in the nursery.

The head tray should be prepared before starting with the child and it should contain the following:

Bowl of disinfectant (usually Dettol, 1 drachm to 1 pint of water)
A bowl or jar of cotton wool swabs
A comb
A Sackers comb
Lethane oil or a DDT preparation or Lorexane
A plastic cape
Derbac soap

If possible the child should be taken to a room where he can be treated alone. A gown is worn by the adult for her protection.

General technique. The child should be seated and made as comfortable as possible. Remove the outer garment and apply the mackintosh cape. Comb the hair and be careful not to fluff it about. Part the hair into sections, and then with the small tooth comb dipped in disinfectant, comb a few strands of hair at a time, examining the result carefully, and wiping the comb with a swab, killing lice in the swab and place the dirty swab in the receiver. After going all over the hair, burn all used swabs. The hair should then be free from lice or pediculi and must be thoroughly washed as already described. The nits or eggs can be seen attached to the hair about a quarter of an inch from the scalp and if not removed will hatch out in about ten day's time. When the hair is half dry it must be combed with the Sackers comb, taking small sections at a time and trying to remove the ad-herent nits. After this treatment apply a few drops of Suleo or Lorex-ane to the scalp in several places, thus helping to destroy any lice or nits. Tidy the hair and leave for twenty-four hours to forty-eight hours according to directions, then thoroughly comb the hair again as it is important to remove all the nits to avoid further infection. As a

FIG. 47. Quiet period with father before going to bed.

preventive measure the preparations mentioned may be applied about once a fortnight.

Nursery children may be infected by older school children in their own homes. Wherever children are cared for, it is important that each should have individual equipment. This does much to prevent the spread of infection and it applies equally to the home and to the nursery.

Bedtime

This is an extremely important period of each day and in many instances it is passed over much too lightly. It is essential that the child should know the person putting him to bed, just as a child at home expects his mother's attention at this time. After his bath he will want his drink of milk and will love to have a story told to him, either before getting into bed or when he is in bed. After passing urine he should be settled down in a comfortable bed, with suitable bedclothes and clothing, which will allow him perfect freedom with the necessary warmth. A favourite cuddly toy is often a great joy and comfort, particularly to the deprived child. At the same time it is wise for the child to be taught to associate bed with sleep.

The room should be well ventilated and the curtains drawn back. Guard against noises, such as rattling windows which might frighten the child. If he is rather nervous allow a safely guarded night light and leave the door open, so that he can hear the normal household sounds which will reassure him. Sound sleep will encourage good growth.

The child's bed and bed-clothes

The bed must be long enough and broad enough to allow full body movement. The mattress should be firm, giving support to the spine. It is important that the mattress is aired each day, before the bed is made. It should also be brushed or cleaned with a vacuum cleaner at regular intervals, preferably in the open air and it should be covered with a washable cover. The same principles apply to bed-clothes as to general clothing – they should be warm, light in weight and easily washed.

Sheets made of cotton or linen should be large enough to tuck in without causing restriction.

Blankets are best when loosely woven, pure wool, light in weight, and large enough to tuck in.

Pillows if used should be of Dunlopillo or flock. They should be as flat as possible to ensure that the head is in the correct relationship to the spine.

Sleeping accommodation

Whether in the home or the nursery the night nursery must allow the maximum of fresh air without draughts. The cot or bed if placed near the open window must be guarded. By four years of age the child is usually perfectly safe in a small single bed, in fact he prides himself on having a grown-up bed. Wherever two or more children are sleeping, their heads must be 6 feet apart, and the cots at least 3 feet apart. Such arrangements will do much to prevent the spread of infection.

A subdued night light is essential in a babies' night nursery to enable the nurse to observe the babies at frequent intervals, without disturbing them.

Chests of drawers are necessary to provide individual accommodation for the children's clothing. For the older child a small locker by his bedside will make the night nursery more homely and give him a place to keep his personal toys or belongings. Chairs are essential, the type varying according to the children's needs. A rug by the bedside suggests warmth and makes the room more attractive.

Day Nurseries

In the day nursery or nursery school where the children spend part of their day, the staff, whatever their basic qualifications are, must cooperate with each other in a genuine team spirit to produce a happy atmosphere. Parents must be encouraged to play their part if the nursery is to be a true extension of the home. Under normal conditions mothers are often interested to come along to sew or mend, as they derive great joy from seeing their children at play under such good conditions. The father can make and mend toys, and if they can do this in view of the children they will be doubly repaid by the interest and pleasure of the children.

Parents' clubs have a great social and educational value, thus encouraging understanding between the staff of the nursery or nursery school. Success is dependent on the sincerity of all the staff and the parents. Naturally the parents' hours of work can make meetings difficult to arrange, but it is well worth the effort to run a parents' club.

The reception of the children is most important. Each child must be made welcome, and if the nursery conditions are good, the child will look forward to his day in the nursery, but he should also enjoy going home. The staff need to be on friendly terms with the parents, and should try to find out a little of what has happened to the child since he was last in the nursery; for example whether he has slept well, whether has has passed a stool, whether he has been irritable or at all difficult. Home conditions vary very much but with the cooperation of the local health visitor who should know the home, a better understanding of the child should be possible. At times a mother may appear careless and even indifferent but on investigation she may be found to have family worries which account for her manner. The private life of each family must be respected, and the staff of the nursery should show sympathetic understanding. Privacy should be given to any mother who wishes to discuss her problems, and if difficulties in the nursery do arise such as a dirty head or dirty clothes, the matron, head teacher or her deputy should talk to the mother or father, remembering the extreme sensitivities of the people concerned and being as kind and helpful as possible.

The mother or father should bring the child to the nursery and take him home in the afternoon whenever possible, and should be free to go into the play rooms and see their children there. Parents should also be made to feel that they can talk to the staff at any time so that the gap between nursery and home is bridged as far as possible.

Day nurseries are provided by the local health authority for the children of working parents who pay according to their income. The function of the nursery is to care for the children if the mother has to work, or if she is ill for any length of time or if there are other difficult circumstances. Children are accepted from the age of six weeks. Lunch and tea are normally provided but breakfast only in rare circumstances. Details vary from one local authority to another. The children's activities vary according to their age, the very young ones following a routine as close as possible to that of a normal home, and those who are two years old or more have a routine similar to a nursery school.

The nursery school service

This is the responsibility of the local education authority. It is provided free but its provision is deplorably inadequate, some local authorities providing almost no nursery school places at all. This situation has given rise to the proliferation of unskilled, untrained and unsatisfactory baby minders, but also to the development of play groups which when well run can be a great asset to a neighbourhood.

Day Nursery routine

Children arrive between 8.30 and 9.30 a.m. and are free to play with a variety of play equipment such as bricks, dolls, books or in a play house, or to sit quietly doing nothing in particular until they wish to be active. Some nursery schools give milk soon after the children arrive.

Between 9.15 and 11.15 a.m. they are free to play. There are indoor and outdoor occupations, and freedom to change round from one occupation to another. During the morning short periods with small groups may be arranged for music, stories, or for a walk, or for looking at living and growing things. Any really tired child should be allowed to rest.

Many nursery schools only keep the children for half a day, either morning or afternoon, but if they are staying all day a charge is made for lunch.

As lunch time approaches small groups should go to the cloakroom to use the lavatory and wash their hands, and some of the older children may help to lay the table.

After lunch small groups should again go to the cloakroom and then prepare for a rest period which can be out of doors if weather permits, otherwise in a well ventilated room with the rest beds well spaced. The children should be alternately head to foot. The length of rest will vary according to the age of the child. Children who do not sleep are encouraged to look at a book or to rest quietly while the others are sleeping.

The period from 2.0 p.m. to 3.30 p.m. is arranged in a similar way to the morning.

In most nursery schools the mother collects her child soon after 3.30 p.m.

Residential Nurseries

These are provided by the Children's Committee of the local authority or more often by a voluntary organisation helped by local authority grants, such as the National Children's Society or Dr. Barnardo's Homes. There is a definite trend away from residential institutions, and wherever possible foster parents are found for deprived children.

The children who enter these homes come for a variety of reasons; the courts may have decided that their parents are temporarily unfit to care for them, they may be from homeless families or be unwanted illegitimate children. But one thing that they all have in common is some degree of deprivation. So their reception on entering the home must be warm and friendly, as the child is bound to be disturbed on leaving his own environment however unsatisfactory it may have been. It is wise for him to meet not only the matron but also the nurse who is going to look after him, and it is up to her to make him feel really wanted. Usually he will gradually come to accept her, and the other children in his own group who form a real family unit.

It is difficult to prevent a residential nursery appearing rather institutional, but the small family groups within it go a long way towards breaking down this image. A great deal depends on the matron of the home and on the kind of atmosphere she creates. The children should be allowed to help wherever possible in the way they would at home. One or two children go into the kitchen 'to help' the cook for short periods, and the domestic workers should also be prepared to accept 'help' from time to time. Seeing the things done that they would normally see in a good home, is of tremendous importance to them and should be encouraged whenever possible. This creates a home-like atmosphere and for any child who has left his home it is most comforting, while to the child who has never known a real home, it gives him something as close to it as possible.

Small family groups of children of mixed ages from one to seven

FIG. 48. The family meal.

are more home-like than a larger group and they are much more satisfactory. In this way two children of the same family can be kept
together, thus strengthening the family ties. Meals taken in small
groups are much more sociable and helpful to the child, especially if
the nurse in charge of the group tries to create a real family feeling.

Birthday parties give great pleasure to the group, and the antici-
pation is often as exciting as the actual party. Shopping expeditions
from the nursery will provide new ideas for the children and enlarge
their whole outlook, and whenever it is possible the older children
should be allowed to help choose their own clothes. Visits to ordinary
homes if only for a few hours, can be very valuable and a weekend
or a few days away with a family are a wonderful experience for
children from a nursery. The wider his experience can be while he is
still in the nursery the more prepared a child will be to fit into the
ordinary world later on. Also, if he can make some real friends outside
his nursery environment it will help him to form good relationships
later on in life.

In the short-stay nursery where children may go if their mother is

FIG. 49. I really have my own possessions.

ill or having another baby and is unable to look after them for a limited period the atmosphere is just as important as in a long-stay nursery. Small children have little or no conception of length of time, and a week or even two days will seem to them like eternity. It is very important that they should be able to take in with them some of their own possessions such as a favourite doll or bear as this will provide some link with their home and known surroundings. To almost every child there is an indescribable charm about his own home, however inadequate it may be and unless the nursery can give the impression that it is a home, their home, they are going to be very seriously upset although this may not be immediately apparent. They must be granted a certain amount of privacy, some territory that is really their own, their own possessions and somewhere to keep them where no one else can interfere (see Fig. 49). And most important of all someone who is really theirs, to whom they can relate, and on whom they can rely, who can fulfil as far as is possible the role of a mother.

Residential nursery routine

The routine for children of from two to five years:

7 a.m. to 7.30 a.m.	Getting up and a fruit drink.
	Toilet. Wash hands and face.
	Dressing, the older children helping any younger ones.
7.45 a.m.	Breakfast with family group. Toilet and wash hands.
8.30 a.m. to 4 p.m.	Nursery school or similar routine within the home.
4.30 p.m.	Tea in family group.
5 to 6 p.m.	A quiet period with books to look at or stories being read or told.
6 p.m. to 6.30 p.m.	Bath and bed. A light snack and a drink of milk.

CHAPTER 7
Play

The need for play

'Play is the child's natural way of learning and developing and is the main business of his life.' Every child plays, and really adequate and satisfying play will help his all round development as nothing else can. All children play and it is significant to find throughout the world that the same patterns of play follow one after the other in a definite order or sequence. It is interesting to consider the play of man in relation to that of animals. Those animals that are most immature at birth, but higher in the scale of intelligence, spend the most time in play, and the human infant the most dependent and the slowest to mature of all takes even longer.

It is possible to tell roughly what a normal child's play should be at a certain age. So from watching play it is possible to discovers whether a child is backward, forward or average in his development.

A child's play is of most value to him when it is completely free and spontaneous, and organised by the child himself, for he instinctively knows what he needs to do at each stage of development. Given adequate materials and the opportunity to play with them in his own way, the child will prepare himself for future life and education.

Purpose of play

The child's play arises spontaneously and freely from his inner needs, and is vitally important for good all round development. Through play he prepares for the important business of growing up. He will teach himself to think and to reason, and to use his mind in many different ways which stimulate the growth of his intelligence. Confidence is encouraged through his experiences, and as the child learns to control his muscles, his bodily skills and movements increase.

He grips and controls his hands, stands, walks, runs and, if he is given a good environment, he will gradually learn to use his body with grace and dexterity.

Through his play the child can express his individuality. Given plenty of scope he can give vent to his feelings, which helps him to establish and eventually maintain a good emotional balance.

As the child grows, he will meet an increasing circle of people. The first relationships with his mother and his immediate family, and later the activities shared with his contemporaries, will all help him to make the right sort of social adjustment which matters so much if he is to grow up to be a happy and valuable member of the community.

The responsibility of the adult

It is essential that the adult in charge of the child should realise the vital importance of play from the very early days. Her role is to provide, not only the right play materials, but equally important, the right atmosphere, to foster the most satisfactory all-round development.

Both in the home and in the nursery the adult must be aware of the child's needs, to enable her to supply play materials of different types in adequate quantities, which will be suitable to the stage of development which he has reached. The arrangement and presentation of these materials needs careful thought in planning, so that the children's interests are stimulated, and so that the best possible use is made of the available space, and the risk of accidents is avoided.

In nurseries and nursery schools the equipment should be arranged and remain in the same position, so that each child will know exactly where to find what he needs; for example the book corner, the Wendy house, painting things and clay for modelling. The adult should watch the children carefully so that she can see whether the materials are within the children's scope. If the apparatus is too easy the child will become bored, and if it is consistently too difficult he may become discouraged and in either case he is very likely to vent his feelings on the toys and damage them. Children use similar materials in a great variety of ways, and each child should be able to achieve a result that is satisfying to him at his particular stage of development.

It will be necessary for the adult to show the children how to use various tools and pieces of equipment, such as scissors and paint-brushes, and also to suggest new ways of using materials, if the children are short of ideas. If a problem arises during play which the children cannot solve and which threatens to spoil their game, then the adult can offer suggestions as to how to overcome the difficulty.

Large apparatus such as slides, climbing frames, and swings which stimulate physical activity, should be kept out of doors. They should be well spaced, giving the children plenty of freedom for movement, so that overcrowding does not lead to dangerous conditions that might cause accidents. They should be positioned so that the children can be easily seen. If weather conditions are suitable activities such as painting, water play and playing with bricks and trains, can be moved outside; this will be good for the children as well as giving them great pleasure, since many children have nowhere at home where they can play outside.

Natural materials such as sand and water are a real necessity to children, and should be provided whenever possible. Children who come from unsatisfactory homes will benefit in every way from attendance at nursery school, a day nursery or play group, where there are adequate facilities to aid and encourage their full development. Probably the best possible play environment is in the country where the child can play in fields and woods, with sand, earth and water, sticks and stones, and where there are rocks to climb, and living plants and animals to watch in their natural environment. But life in the country is the privilege of an ever decreasing number so that parks and play-grounds become of more and more importance in all built up areas.

An understanding adult will be able to create a calm happy atmosphere, in which the child can make the best use of his play materials. She should be aware of the problems of her charges, and should guide rather than command, so that the child learns to find his own solution to his difficulties, and to adjust his behaviour in varied circumstances. Independence should always be encouraged, but the adult must be at hand to help and encourage a timid, frightened or unhappy child.

Through the companionship of children of a similar age or stage of development there will be opportunities for the child to lead and follow in turn, to give and take, and to be considerate and kind in his attitude to other people. He should have freedom to learn by trial and error, which will ultimately give confidence and satisfaction.

An over-anxious adult can be a handicap to the child as he quickly senses her anxiety or disappointment. It is important too that she should understand the child's background; for example, she should know if there is any emotional stress, such as fear, jealousy or even a slight physical handicap which might slow down development or the growth of confidence. Adults who have the care of children should try to work together in matters of discipline, as if there are inconsistencies the children will not know what is expected of them and will feel uncertain and insecure. Expert advice on behaviour problems can be obtained at a child guidance clinic (see Chapter 31).

Stages of play up to one year

A child's stages of play are closely linked with his general development. During these early years the two most important factors in a child's development are learning to control and use his body, and his five senses, and getting to know and come to terms with his environment. It must not be assumed that all children will walk at one year and start talking then, or that certain definite stages will have been reached by two, three, four or even five years; a child should be judged by his own development and not only by his age. A child who develops slowly will probably be perfectly normal when he reaches maturity. As every child is an individual he will go through each stage of his development at his own pace.

The first three months

During the first three months of life the baby gains much experience through his own reactions to handling, feeding, and general comfort. He has no need of toys nor of play in the ordinary sense of the word. By about six weeks he is gradually becoming aware of his surroundings. This awakening may be encouraged by suitable play materials such as bright beads or a rattle tied to his pram. Unless the toys are fastened to the pram where he can see them, he will quickly lose sight of them and forget them.

In the early weeks he will automatically grip with the palm when a small object is placed there, but his muscles will quickly relax again and the toy will drop. Gradually as the muscles become stronger he will grip for longer periods, and appear to look at the toy or put it in his mouth. Thus he is using all his capabilities to investigate and learn. In these early weeks it will be the colour and sometimes the sound of the article which will attract him rather than its actual shape.

Careful note should be made of any reaction to different textures. For example, fur is sometimes disliked and the baby reacts by quickly withdrawing his hand or fingers. In such instances the toy should be removed and given again later on, when he may accept it. At this stage a known voice will please him, and he may respond by looking and smiling.

The infant's daily bath must not only be considered as a hygienic necessity, but also as a valuable play period when he is in close contact with someone he knows who chats and encourages him to use his arms and legs when he is in the water. Through the secure hold by the adult he is free to move and splash. Most children get great delight from this splashing and freedom. This is the beginning of water play, which is so valuable to his development. Through this daily experience he begins to be really interested in his hands and feet.

Three to six months

The baby is now becoming more capable of movement, particularly associated with his limbs. Opportunities must be provided for him to exercise with perfect freedom on a rug or in a playpen. During this period he becomes very interested in his hands and feet, and when on his back he will try and eventually succeed in getting his toes into his mouth. This demonstrates how quickly he learns by his own efforts and experiments. Naturally he quickly tires, but he must have this freedom. He should have a few colourful toys available for him to handle or throw about if he wishes.

He will often take notice of music and singing and in time show an interest by turning his head in the direction of the sound. Sometimes a child will show enjoyment by waving his arms and smiling, while another remains quite calm although he likes the music too. Babies respond differently to similar circumstances, just as they will when they are grown up.

Children will handle toys in similar ways according to their own abilities, but concentration is still very limited so another toy should be available when interest in the first one is lost. Having only one toy to play with at a time, prevents the child from becoming confused. Gradually he may show a preference for some colours, and for slightly bigger toys and often at this stage a toy or a wooden spoon which the child can bang will give great delight to him, if not to his mother.

Sitting up with support is often achieved at about six months, and the baby will try to clap his hands when encouraged by the adult. This shows the beginnings of neuro-muscular coordination and is very satisfying to most children. He can now handle toys such as a small teddy bear and will often show a marked sense of possession.

Six to nine months

At this stage the baby may have developed sufficient muscular ability to start crawling, or moving around by some less conventional method. He will begin to show interest in bricks and balls and in anything that will make a noise. He will sometimes use both hands at once, and may even look at a simple and colourful picture. One favourite occupation is to feel and crush pieces of paper, but he will need watching carefully to make sure that he does not eat it.

If he is well developed he may be interested in a fairly stable push along toy, such as a dog or horse or lorry, which he may examine by feeling, licking or patting according to how he feels. The family pet, a cat or a dog, may interest him but he will not realise the difference between his toy dog and the real animal. This means that he needs watching to make sure that he does not hurt the animal, or do anything that might upset it and make it bite or scratch him. Many small children develop fears of animals through some very minor incident, which can be very hard to eradicate.

Small trucks to push are interesting, and he may be able to put bricks into them, using both hands and gripping with his fingers. By copying an adult, or older child, he may be able to put one or two small bricks on top of each other, a feat which will impress him greatly.

He may begin to understand what is meant when a familiar toy is named, and he may even point to it showing that he does understand simple words, although he is not yet able to express himself.

His activities are usually spasmodic; he contacts the adult for a few brief moments to assure himself that she is still there. Then he will turn away with renewed confidence to handle anything that attracts his attention. Although a choice of play materials is essential, too many toys at one time will confuse him so that he cannot benefit or learn from them.

Mealtimes should be happy, and of great interest to the child, and he must be allowed to try to feed himself if he wants to, to help him master this skill, even if the result is not very successful.

He will enjoy singing games such as 'This little pig went to market' and listening to the jingle of nursery rhymes.

Nine to twelve months

Many children develop very rapidly during this period and need the freedom to explore whatever new fields they can find. Great care needs to be taken to avoid accidents which can so easily happen because of the child's lack of skill and experience. The adult should avoid showing anxiety whenever possible as this can have a bad effect on the child's progress.

Some rather stronger play materials, such as a small rocking horse, trucks, animals on wheels or any improvised wheel toys made from strong boxes, should now be provided.

Towards the latter part of this period a small sturdy chair will be useful. The child may use it to sit in and to try to pull himself to a standing position. Some children may try to shuffle along in a chair, thus fulfilling their great urge to move about. Crawling after balls or bricks will give a sense of achievement and many children derive great pleasure from shaking a tin with one or two pebbles inside.

By this stage the child is really working with a sense of purpose, and he is most earnest about it all, but with such hard work he will need short periods when he can sit quietly with an adult, who may talk or sing or read to him, until he has regained his energy and wants to be off again. He will probably develop a technique to enable him to slither quite safely from a chair to the floor, and by one year he will probably have his own particular method of trying to climb onto an armchair or other accessible piece of furniture.

The more children can be out of doors the better, though close supervision is essential when any new activities are being introduced, such as sitting in a baby swing, or crawling across a stretch of grass to fetch a ball. Most children enjoy going for walks in a pram, and will show interest in anyone or anything that passes by. Going on a bus or train for a short journey and noticing the goings on of the other passengers all helps to enrich experience.

The more varied the child's play and experience can be the better it is for his all round development.

Suggestion for play materials during the first year

0–6 months

    Various types of small rattles
    Coloured beads or discs on a ring or chain
    Bell or ring on stick
    Teething ring
    Small soft ball
    Rubber or plastic animals to squeeze
    Small washable dolls and soft toys
    Toys for the bath

Improvised equipment:
Small empty tins with something inside that rattles
Plastic cup and spoon

6–12 months

All the things provided for the first six months which will be used
much more expertly, together with:
Small building bricks
Nesting boxes
Larger balls
Strong books with large simple pictures
Small toys on wheels to push or pull
Pouffe to climb on

Improvised equipment:
Bigger tins and boxes with cotton reels to put in them
Tins of different sizes fitting into each other to make a nest of tins
(It is of course important that any tins used should not have sharp
edges)
Tin tray or saucepan lid and wooden spoon

Special precautions to take with toys during the early months
The baby is inclined to put everything into his mouth during the
first months, so play materials must be washable and quite safe when
sucked. Polythene is a good material and much more satisfactory than
brittle plastic or painted wood, or metal. Objects must not be so
small that there is a danger of their being swallowed or pushed into
the nose or ears. On the other hand they must not be so large that the
baby can not grasp them.

It is important that all play material is safe and strong. There must
be no rough edges or surfaces that can rust. Beads must be firmly
threaded, rattles should be strong, and all toys should be regularly
inspected for signs of damage.

Stages of play from one to five years

Twelve to eighteen months
During this period the child makes rapid strides in physical skills
and control. He greatly enjoys using his body, learning to walk and
to climb. The pace of development varies very much from one child
to another at this stage but most of them will go through similar
stages at some time or another. By the time they are one, most children
can pull themselves up to a standing position, and some will be trying
to stand alone or even to take their first few faltering steps. By some

means or other the child will move from place to place. Everything fascinates him, and he is into everything so that any fragile or unsteady furniture should be well out of reach.

The child can now amuse himself in his play pen for short periods, where such toys as beakers or containers are put to many uses. He will put an object in and out of a container and will throw it, pick it up, and throw it again. He can use his hands to bang or hammer and loves the feel of sand or water or clay. His span of concentration is still very short, so he will need a variety of toys to hold his attention. Pull-along toys will be especially popular at this stage.

As physical growth and intelligence develop, so the child's interests increase. Towards the end of this stage a brave adult may try to introduce painting having first assured herself that nothing in the vicinity or a good way beyond it can be spoiled by paint. The first

FIG. 50. Water play in the home.

attempts will be extremely crude; the child will grip the brush in his fist and using his whole arm will scrub the colour on to the paper. This primitive movement will give tremendous pleasure and satisfaction, although he may only make two or three strokes before losing interest.

Sand and water are both sources of endless pleasure, and are fascinating to children at this stage. The sand is tractable and has a pleasant texture and the child will spend a long time patting it, emptying and filling a bucket, and letting the sand run through his fingers. Water will be poured from one container to another, dolls can be washed and boats floated. Even if it is difficult to provide facilities for water play, it should be possible to allow the child time to play in his bath. Toys which float and containers for pouring

FIG. 51. Water play in the nursery school.

should be provided. Used and washed out yoghurt cartons are ideal for this. All these activities give the child practice in using his hands and help to develop coordination between hands and eyes. At the same time the great feeling of pleasure and emotional satisfaction which they give him contributes substantially to his development.

The child is now more responsive to adults than to children of his own age, and demands a great deal of attention. As he is not yet fluent in speech he will often take the adult's hand and pull her along towards the thing to which he wants to attract her attention.

Eighteen months to two years

The child is now likely to be walking and climbing although he is still unsteady on his feet, which sometimes seem to run away from him. He is still very active and needs a good deal of space to run about in. There is more control of the hands and with this increase in skill comes a great interest in fitting one thing into another. Nesting beakers are a favourite toy. He has gained more confidence in feeding himself, although he will probably tire before the end of the meal and need some assistance to finish.

The child may now become especially attached to a particular toy or other object, for example a piece of material or a doll or teddy

FIG. 52. His very own teddy bear gives pride of possession.

bear, and this is comforting to him. When his mother is busy with domestic duties, he may often attempt to copy her and he will industriously, though not very efficiently, dust and sweep. He will find it difficult to share his mother or her substitute with other children. She must be very patient and tactful, especially when dealing with a small group. Although he is interested and enjoys playing with other children there is no real cooperation between children at this stage. There is little social give and take, but children are inclined to use each other as if they were physical objects, and defend their rights by pulling and pushing or even kicking or biting. Therefore the adult must always be watchful and ready to protect them from each other.

Too many companions might be over-stimulating, and it is essential for the child to have sufficient rest.

The wrist movement is now more flexible, allowing easier brush strokes when trying to paint, even with a brush in each hand. He still scrubs the coloured paint over the paper, often putting one colour over another, giving a muddy effect. His vigorous movements may even rub a hole in the paper. At this stage it is the act of painting which is important, the result does not matter.

Modelling with clay or dough is much enjoyed. This will be slapped with the palm of the hand with great enthusiasm. Some children dislike the feel and texture at first, but they soon overcome this. Some may taste it as this is a time for experimenting and finding out.

From about eighteen months to two years children begin to enjoy looking at picture books with clear, large pictures of animals or things they have seen. They love going through them with an adult helping to turn the pages, and naming the various things they are familiar with. Nursery rhymes give great pleasure too, and the child will often repeat them with an adult, usually managing to supply the last word when encouraged to do so. Their attempts at singing at this stage are usually enthusiastic but out of tune, though the occasional child sings in tune at a very early stage.

Two to two-and-a-half years

This is a stage when all the child's activities are accompanied by talking. His speech is becoming more fluent and he loves to practise his skill. There is a quick shift of attention and the child flits from one activity to another. He continues to be interested in all previous activities, with some additions such as a very simple jigsaw puzzle, and threading large beads. When painting, the child will usually start with a great deal of care to make lines, but this very soon deteriorates as he loses interest. He seems to find modelling relaxing, and will often spend long periods playing with clay, dough or plasticine (see Fig. 53). Sand will be used to make cakes and pies,

E

FIG. 53. Playing together with dough.

with increasing skill in turning out the buckets and patty tins or pans. Blowing bubbles, washing doll's clothes and scrubbing, all of which incorporate water play, give great emotional satisfaction. The child will show more interest in books and enjoy rhythm, and repetition in rhymes and stories. He also likes the adult to improvise stories about himself and his activities.

Two-and-a-half to three years

Now dramatisation and imagination are beginning to enter into the children's activities to a far greater extent. Their speech becomes more and more fluent and thus they become better able to talk about what they are doing, and their play is still accompanied by a running commentary.

In block building there is increasing interest in a variety of shapes and sizes, and the child will often combine the blocks with other playthings, such as cars, garages and sand to make roads and mountains. This type of game leads to increased sociability with other children in a group.

In painting, the strokes will become more and more varied and the beginning of design is emerging. Sometimes a whole page is covered in one colour. The child may tell you what he is painting, but the finished result will seldom be recognizable. The adult will be in great demand to admire the painting, and the child is usually very proud of the result. He will also enjoy drawing with crayons, and these drawings are often more advanced than his paintings (see Fig. 54).

FIG. 54. Learning to express himself through painting.

The beginning of form is to be seen in the child's use of clay. He enjoys manipulating it with his hands; patting, squeezing, and poking holes with his fingers. He will make long snakes and balls.

Dramatic and imaginative play will take place indoors and outdoors in many forms. Sometimes the bath tub becomes a ship or an aeroplane; the dolls corner will be transformed into a hospital with sick patients well wrapped up, being given frequent doses of imaginary medicine. Such play is very revealing as well as being entertaining, and the adult gets a real insight into the personalities and problems of the children. It is also highly likely that she will see a reflection of herself in the way the children treat each other and their dolls. One child may be docile and do exactly as he is told, but another will insist on being the leader and organiser of the group. The quiet

FIG. 55. Make-believe play – the doctor and the nurse.

child can be helped by the support of the adult to assert himself, while at the same time she should try to guide the dominating child to be kind and gentle to those who are more timid.

The child's interest in books and stories is constantly increasing and he will begin to show a keen interest in details. Sometimes children will insist on stories that they know being told in exactly the same way each time, and become very annoyed if a single word is altered.

Imaginative stories are enjoyed especially if they are based on real people, and a repetitive element as in 'The three little pigs' or 'The three bears' usually goes down well. The children may interrupt during the telling of a story, especially if it is about an experience which they have had themselves, for example, a story about a birthday party, or a trip to the zoo. The adult should encourage the children to discuss their experiences if possible, saving them until the end of the story. This will stimulate their fluency of speech. All sorts of facts about the world around them are conveyed to children through stories, and this helps them to become familiar with a much wider world than their own, and opens the doors to a whole new realm of fantasy and imagination. Some children may enjoy sitting and looking at books on their own, and it is a good thing if they do this at a table as their laps are too small to hold a book comfortably or safely.

FIG. 56. Enjoying books.

Music will stimulate them to tremendous activity so that the more space they have the better. They will want to walk, run, jump, or gallop and some will quickly become quite good at moving in time to the music. They like to experiment with percussion instruments, and can march beating time with a fairly good rhythm. Although most children cannot sing in tune at this stage, they enjoy singing and dramatising songs, especially if there are some things to dress up in.

A child will need to be told about putting away his toys but this can be fun if the adult turns it into a game. The children can become furniture removers, or dustbin men, and have the room cleared up in record time.

Three to four years

Much of the play during this stage is still imitation of the child's experiences and observations of all that he sees going on around him, but now because his life is fuller he will have much more to draw on. Outings to the circus or the zoo, to the sea or to a farm, a visit to the doctor or dentist will all reappear in games, especially if there are several children playing.

At this stage too, the child often has complicated ideas, which he has difficulty in expressing. A very considerable increase in the use of constructive materials of all kinds will probably take place. Not only physical activities, such as running and jumping and climbing, but also intelligence and self confidence make great strides forward, and the child can really be seen to be growing up.

He likes to be physically active and his muscular control is improving. He will run up and down stairs, dash about on his tricycle, and perform with great skill on large apparatus, such as a climbing frame or nesting bridge. He often seems fearless in such situations and he may have to be persuaded to try to use more restraint, although his confidence in his ability should not be lost. By using his fine muscles he also shows increased dexterity.

Threading beads and cutting out with scissors, activities which were formerly rather laboriously performed, are now tackled with great speed and assurance. The child is capable of sitting still for quite long periods if he is sufficiently interested in what he is doing.

Towards the end of this stage the child becomes more sociable. He will really enjoy attending a nursery school or nursery class, and he may want to have his friends home to play. Although there may be many arguments and disagreements, the child will be able to cooperate well in his social and imaginative play. He still enjoys playing at 'families' and there will be a surprising amount of accurate detail in this type of play.

There is also a tremendous surge forward in the development of creative activities. When the child paints the brush is held in an adult manner, and he may spend a long time working with great care on one painting. He makes designs and patterns, and sometimes letters. He can also draw definite objects, though these may be rather primitive to begin with, and he knows the names of many colours and will often experiment in mixing them. The finished article has now assumed a definite value to the child. He will want to take his painting home, and will be very proud if it is hung on the wall.

When he is modelling the child needs a lot of clay, and the things he makes become gradually more recognisable. If the models can be kept he will enjoy painting them when they are hard.

Voice control is increasing and the child can sing much more tunefully. He will get pleasure from group singing though some children prefer to sing alone. The acting of songs is still popular and even the child who is shy may begin to join in. Most children love a percussion band and respond well to varied rhythms. A favourite game is to guess tunes that are played on the piano or another instrument.

Children enjoy listening to gramophone records and the favourites will be played over and over again. Some will quickly learn the current popular songs which they hear on the radio or television. Television viewing, which should be supervised, is almost always popular, and the programmes for young children have a strong appeal and many of them teach a great deal.

As the child's powers of concentration develop he becomes able to listen to longer stories. Children of this age love being read to and will also look at books themselves and pretend to read them. They may even know a story completely by heart and will manage to turn the pages at just the right time. They may be able to pick out and name several letters, particularly those in their own name. Stories which deal with people's every day lives are popular, as are those containing information, and a whole store of knowledge can be acquired in this way.

Four to five years

It is usually towards the end of this period that the child has to face the tremendous adjustment of going to big school. If his opportunities for all round development have been good, he should take this in his stride, but it is important to watch for any sign of strain. He is now becoming more independent in his play and does not need so much adult supervision and help, though he still needs to know that there is a grown up somewhere in the background.

There is a greater ability to play with other children, and although he may show a protective attitude towards younger children, he generally prefers to play with his own contemporaries. Occasionally two children will gang up on a third and tease him. At home it may be better to have only one friend at a time to play, to avoid this happening.

Physical control is well established though there are marked differences in each individual. Some children may be nervous about using large apparatus, such as a climbing frame. Differences in sex and personality become more apparent in play; boys may have a genuine interest in tools and become quite proficient in their use, while girls will prefer more domestic activities such as cooking and playing at families.

Blocks and junk materials of all kinds are favourite materials for boys and girls. The girls will probably build houses and kitchens while the boys make airports, garages and bridges. Games of cowboys and Indians, space men or soldiers, hospitals and schools, will provide many hours of fun.

Choice of suitable play materials

When choosing suitable play material and toys for children, there are several points which should be borne in mind. All too often adults buy articles which look attractive, but which are of little or no value to the child. When buying toys, especially on a limited budget, the best ones are those which can be used in a variety of ways, and in which interest will be maintained, and which encourage cooperative effort. It is essential that every article should be of such a shape and size that it cannot hurt the children's eyes, ears, nose and throat. There should be no jagged edges, or any splinters on wooden or metal toys, and care should be taken to make sure that any paint used is non-toxic.

Manipulative and constructional material

These are toys which help muscular control, and coordination between the brain and muscles.

Graded nesting beakers in bright colours and posting boxes, whose lids have specially shaped holes, through which blocks of corresponding shapes can be dropped are useful in the early stages. Peg boards and spool boards for making patterns and matching colours, can either be bought or improvised without too much difficulty. The first jigsaw puzzles should be wooden and should consist of not more than eight large simple-shaped pieces. As the children progress they can be given harder puzzles to do but their capability and interest will vary considerably.

Pull along toys, wooden trains and hammer peg toys will all be of value.

Blocks are an essential play material, and will be used in an enormous variety of ways by children of all ages. It is important that the child should be able to handle the blocks easily, and so if the large ones are hollow they are much easier for a small child to pick up. The more variety in size and shape and colour the better, as this should stimulate the child's imagination.

Carpentry is popular from an early age but it should always be carefully supervised. Children need to be shown how to handle tools properly, but they usually have very definite ideas about what they

FIG. 57. Woodwork – using the tools.

intend to make. A low work bench should be provided with a few good quality tools, such as 7–10 oz (200–300 g) hammers, a small tenon saw, screwdrivers, a gimlet and some screws, and some large headed nails. The wood used should be soft, and usually enough odd bits and pieces can be found lying about to save buying any specially (see Fig. 57).

Junk modelling from old cardboard boxes of various shapes, cardboard rolls, newspaper and glue can lead to all sorts of exciting ideas. Scissors sharp enough to cut the cardboard will be needed but these must have rounded ends.

Plastic materials

This does not refer to plastics in the technical sense but to those materials that can be moulded and shaped such as clay and sand and dough. Also included under this heading are water and paint.

Painting

Before any painting is attempted the children should be properly clothed, with aprons that cover them effectively. The adult too will probably need to be well protected. Powder paint is the best type of

FIG. 58. Serious work with suitable equipment.

paint to use, and for young children this should be mixed before hand in jam jars, and a separate brush provided for each colour. If this is not done everything will be mud coloured in no time at all. Sugar paper or even newspaper is a satisfactory and economical type of paper to use, and the brushes should be fairly large and have long handles. Easels are better for children to paint on than tables, though for really large combined efforts the floor is often the best place. For finger painting the paint should be thickened with a paste of starch and a thick paper should be used as thinner types will disintegrate.

Modelling

Potters' clay is the most satisfactory material for children to use, providing it is kept moist and clean. The modelling should be done on boards, and when the models have dried out they can be painted and varnished with very good results.

Plasticine is also a good material to use, and dough made of flour and water and salt gives great pleasure, especially if pastry cutters are provided. The salt keeps the dough moist, as well as making it very unpleasant to eat.

There is a variety of other modelling materials available, but they tend to be expensive and not as satisfactory for the children as those mentioned.

Sand

An outdoor sandpit is ideal. If possible it should be large enough for a group of children to play in, and deep enough for them to dig holes. A flat ledge around the edge is useful for making pies and also for sitting on. Sea sand or washed sand is the most suitable type to use and it will probably need renewing every six months. The sand pit should be covered when not in use.

Indoors a polythene bath or special sand tray can be used. It should have as deep sides as possible, otherwise the sand will very quickly disappear.

Water

Water is an essential play material. Again a deep bath should be used and objects provided for experiments in floating and sinking and pouring. Children also enjoy washing doll's clothes, scrubbing dirty wooden or plastic toys and blowing bubbles.

Some mess is bound to be made when children play with sand and water and clay and if they are made to feel afraid of making any mess at all their play will be very inhibited. On the other hand a wise teacher will make adequate precautions before hand so that no real damage is done to clothes or furniture or the floor.

Imaginative and dramatic play

A very large part of children's play is imitation of what they see going on around them, so one very important piece of equipment in any nursery is a Wendy House where they can play at mothers and fathers, or schools, or hospitals. It can contain small strong pieces of furniture, such as chairs, tables, cupboards and beds; a cooking stove and some pots and pans, a toy iron and ironing board and some dusters and brushes. Dolls or teddy bears will also be needed and the children will probably think of many other things themselves (see Fig. 59).

FIG. 59. Imaginative play – building a house.

A box of dressing up clothes will be used endlessly in dramatic play. Old adult clothes can be adapted so that children can wear them, and a selection of old hats, handbags and necklaces will give great pleasure.

Equipment for muscular development

This will include all the large apparatus which is mainly used out of doors. A climbing frame with graduated spaces between the rungs should be carefully chosen. It should be firmly constructed and firmly attached to the ground. Trestles, nesting bridges and small ladders can be used in conjunction with each other and with planks. They should be free from splinters and should always be set out under the supervision of an adult. This type of equipment is expensive to buy but is worth the cost as badly constructed material can lead to serious accidents.

Swings, old tyres, knotted ropes and rope ladders will give added opportunities for swinging and climbing.

Tricycles and cars should be very strong and durable, especially if they are to be used by a group of children. They should be regularly checked to make sure there are no loose screws or unsteady parts. Well-made carts made of strong wooden boxes mounted on pram wheels provide a great deal of fun as do wheel-barrows.

Books

Books should be strong and with large clear colourful pictures which are well drawn and well spaced on the page. A few home made books with pictures pasted in are useful for young children. When choosing books, the children's interests are important. Until approximately three years of age the pictures should be of familiar objects such as toys, cats and dogs, cars, buses, fruit and flowers. Later there should be clear illustrations which will increase the child's knowledge of the world around him, wild animals and farms, factories and mines, different methods of transport and pictures of life in other countries.

Stories for reading to children should be chosen with great care and the adult should always read them through to herself if they are unfamiliar to her to make sure they will be good for reading aloud. It is important that the adult should enjoy the story herself as her enthusiasm or lack of it will affect the children. Through listening, the child enlarges his vocabulary and increases the scope of his ideas and for many children sitting quietly and listening to a story is the happiest part of the day.

Musical equipment

Almost all children enjoy making a noise, and so making music is always popular. Percussion instruments can be improvised in a variety of ways and as such instruments are very expensive to buy this is a useful saving. Shakers can be made from tins containing sand, small pebbles or other similar material, providing that the lids are always firmly secured. Sticks can be used to beat time to rhythms, and can have bells or rattles attached. Improvised drums can also be made. If there is space a music corner can be set aside for keeping the instruments. A piano and record player or tape recorder, are a tremendous help and there are many excellent music programmes for children on television and radio.

Television

Television has an enormous appeal to the majority of children and offers a good form of relaxation for children at the end of an exhausting day. There are a great many good programmes and the children can increase their fund of general knowledge to a very large extent. But it is important that the children should not be allowed to switch on just because they cannot think of anything better to do. Their viewing should be supervised and carefully regulated so that they really enjoy what they do see and benefit from it.

Care of equipment

Equipment should always be kept clean and in good repair, and it should be inspected regularly to make sure that it is. Damaged toys should be removed from the garden as soon as they are broken if the children are to learn to take care of their toys.

A child cannot be expected to respect and care for shabby and incomplete material; but if he is encouraged to clean and look after the toys as much as he can himself he will begin to take a pride in them.

Wooden articles should be washed regularly and scrubbed when necessary; and if any splinters appear the toy should be sandpapered. Screws are more efficient and safer to use for repairs than nails. If toys need repainting this should be done with washable non-toxic paint. Wooden out-door equipment such as climbing frames and swings, should be inspected regularly and oiled from time to time to protect them from the weather. Plastic materials should be kept clean by washing, and paint brushes should be well washed after use and stored with the bristles uppermost.

Toys used in sand and water play should be washed and well dried after use, and any rusty toys should be discarded. The sand should be raked daily when it is in use and cleaned once a week by watering it with a disinfectant solution. It should be covered up at night.

Dolls and soft toys should be washed regularly, so it is important when buying these toys, to make sure that they can be washed. Dolls clothes and dressing up clothes may need a weekly wash if they are in constant use.

Books should be removed as soon as they are torn and mended with transparent tape. Covers to protect the books can be made from children's finger paintings or drawings, and this will give them great pleasure in the books. If possible there should be a book corner where the books can be attractively displayed.

PART TWO
Nutrition

CHAPTER 8

General Nutrition

The science of nutrition is the study of foods and their uses in the body. It is a comparatively young science which embraces a very large field. It is important that all people responsible for the care of young children should have a good knowledge of this subject. Good nutrition is one of the chief factors in building and maintaining physical and mental health, and it plays a major part in good nursing and general care. The correct foods in adequate amounts can promote and maintain not only good health, but radiant health. The child's development is judged not only by his height and weight, but on his whole make-up, the condition of his skin, eyes, hair, bones, and muscles, his general activity, alertness and habits. All of which will be affected by his diet.

Functions of food
1. To provide materials for growth and for the repair of tissues.
2. To promote health, regulate the body processes, and increase resistance to disease.
3. To provide heat and energy.

Foods, with rare exceptions, are complex in structure, and because of this they often fulfil more than one function. It is necessary for any diet to be complete and well-balanced and to provide all the needs of a growing child.

Classification of foods

Foods are classed in the following groups and in relation to their chief purpose:
1. Proteins – body building and repairing foods.
2. Carbohydrates and fats – warming and energy giving foods.

3. Mineral elements – essential and protective substances, valuable for health and growth.
4. Vitamins – protective substances and essential for health and growth.
5. Water – necessary for production of body fluids and secretions and the elimination of waste from the body.

See Table I, page 136, for the content of foods in common use.

Proteins

These are nitrogenous substances which are present in every cell in the human body, but they differ according to the organs in which they are present and the functions they perform. They have a very complicated structure, being made up of minute chemical bodies called *amino-acids*, which make up the complex compounds known as proteins. Proteins have three important functions in human nutrition:

1. They are used to build tissues in a growing body.
2. They are responsible for the repair of daily wear and tear due to the rubbing away of dead skin cells, the loss of mucus from intestinal and nasal tracts, and the growth of hair and nails.
3. They are the source of many of the catalysts or agents which regulate body processes, and they are responsible for the combination of antibodies which resist the invasion of the body.

Too much protein in the body can be oxidized for the release of energy. Amounts eaten in excess of requirements are disposed of in this way, and when other energy releasing foods are lacking, as in starvation, body proteins are used as fuel. Excess protein is excreted as urea in the urine. Proteins may contain twenty or more amino-acids, eight to ten of which are considered essential for the growth and well-being of the human body. Some amino-acids can be manufactured by the body from others in the diet, but eight essential ones must be supplied directly by food. Foods rich in these essential amino-acids are of great importance in the child's early years.

Protein foods are of both animal and vegetable origin and most foods contain several proteins. Their value depends on the total amount of amino-acids present. A food which contains all the essential amino-acids is said to be *first class* or *complete protein*; examples are lean meat, fish, eggs, milk and cheese. Milk is especially valuable as it is easily digested and because of this it is necessary for all children to have at least one pint each day. The body's most rapid growth takes place in the first six months, during which time the infant doubles his birth weight. During this time, if the baby is being breastfed, all the materials forming his new body substance are derived from the mother's milk, or if bottlefed from cows' milk.

Second class or incomplete proteins are derived from vegetable sources. They lack one or more of the essential amino-acids, but they are useful in conjunction with the more valuable protein foods; examples of these are the seeds of leguminous plants, peas, beans and lentils. Also cereals, where the protein is found in concentrated form around the germ of the seed; wholemeal flour contains this. Vegetable protein is not so good as first class protein and is more difficult to digest, but it is a useful source of cheap protein, and is satisfactory, providing it does not exceed 30 per cent of the whole daily intake for the child under seven years.

Children need a high proportion of animal protein to maintain their growth and this need continues right through and in adolescence. The protein should be present in the three main meals of the day, and not concentrated into one.

Carbohydrates

This is an inclusive term used to describe starches, sugars, pectins and cellulose. Its presence is essential for the release of energy, which has two primary purposes, firstly to produce heat which will maintain the normal temperature of the body, and secondly, to keep the unconscious and automatic mechanisms of the body going, such as digestion, metabolism, respiration and the pumping of blood round the body by the heart; also the more apparent activities, such as walking, talking, eating and generally being. All the energy requirements of the body are supplied by food, and the activity of the individual combined with the climatic conditions control the carbohydrate intake required.

During normal digestion, starch is converted into sugar, and then enters the circulation, very gradually, to maintain a normal balance of sugar in the blood. Any carbohydrate in excess of the body's immediate needs is stored in the liver as glycogen, and this forms a reserve supply. The liver will reconvert the glycogen into glucose and release it when required to keep the blood sugar at a constant level. Any carbohydrate consumed over and above what the liver can store is converted into fat, and is stored under the skin and around the internal organs. Carbohydrate taken in the form of sugar is quickly digested, and if taken in too large quantities by small children is liable to flood the digestive tract and may cause irritation to the lining membrane, resulting in loose green stools. In cheap diets starches and sugars are often taken in excess and will fatten the child without building healthy tissue.

Starch is the form in which carbohydrates are stored in plants, and so it is present in many foods of vegetable origin. There are no pure carbohydrate foods in their natural state, but refined sugar is pure carbohydrate.

Starches

Starches are derived from the following sources:

a. *Cereals*, such as wheat, oats, barley and rice.
b. *Tubers*, such as potatoes.
c. *Roots*, such as carrots, parsnips.
d. *Pulses*, such as peas, beans, and lentils.
e. *Fruits*, such as unripe bananas, or apples.
f. *Nuts*, such as chestnuts, peanuts, walnuts, almonds and brazils.

Although the word 'cereal' strictly means a grain product, foods classed in this way include some which are produced from roots or underground stems, for example:

a. Arrowroot, almost pure starch, and contains no other nutrients of value.
b. Tapioca, prepared from the roots of the Cassava plant, consists mainly of starch, but contains small quantities of iron.
c. Sago is prepared from the pith of the trunk of the sago palm. Mainly starch and has little nutritive value.

All these contain negligible amounts of either protein or fat. Cereals are, usually, the cheapest form of food, and form the staple diet in most poor and underdeveloped countries.

The *wheat grain*, which is used for bread, consists of:

a. the *germ* or embryo, which although minute is rich in vegetable protein and fat. The embryo is situated at one end of the grain and is very small compared with the rest of the grain.
b. the *kernel*, or endosperm, which makes up 85 per cent of the whole grain and is tightly packed with starch. It is the food store for the new plant.
c. the *bran* and middlings or outer husk. This is the inner layer of the seed coat; it is dark in colour and is largely composed of cellulose, combined with mineral material.

During the baking of bread, there is some loss of nutritive value, but this is not extensive.

Macaroni, vermicelli, spaghetti and semolina are all preparations of wheat.

Barley is rich in mineral matter. It is seldom used for bread, but is used for soups, savouries and puddings. Pearl barley is prepared by steaming and polishing husked barley. This is used in soups, and for barley water. Malt is also obtained from steeping barley in water; it is used in the preparation of malt extracts, cereals, vinegar and beer.

Rye is closely related to wheat and is widely used in Northern Europe for bread making. It contains good quality protein so that rye flour has a high nutritive value.

Oats is one of the most nutritious of all cereals, with valuable amounts of protein, fats, minerals and vitamins. It is cleaned and ground to produce oatmeal. The flattened, partly cooked oats, known as rolled oats or quick porridge oats are treated by a heated rolling process. Oatmeal is useful for cakes, biscuits, savouries and porridge.

Maize or Indian Corn – there are two varieties of maize, yellow which contains carotene, and white which has none. Cornflakes and cornflour are derived from maize and it forms the basis of custard and blancmange powders.

Rice is still the staple food in a large part of the world. It can be used for making puddings and savouries and is more valuable if unpolished.

Sugars

The best known are cane sugar and beet sugar, both used as ordinary sugar for general purposes. This sugar is known as *sucrose* and also occurs in the roots of carrots and parsnips, and in the sap of the maple. *Fructose* is a sugar found in fruit and honey. It is a very sweet sugar. Combined with glucose it forms sucrose.

Malt sugar is produced from sprouted barley and is used for a base for some patent foods.

Lactose is a sugar found in milk; when fermented it forms lactic acid and turns the milk sour. It is also the acid which causes the precipitation of casein in the production of cheese. It is sometimes known as milk sugar and is white, fine in texture and practically tasteless.

Glucose is sometimes called dextrose. It occurs in most natural plant foods, and its concentration is particularly high in grapes, hence its other name: grape sugar. It is prepared commercially from starch and is available as a proprietary preparation. It is absorbed very quickly and is therefore immediately available in the body. It is sometimes taken by athletes before competing to give them added energy. Sugar acts as a preservative for fruit as in jam, marmalade, and candied peel.

Fats and oils

These are derived from the animal and vegetable world, and differ only in consistency. They are valuable fuel foods and weight for weight they produce twice as much heat and energy as carbohydrates or proteins. They are not so easily digested as starch and must be taken in conjunction with carbohydrate in suitable proportions to keep the combustion of the foods in the body properly balanced.

In the body fats form a padding around organs, such as the kidneys, and are stored as adipose tissue under the skin and between the muscles. Body fat is derived both from fat and carbohydrates eaten in excess of needs and can very easily make children overweight and have a detrimental effect on their health. Being a bad conductor of heat fat insulates the interior of the body from changes in environmental temperature.

Some people can tolerate fats much better than others, therefore it is important that the needs of each individual, and particularly children, are considered. Fats eaten with protein, and little or no carbohydrate, may cause headaches, nausea and sickness, but the presence of fat in the diet can prolong the satisfied feeling after a meal.

Animal fats most common in the diet are suet, butter, lard, dripping and fish oils. *Vegetable fats* in everyday use are corn oil and peanut oil, vegetable oil, olive oil and margarine. These are used for frying and in salad dressings. Fish oils are given to children in the form of capsules or liquid. Cod liver oil is the most common one. Herring, mackerel, salmon and sardines are rich in fat.

Lard is the purest animal fat, but bacon, fat meats, cheese, egg yolks and nuts all contain a good proportion of fat. Cereals have a trace. Vegetables cooked in fat absorb a great deal of it.

Minerals and vitamins

Foods which are rich in minerals and vitamins are sometimes called protective foods because they play a vital part in the growth and maintenance of health. The lack of minerals and vitamins gives rise to conditions known as deficiency diseases. Dairy produce and fresh fruit and vegetables are rich in vitamins (see Table II, page 142),

TABLE I

Content of Foods in Common Use

PROTEIN		CARBOHYDRATES		FATS	MINERAL ELEMENTS	
Class I	*Class II*	*Sugars*	*Starches*		*Calcium and phosphorus*	*Iron*
Milk Cheese Lean meat Eggs Liver, kidneys, etc. Poultry Fish (herring, sprats, mackerel, salmon, roes, sardines)	Cereals Nuts Peas, beans Lentils Potatoes	Milk (lactose) Jam Honey Syrup Sugar Ripe fruit	Flour Bread Cereals Nuts Peas, beans Lentils Potatoes Root vegetables Ripe fruit	Cheese Eggs Poultry Fish and fish oils Nuts Butter, dripping, suet, lard, margarine	Milk Cheese Lean meat Liver, kidneys, etc. Poultry Fish Peas, beans Lentils Green vegetables	Lean meat Eggs (yolk) Liver, kidneys, etc. Poultry Fish Green vegetables

but cooking and storing destroy a good deal of the vitamin content. Some of these foods are expensive but they should not be omitted from the diet as they promote a higher level of health. Health and normal growth would be at risk if chemically purified foods only were eaten and so frequently extra vitamins are added. See the list of ingredients on many foods, such as breakfast cereals and margarine.

Minerals

Calcium is essential for the structure and growth of bones and teeth. It is vital to a growing child to have adequate amounts. Calcium circulates in the blood and is essential if normal clotting is to occur. Additional calcium is needed by the pregnant woman to ensure that her own needs are met as well as those of the developing foetal skeleton. Women who are breast feeding also require more since a great deal is lost from the body in milk.

Calcium is also necessary for the proper functioning of nerves and muscles. If both calcium and vitamin D are deficient this will cause rickets, poor growth of bone, slow dentition and dental caries.

The richest sources of calcium are cheese and milk, including skimmed milk, but it is also present in smaller quantities in eggs, sardines, whitebait and watercress.

Even if there is sufficient in the food, the body may show signs of a deficit if there is a lack of vitamin D, without which calcium cannot be properly absorbed and utilized.

Phosphorus constitutes about one fourth of all the body minerals and is often associated with calcium and takes part in the formation of bones and teeth. The rest is present in soft tissues and body fluids. It is also present in the blood and there are higher concentrations in nervous tissues, especially in the brain. Children need equal amounts of phosphorus and calcium as do nursing and expectant mothers. Mature adults need more phosphorus than calcium. The chief sources are milk, cheese, eggs, fish, white and wholemeal bread and cereals. Fruits and vegetables contain much smaller quantities.

Iron is very important indeed. It is used for the manufacture of a red pigment called haemoglobin which gives blood its red colour. Haemoglobin owes its property of carrying oxygen to its iron content, whereby oxygen is transported round the body to all tissues and carbon dioxide is returned from the tissues to the lungs, where it is excreted. Iron is used in the manufacture of red cells in the blood; these are called the red blood corpuscles and they contain haemoglobin. They are made in the red marrow of bones, and then enter the blood stream; eventually they are stored in the liver. It is for this reason that the liver of animals is an excellent source of iron in a diet.

Whenever bleeding occurs iron is lost and this should be replenished. Menstruation causes a considerable depletion of a woman's store of iron. Some iron is lost each day by normal wear and tear. Babies are born with a store of iron in their liver which is used during the first few months, while their diet of milk has a low iron content. Children need relatively more iron than adults. Any shortage of iron in the diet will cause anaemia.

Good sources of iron are liver, kidney, egg yolk, meat and sardines. Green vegetables are valuable sources, turnip tops, spinach, spring onions, mustard and cress, and watercress being the best. Fresh and dried fruits, especially blackcurrants, are equally useful. Curry powder and cocoa also contain iron.

Vitamin C increases the absorption and use of iron; this occurs in the intestines. Iron is present in drinking water in certain areas and it may also be transferred to food from cooking utensils.

Iodine. This is essential to the body, but only in minute quantities. Lack or shortage causes cretinism in children. During pregnancy more iodine is required; it is also needed during lactation. Children need extra amounts in adolescence.

The best sources are sea foods, since sea water contains more iodine than fresh water. In most areas there is iodine in the soil and certain vegetables grown on it contain traces of iodine. The use of iodised table salt will ensure the provision of an adequate amount of iodine.

Fluoride is found in bones and teeth. It has been found in very small amounts in water, and is valuable in maintaining good teeth, but too much may lead to a mottling of the enamel. Little is known about its distribution in food. Local authorities are now empowered to add minute quantities to the general water supply.

Common salt or sodium chloride helps in the secretion of the hydrochloric acid in the gastric juice, and for maintaining the correct balance of fluids in the tissues. It is, in fact, found all over the body and there is very little risk of any shortage of this mineral in any normal diet. Salt is excreted in the urine and in perspiration. Extra salt is needed in hot climates and in hot weather. It is present in most animal foods, preserved, cured and pickled meats and fish, such as kippers. Shell fish and cheese also contain salt.

Vitamins

It is only in the twentieth century that the true value of vitamins has come to light. Some vitamins are concerned with growth, others with energy release, but all play some part in the maintenance of health. They circulate in the body fluids and occur in tissues where they have various functions to perform. They exist in minute quantities, which at first made it very difficult to assess the amount found in food, or needed to maintain health. The term *international unit* is used as a measure to indicate the quantity of vitamins necessary in the diet. Vitamins have become known by the letters of the alphabet and their importance cannot be over-estimated, in spite of the minute quantities found in foods. Although the chemical names and formulae of vitamins have been determined, they are most easily remembered by their alphabetical names.

The chemical composition of many of the vitamins has been revealed by research, so that many of them can be artificially produced, used to supplement the diet and treat deficiency diseases. Each vitamin has its own specific role, but frequently two or more are concerned in one process; for example, vitamins A, C and D are all concerned with calcium and phosphorus in the growth and maintenance of the skeleton. Everyone requires all the principal vitamins in their daily diet, and this is especially important in the winter months because the body needs extra resistance to infection and to be able to cope with the debilitating effects of winter conditions. Deficiency, even if only slight, can affect the growth and general health of the individual, and it is important that slight shortages should be diagnosed and made up in the early stages.

Vitamin A is soluble in fat, but not in water. It is important to all parts of the body, to promote growth of bone and for the health of the skin and mucous membranes, thus resisting infection of the respiratory passage. It is also concerned with vision and is necessary for the retina of the eye, making vision possible in a dim light. It is found in milk, butter, liver, animal and fish fats, such as cod liver oil, halibut liver oil and egg yolk. Margarine has vitamin A and D added.

Carotene is the yellow pigment found in carrots and the green leaves of vegetables, especially the dark green leaves; examples of these are parsley, spinach and turnip tops. It is also present in various fruits, such as apricots and plums. It is similar in chemical structure to vitamin A and is converted into it by the liver.

Vitamin A is not destroyed by cooking and canning. The body can store it in the liver and draw upon it when needed, hence the value of cod liver and halibut liver oil. Deficiency of vitamin A will retard growth, lower resistance to infection and cause night blindness.

Vitamin D is another fat soluble vitamin. There is a group of complex organic substances which occur in many foods. These substances are sterols, one of which, ergosterol, is present in the fat under the skin. When acted upon by direct sunlight or by artificial sunlight it is converted into one form of vitamin D. This vitamin promotes the absorption of calcium from food and its deposition in bones and teeth, so that sound structures are formed and maintained. Vitamin D may help in the prevention of dental decay and also aids some abnormal skin conditions. Exposure to sunlight enables the body to produce a store of vitamin D, which can be used during the winter months.

The chief sources of vitamin D are some animal fats, fish liver oils, salmon, sardines, herrings and butter. Margarine has synthetic vitamin D added.

Deficiency of this vitamin may cause rickets, a formerly common disease amongst children, due to poor bone growth, which has been almost wiped out since it was discovered that adequate vitamin A prevented this condition. Cooking, canning, curing or smoking does not affect vitamin D.

Vitamin B is an inclusive term for a group of vitamins, all of which are soluble in water but not in fat. At first vitamin B was thought to be only one substance, but now various vitamins have been isolated, each with its own chemical characteristics.

Vitamin B_1 is one of the most important. It is used in the body in the oxidation of carbohydrates; it is also necessary for growth and for the normal functioning of the nervous tissues and good health.

It is found in yeast, cereal germ (Bemax), liver, egg yolk, peas and beans, wholemeal bread, white bread, oatmeal and other cereals. Cabbage, carrots, potatoes and tomatoes are also good sources. All meats contain some vitamin B_1, but pork and bacon have by far the largest content.

When vitamin B_1 is deficient it will cause loss of appetite, nausea, constipation, anaemia, poor growth and various nervous conditions. Vitamin B_1 is often lost in storage, cooking and processing.

Vitamin B_2 group. This consists of a number of vitamins, some known by number, such as B_6, B_{12}, and others by names, such as riboflavine, nicotinic acid, and folic acid. Riboflavine is essential to growth in children and adults, and plays a part in the release of energy from foods. Nicotinic acid is necessary to keep the mucous membranes and the nervous system healthy. Folic acid is essential for the blood.

These vitamins are found in yeast, kidney, liver, meat, milk, eggs, Bemax, butter, leaf vegetables, and in certain fish. Deficiency of these vitamins causes skin disorders, inflammation of the mouth, some forms of anaemia, digestive disturbances and an unhealthy nervous system.

Cooking and storage may cause some loss of vitamin B_2 group.

Vitamin C is known as ascorbic acid and is soluble in water. Children and expectant mothers require more vitamin C than others. Vitamin C has many functions in the body. In association with calcium, phosphorus and vitamins A and D it plays an important part in the formation and maintenance of good teeth, and affects the calcification of bone. It is concerned with the metabolism of carbohydrates. It prevents some forms of anaemia and is vital for regulating the muscles of the body, including the heart muscle.

Vitamin C is present in large amounts in citrus fruits, in rose hips, and in blackcurrants. The highest concentration occurs at the growing points, and especially in spring when growth is rapid. The best sources amongst green vegetables are brussel sprouts, cabbage, cauliflower, turnip tops, watercress, parsley, spinach, mustard and cress and tomatoes. Strawberries, redcurrants, loganberries and gooseberries also contain valuable amounts. Germinated seeds or pulses are useful sources when fresh fruits and vegetables are not available. When young potatoes are first harvested they have a good content, but this is reduced by storage. Vitamin C is the vitamin most affected by heat, therefore cooking and reheating should be reduced to a minimum and avoided altogether when possible. As it dissolves in the water in which fruit and vegetables are cooked, green vegetables should be plunged into a small amount of boiling water; the remaining water should be made at once into gravy, then the additional vitamin C is obtained. The lid must be kept on the saucepan to prevent the escape of vitamin C in the steam. Storage and soaking also reduce the vitamin content. Canned vegetables and fruits compare well with home cooked vegetables and fruit, because of the methods used in canning, and also because the contents are usually canned within two hours of gathering. Canned vegetables for babies retain a high percentage of vitamin C.

TABLE II

Vitamin content of foods in common use

Vitamin A	Vitamin D	Vitamin B₁	Vitamin B₂	Vitamin C	Vitamin E
Milk	Milk (especially summer)	Yeast	Yeast	Citrus fruits	Wheat germ
Cheese	Cheese	Cereal germ	Cereal germ	Green vegetables	Eggs
Eggs	Eggs	Eggs	Eggs	Rose hips	
Butter	Butter		Butter	Blackcurrants	
Fish & fish oils	Fish & fish oils		Fish		
Margarine	Margarine				
Dark green leaved vegetables	Animal fat		Leaf vegetables		
Carrots, tomatoes, (carotene)		Carrots, tomatoes, potatoes			
Dried fruits (apricots, etc.)					
Liver (offal)		Liver (offal)	Kidney & liver		Liver
Meat		Meat			

New methods of dehydration of vegetables retain most of their vitamin C content, and even less is lost during quick freezing of vegetables.

Deficiency of vitamin C leads to bleeding of the gums and anaemia, poor bone and tooth structure. Wounds do not heal well and broken bones do not unite. Small haemorrhages may occur under the skin due to the blood vessels or capillaries becoming fragile. Scurvy may occur if this vitamin is lacking over a long period. This disease is rarely met in this country today, but is common in under-developed countries.

There are several lesser known vitamins, for example vitamins E, K and P.

Vitamin E is fat soluble. It influences the function of the muscular system and is thought to protect vitamin A in the body. It has been found to have effect on the fertility of some animals, and may prove beneficial to man. It has been found valuable in prevention of some types of habitual abortion. So far it is not known how much is required in the diet.

The chief sources are wheat germ oil, cereals, liver, eggs, and green vegetables. A good diet should be sufficient to supply the amount required.

Vitamin K is also fat soluble. It is essential for the clotting of blood and therefore prevents haemorrhage. No intake level has been specified since a normal diet usually contains enough. If vitamins A and C are present in sufficient quantities vitamin K will be there as well. The chief sources are found in green vegetables such as cabbage, spinach, peas, soya beans, tomatoes, liver, fish, rose hips and straw-berries.

Vitamin P is closely associated with vitamin C. A diet supplying sufficient vitamin C will ensure an adequate intake of vitamin P. It is found in the juice of citrus fruits, blackcurrants, rose hips, cabbage, spinach and tomatoes. Some fruits deficient in vitamin C should be eaten for the vitamin P they contain.

A deficit of vitamin P may be responsible for small patches of haemorrhage in the skin, through poor or weak capillary walls, but there is still a great deal of research to be done in this field.

Water

Strictly speaking water is a food. It is not possible to live without water for more than a few days. It forms about three-quarters of the total weight of the body and is the major constituent of blood and the digestive juices. It is also essential to the building of tissues. Water is necessary in the diet for the following purposes:

1. To enable dissolved food material to be distributed by the blood stream to every part of the body.
2. To carry ferments and internal secretions (hormones) throughout the system.
3. To regulate the body temperature.
4. To cleanse the tissues and eliminate waste material. Water is constantly lost from the body, in urine, faeces, perspiration, and in the breath. This loss must be made good.
5. To help in preventing constipation.

There is a large proportion of water in solid food, but approximately two to three pints of water are required per day by the adult in addition to that in various foods. Water is essential for children and should always be available for them. More is needed in hot weather, after exercise, in fever, diarrhoea, and in diseases in which the kidneys are involved.

Water is usually spoken of as hard or soft, the hard containing a high percentage of lime (calcium) and magnesium salts. Fluoride is present in water in some parts of Britain, and where it is not local authorities add it as it helps to prevent dental decay.

Water is purified, both bacteriologically and chemically, before distribution through the pipes, but in remote country districts well or spring water is sometimes used for drinking purposes. This should be boiled for young children.

It is important that the water supply is pure otherwise it can be a real source of infection. Samples of water are taken at every stage of its journey to the consumer's tap by the local health authorities.

Beverages. The importance of water in the diet has been stressed. Beverages commonly used in this country are useful ways of introducing water with variety. Drinks may be taken hot or cold, flat or aerated, with meals or between meals, sweetened or unsweetened. Fluids drunk with meals are not excreted so quickly as those taken between meals. Drinking with meals also softens food and facilitates its absorption. Tea and coffee are the most popular fluids taken. Both contain tannin and caffeine which are stimulants and so affect the brain; they are of great help when mental work has to be done. Strong black coffee is a valuable stimulant for shock and narcotic poisoning.

Cocoa contains a little protein, fat, carbohydrate, calcium, iron, vitamins A and of the B complex. When cocoa is prepared it should be boiled on account of its carbohydrate content.

According to the amount of milk used in cocoa, coffee and drinking chocolate, the nutritive value is increased, and it is generally made more palatable.

Fruit drinks. These vary from flavoured and coloured water, which has little value apart from being fluid, to pure fruit juice which can be high in vitamin and mineral content. Drinks from fresh fruit are preferable to bought preparations.

Soups add fluid to the diet and act as a stimulus to the digestion at the beginning of a meal, but the nutritional value depends on the content of the soup. The average soup has little food value, but it can be made more nutritious and it is useful for an invalid diet.

Meat extracts are useful for hot drinks, but unless they contain pulverised muscle they have little food value.

Roughage

This is chiefly cellulose from fruit, vegetables and wholemeal bread. It is not absorbed, but makes bulk in the intestines and stimulates peristalsis, so preventing constipation.

Foods containing roughage are brown bread, oatmeal, vegetables, fruits, nuts, and jams that contain pips and skins.

How the body uses food

If diets are to be planned it is important to know what happens to food after it has been taken into the mouth. The changes involved are very complicated ones and some of the details are still only partly understood, but the broad outlines have been fairly well worked out.

Digestion is the process by which foods are dealt with in the alimentary canal and prepared for entry into the blood stream. Digestion involves two processes, one chemical and one mechanical. The chemical changes are brought about by enzymes which break down the food to its basic constituents. Solid foods are gradually reduced to a solution and into a simple form, fine enough to be absorbed by the tissues and to be able to pass through the wall of the alimentary tract. In the process the food substances are divided into two main groups, soluble substances which are used by the body, and cellulose or roughage which is excreted undigested.

Absorption. The absorption of foodstuffs into the blood takes place almost entirely in the small intestine. Its inner surface is covered with tiny finger-like projections, the villi, which greatly increase the absorbing surface. As the digested food passes down the intestine, the villi take up the digested carbohydrate in the form of simple sugars, the protein as amino-acids. Ordinary salts such as common salt or iron are absorbed, together with a great deal of water. The fats in oil form are absorbed by the lacteal in the villi and taken through the lymphatic system into the blood stream.

Metabolism is the term used to describe what uses the tissues make of the food substances, which have been digested and absorbed into the blood stream. Protein takes a very special place in the diet for the body cannot make protein from fat or carbohydrate. The tissues of the body are constantly changing, breaking down and building up and a continuous supply of protein is required. Clearly in children, in whom there is a constant addition of new tissue throughout the growing period, the need of protein is even more urgent. The various cells in the tissues select foods for their own particular needs, and a process of oxidation takes place between the tissues, the oxygen and the food substances, and waste products, such as urine and carbon dioxide, are eliminated from the body.

Defective metabolism may occur, due to some deficiency in the process of digestion and this can cause severe damage to a child (see Chapter 27).

Metabolic rate. This is the term used to express the rate at which the cells of the body work and burn fuel and oxygen. It varies in different people, depending on their activity and occupation. The metabolic rate is at its lowest when all the cells are at rest, except those that must work to keep the body alive – the heart, blood vessels and respiratory organs. This is known as the *basal metabolic rate*, and can be calculated by measuring the amount of oxygen an individual uses and the carbon dioxide he produces in a given time, when in bed, at rest and fasting. All food taken beyond this supplies the energy needed for work and muscle activity.

Calorie values

All cell activities involve the burning of sugar with oxygen with the production of energy, including heat. This is what is meant by oxidization. Fat is another fuel food, and part of excess protein is also available for fuel. The value of these three foods as fuel can be estimated by the amount of heat produced when they are burned or oxidized. This is expressed in calories.

A *Calorie* (with a capital C) is the amount of heat required to raise the temperature of 1 kilogram of water through 1 degree centigrade. (The small C calorie used in science laboratories is the amount of heat required to raise 1 gram of water through 1 degree centigrade).

The amount of heat produced varies with each kind of food. Fat produces most heat, but it needs to be burned with sugar. The caloric value of foods can be found in food tables, and from these calculations it can be ascertained how many Calories there are in any given diet. The normal standard used as a basis for comparison is usually taken to be a man doing average work. He would require 3,000 Calories in a day. Using this scale, it is calculated that a woman requires less food than a man, but during adolescence, which is an important growth period, a little more than the full adult ration is needed by both sexes. It is generally accepted that babies require 50 calories to each pound of body weight. Milk yields 20 Calories per ounce.

If a person is in good health and his weight remains constant, appetite is usually a satisfactory guide to Calorie intake.

Growing children need relatively more food in proportion to their size and weight than adults. The amount of food eaten is partly governed by habit, but it also depends on whether the food is presented attractively. Well-cooked food is much more appetizing and readily eaten than dull uninteresting meals.

The Ministry of Agriculture, Fisheries and Food, after considerable research into the dietary requirements of young people, produced a series of menus for children of 1–7 years. Certain foods are omitted, for example, pickles, soft new bread, and other foods likely to be indigestible. They stress the importance of milk, cod liver oil, orange juice and of school meals. Children should enjoy mealtimes and look forward to them with pleasure. There is nothing more harmful to the young child than to be continually chastized at mealtimes, which may well affect his attitude to food for life. Worry and overtiredness are harmful to the appetite and digestion. Rest, adequate sleep, plenty of fresh air and a happy atmosphere will help to develop a healthy appetite and a good digestion.

Balanced diet

It is important that everyone should eat a good, balanced, mixed diet, with an adequate amount of all the different foods. The following proportions are a good average for an adult: one-sixth protein, one-sixth or less fat, and two-thirds carbohydrate. Growing children and expectant and nursing mothers need more protein. Foods are eaten as complex substances, and not as pure proteins, or pure carbohydrates, hence the need for a good mixed diet. Cheese, rich in protein, is eaten with bread which contains carbohydrate; meat rich

F

in protein and fat is eaten with potatoes, which are rich in carbohydrate. In this way one food balances the other.

For children it is necessary to begin with small helpings, and because appetites vary, new foods should be introduced gradually.

A child should be comfortably seated at a table, so that he can reach his plate and mug easily, and young children need a deep plate so that they can get the food into a spoon without spilling it. Spoons and forks should be of a convenient size. The cup should be only partly filled to avoid accidents. A child should be encouraged to cope with his food himself as far as possible.

The feeding of school children

By a Department of Education and Science regulation, the school dinner must provide a substantial proportion of the child's daily requirement. It should provide from 650 to 1,000 Calories, according to the age of the children and with this, 20 grams of animal protein.

Children of school age are not only growing fast but are physically active. Their need for Calories is relatively high, as is their need for protein and all the protective nutrients. Their large appetites represent a real need and are not due merely to greediness. The points to remember are that they need energy foods, but excessive bulk should be avoided because small children have small stomachs.

CHAPTER 9

Breast Feeding

An expectant mother has special nutritional requirements, because as well as providing for her own needs, she must supply the food for the growing uterus and the foetus within it. This does not mean that she must eat twice as much as usual, or that she should allow herself to develop and give way to strange dietary fancies. The expectant mother must eat wisely so as to provide the particular food stuffs required by the growing foetus and to keep herself fit, healthy and not overweight. She also has to build up reserves for the strenuous activities of labour and for lactation. Mothers who are well fed throughout pregnancy are more likely to have healthy babies, and there is less chance of their giving birth prematurely.

During the antenatal period the expectant mother will receive advice about her diet and the value of additional milk, calcium and vitamins A, D and C. It may also be possible for her to go to classes where she can learn about the care of her baby and about problems and difficulties that may arise during and after her pregnancy. Husbands are often welcomed at these classes and this helps them to realize that fathers too have an important part to play right from the beginning of the baby's life.

Once the baby has arrived his first and foremost need is food. This can either be natural breast milk or an artificial food.

Many mothers today prefer not to breast feed their babies as they feel it ties them too much to the home when they are anxious to get out or back to work, and it is clear that bottle fed babies do thrive and develop into healthy children. But there are important advantages in breast feeding and these need to be presented clearly to the mother. The mother's milk is designed for and entirely suited to the baby, and it provides all that he needs for growth. Breast feeding also provides intimate contact between the mother and baby. This feeling of warmth, security and love lays down firm foundations for later physical and mental development.

Breast feeding is safer for the baby. Young babies have very little immunity to common infections such as colds, coughs and diarrhoea, and breast fed babies are less likely than artificially fed babies to contract these infections. This is because breast milk is sterile and possibly also because some of the mother's antibodies are ingested in the milk. Gastro-enteritis which is the most dangerous of all infections in young babies is very rarely found in breast fed babies.

The vigorous sucking needed to obtain the breast milk helps the baby's jaws to develop well and prepares them for the eruption of the first teeth.

A great deal of time and trouble can be spent in preparing and mixing artificial feeds, and in sterilizing the teats and bottles afterwards. In comparison with this the mother who breast feeds her baby has only to see that her nipples are kept clean and in good condition.

The healthy mother who can breast feed her baby successfully will be happy in the knowledge that she is giving her baby the best possible start in life. But for those who for one reason or another are unable to do so the wide range of powdered and evaporated milk available provides a good though more expensive substitute.

The mother will have been given advice about breast feeding at her antenatal clinic and this should have included instructions in the care of her breasts. This is very important because lack of care can prevent the establishment of breast milk.

During pregnancy the breasts enlarge and become heavy. This may cause discomfort unless a good brassiere is worn which gives support without pressure on the nipples. The breasts should be washed daily and the nipples gently massaged and pulled out. If the skin is at all dry, lanolin can be applied.

Doctors vary in their opinions as to how soon a baby should be put to the breast. Some say as soon as it is born, while others would wait for up to two days. But it depends primarily on the condition of the mother and the child.

Approximately three days after the baby is born the breasts fill up quite rapidly with milk and may become uncomfortable and painful. The first breast secretion is called colostrum. It is watery in appearance and is mainly made up of protein and a cleaning agent, which prepares the digestive tract for the absorption of true milk. The colostrum changes to a yellow fluid and then to milk two or three days after the baby has started sucking.

The amount of milk present is largely regulated by demand, though it may become established very easily while the mother is resting in bed, and then become scanty and inadequate once she is up and about again. She should have been warned of this and advised to have as much rest as possible during the first few weeks of her baby's life. Worry about lack of milk or indeed about any other problems can reduce the milk supply. This is one reason why antenatal training is so important.

Essentials for successful breast feeding

Diet. The nursing mother requires a well-balanced diet, with additional fluids to her normal intake, taken before or during feeding times. Some mothers become thirsty while feeding and a drink near at hand may be helpful. Approximately $1\frac{1}{2}$ pints of milk per day and plenty of fresh vegetables and fruit are essentials. The supply of breast milk is seriously affected by any deficiencies in the diet.

Alcohol is not advised, and any food which is bound to be indigestible should be avoided.

Rest and sleep are important. One or two short rests taken during the day will prove a great help to the establishment and maintenance of breast feeding, and while she is feeding the mother can put her feet up.

Exercise in the open air is good, but the mother must not overtire herself.

Clothing should be comfortable and suitable. The breasts must be kept scrupulously clean, and it is advisable to place a clean piece of cotton wool inside the brassiere to avoid milk leaking onto the clothes.

Important aids to breast feeding

A peaceful home atmosphere and a real wish to feed the baby both contribute greatly to satisfactory breast feeding.

Comfort. Both mother and baby must be comfortable. The mother should sit on a low chair with her back supported. With the baby on her lap, she should hold him in a comfortable position, with his head resting in the bend of the elbow, and the hand supporting the buttocks. When feeding from the right breast he lies on the right arm. He should be half sitting up with the mother leaning very slightly over him, so that the nipple is well into his mouth (see Fig. 60). With a full heavy breast it may be necessary for the mother to hold the

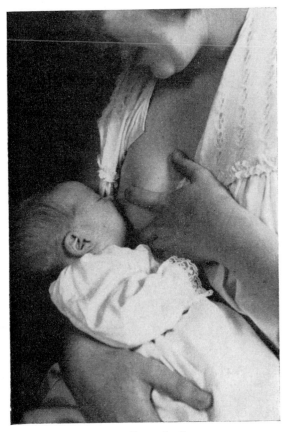

Fig. 60. Breast feeding.

breast between her first and second fingers to prevent it blocking his
nose and making sucking difficult. It is wrong to force a baby to suck
by holding his head. He gets a large percentage of the feed in the first
few minutes and after this he slows down. The hungry baby who
swallows the milk too quickly, causing indigestion, is often helped by
being given a few teaspoonfuls of cool boiled water before his feed.

Both breasts should be used at each feed as the best stimulus to
milk production is the emptying of the breast. When the milk is well
established and there is a good supply, the feed can be given from one
breast only, provided the infant is having sufficient food.

It is not possible to lay down hard and fast rules about the time
allowed for feeding. Some babies suck more quickly than others, and

a baby may suck more quickly at one feed than at another. This may be evident at the early morning feed when the breast is fuller. The average time at each breast is usually ten minutes, or fifteen to twenty minutes for the whole feed, though some babies will be satisfied in a shorter time. In the first weeks of life the baby will take a little longer, but as he grows older he will suck more quickly.

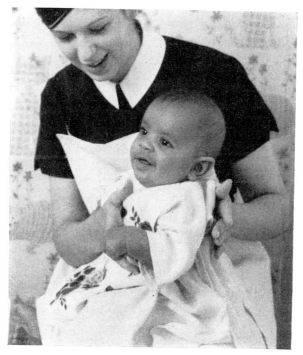

FIG. 61. Getting baby's wind up.

While the baby is feeding it may be necessary to stop once or twice to enable him to get up his wind, though occasionally the infant will resent having his feed interrupted and refuse to take the remainder of his food. In this case it is best not to attempt to bring up any wind until the end of the feed. The best way to bring the wind up is for the mother to lift the baby up to her shoulder and gently rub his back (see Fig. 61). It is quite unnecessary to give him any medicine to bring his wind up. A baby should not be returned to his cot until all his wind has been brought up, as he will be uncomfortable and unhappy. It can also be very dangerous by causing sickness which could lead to asphyxiation.

If the baby is wet or dirty he should be changed, as gently as possible, as many babies are sick if they are handled much after a feed. Throughout the whole feeding period the child must have a peaceful atmosphere, and the undivided attention of his mother.

As every baby is different it is impossible to lay down a rigid time-table. Most babies are satisfied with 3 or 4 hourly feeds, and even if they are fed whenever they demand it to begin with, they will settle into a fairly regular routine within a few weeks. The mother may have to adjust her household routines to suit the needs of her baby. Some babies will wake and need a night feed, while others will sleep through the night from the very beginning. It is wrong to allow a baby to cry for hours during the night and to give him only sterile water when he requires a proper feed, and usually the need for a night feed will disappear after two or three months.

The average baby requires approximately $2\frac{1}{2}$ ounces (75 ml) of breast milk for each pound (0.454 kg) of its body weight per day, e.g. a 10 lb baby (4.54 kg) requires 25 ounces (750 ml) of breast milk each day. Some babies are satisfied with rather less, but others will take up to 3 ounces (90 ml) per lb (0.454 kg) of body weight.

A baby is having sufficient breast milk if he is gaining weight regularly and is happy and contented, and is passing normal stools.

If there is any doubt as to whether the baby is getting sufficient milk or not he should be 'test weighed' to find out how much milk he is taking. This needs to be done over a whole day because the infant will not always get the same amount at each feed.

Test weighing

The baby is changed and weighed – complete in clothes and nap-kin, immediately before going to the breast. Then on completion of the feed he is weighed again in exactly the same clothing, and before he has been changed. The difference in weight will be the amount of milk he has taken, so that if this is done at every feed in 24 hours his total intake can be calculated.

Test weighing is a useful guide if the baby does not appear to be gaining weight, but if done too frequently may worry the mother and do more harm than good. It is important to remember that test weighing does not show the amount of milk in the breasts but only the amount of milk the baby is taking.

The baby's requirements should be calculated, not on his actual weight but on the expected weight for his age based on his birth weight, because babies who have been underfed often have a compensatory increase of appetite until they have caught up the average weight.

Complementary feeding is a term used for a feed of cows' milk, dried or otherwise, or the mother's milk that has been expressed, given immediately after the breast feed to make up the baby's requirements. It is often better to give the complementary feed by a spoon as some babies become lazy when introduced to a bottle and are not prepared to go back to the harder work necessary when sucking from the breast. A complementary feed is calculated according to the difference between the total day's intake from the mother and the amount necessary according to the baby's body weight.

Care must be taken not to introduce too sweet a feed. It may well be necessary to stimulate the breast by expressing the milk after the baby has fed from it, in order to increase the milk supply. The expressed milk can be used for a later complementary feed, but it should be boiled first.

A supplementary feed replaces the breast feed in an emergency, for example if a mother had to leave home for some hours without the baby. But this should not be allowed to happen regularly. The feed should be given in a bottle to provide the necessary sucking satisfaction. It is unwise to supplement a feed in the hope that there will be more breast milk for the next feed for the result would be the reverse as the lack of stimulation through sucking in fact reduces the milk supply.

All breast fed babies from one month of age should have vitamin C in the form of orange juice or its equivalent. This should be given diluted with cool, boiled water, one teaspoonful of fresh orange juice to three teaspoonfuls of water to begin with, and gradually increased to full strength. Half a teaspoonful of sugar can be dissolved in a little boiled water and allowed to cool before adding the fresh orange juice. The orange should always be washed before squeezing and sterile utensils used. The disease of scurvy has almost been eliminated in this country by the regular administration of vitamin C.

Concentrated orange juice must be proportionately diluted, as one teaspoonful (4 ml) made up to one ounce (30 ml) with cool boiled water is equal to full strength orange juice.

It is also important to give vitamin D, as breast milk does not contain enough to ensure the prevention of deficiency diseases such as rickets. It is given in the form of cod liver oil or in a more concentrated form such as Adexolin. This should be given from the first month, starting with about 8 drops, then gradually increasing to a teaspoonful (4 ml) daily by two months of age. Cod liver oil should never be given in the feed, but before or afterwards on a warmed plastic spoon. When the baby is a little older, the bath is often the best place in which to give cod liver oil, as it is very hard to remove the unpleasant smell once it is spilt on clothes.

Premature babies and twins require rather more cod liver oil than other babies, but the infant welfare clinic will give advice about the correct dosage, and the vitamin preparations can be obtained there.

It is important to know the correct dosage of whatever preparation is used to ensure that the child gets his full requirements of vitamins A and D but any overdose may be harmful and cause hypercalcaemia.

In hot weather babies may become very thirsty, and they can be given additional drinks of cool, boiled water between feeds if necessary.

The duration of breast feeding depends largely on the mother's circumstances and wishes. If possible she should continue for at least four months. By this time the baby will be getting used to his new foods in the process of weaning. The change from breast milk to cow's milk should be done gradually by introducing cow's milk or dried milk as a complementary feed. Very gradually the artificial feeds can be increased and the time at the breast reduced. About two weeks should be allowed for the complete change; this will give the baby time to adjust himself without causing digestive upsets. Through lack of stimulus the breast milk will gradually decrease and disappear.

Difficulties in breast feeding

Depressed nipples need not be a very serious handicap. Regular care of the breasts in the latter months of pregnancy is important in preventing this condition. The use of a nipple shield may help, but the baby who sucks vigorously is the best cure of all.

Cracked nipples may be caused by allowing a child to suck too long, or too vigorously at an empty breast. The condition is very painful and the baby should be kept away from the breast until the crack is safely healed. If the affected breast becomes hard, swollen or painful it is wise to have medical advice. Care must be taken to keep the nipple clean and dry.

Breast abscess is a very painful condition which requires medical attention. The infection may have started from a cracked or sore nipple. For a period it will not be possible to allow the baby to suck from the breast, although the milk should be expressed by hand. The infant should have the other breast and when the breast has healed, the breast milk can be re-established. It may be necessary to give a complementary feed if the amount of milk is insufficient.

Malformations of the baby's mouth, e.g. cleft palate, hare lip, may make breast feeding impossible. It is sometimes possible for the mother to express her milk, then give it to the baby with a special spoon used for feeding these babies.

Tuberculosis. The baby should be taken off the breast immediately it is realised that the mother has a lung infection. It will be necessary to consult the doctor, as the breasts will probably become distended and painful and it will be necessary for the mother to have a special medicine to prevent milk forming.

Pregnancy. If a new pregnancy begins it will be wise to take the baby off the breast.

Any illness of the mother would be considered individually by the doctor.

CHAPTER 10

Artificial Feeding

If for one reason or another a baby cannot be breast fed, then there is a wide choice of artificial feeds derived from cows' milk which provide an adequate substitute. It is usually necessary to modify the cows' milk in some way as it is designed for the calf who has very different needs from the human baby. A calf is able to stand on its legs and walk almost as soon as it is born, it has a fur coat to keep it warm, it grows so fast that it doubles its birthweight in about eight weeks, and it has digestive organs capable of dealing with the heavy curds formed by the protein in cows' milk. The human baby on the other hand is helpless at birth, has a very thin skin and so cannot keep himself warm, takes three times as long as a calf to double his birthweight and has digestive organs designed for a very different diet from that of a cow.

The following table illustrates the main differences between cows' milk and human milk.

TABLE III

	Cow's milk		Human milk	
Protein	4%	{3·4% caseinogen {0·6% lactalbumin	2%	{0·6% caseinogen {1·4% lactalbumin
Sugar (lactose)	4%		6%	
Fat (butter fat)	4%		4%	
Mineral salts	·75%		·25%	
Water	87·25		87·25	

The most important difference is that cows' milk contains six times as much casein as human milk, and the curds that form in the stomach from casein are much tougher and less digestible than the finer curds of human milk. This is why it is necessary to dilute cows' milk for babies thus reducing the protein percentage.

Usually the fat content is equal in cows' milk and human milk, but Channel Island milk is an exception, being richer and having considerably more fat. The fat droplets are suspended in the milk and on standing rise to the surface as cream.

As human milk contains more sugar (lactose) than cows' milk it is sometimes necessary to add sugar (sucrose) to cows' milk to make it acceptable to babies, but this alters the flavour whereas lactose is not sweet to taste.

The mineral salts are mainly calcium and phosphorus and a little sodium chloride (common salt), all of which contribute to the development of bones and teeth.

Vitamins A, D and B are present in both milks, but the amount depends on the diet of the mother or of the cow, the latter producing milk with a higher vitamin content during the summer.

To make cows' milk suitable for young babies the following modifications are necessary:

(1) The amount of casein must be reduced, and it must be broken up to make it more digestible.

(2) The fat content must be reduced.

(3) The sugar should be raised to the level present in human milk.

These changes are usually achieved by boiling or pasteurising the milk to make the casein curd more digestible, by diluting the milk with water, by drying it to produce milk powder, and by skimming off some of the fat.

There are many different prepared milks for infant feeding but the three main categories are:

(1) Fresh boiled or pasteurised cows' milk, suitably diluted.

(2) Reconstituted dried milk.

(3) Canned evaporated milk, suitably diluted. (Sweetened evaporated milk is not recommended.)

Cows' milk

Grading of milk

There are four categories of milk available to the public, these are untreated milk, and three types of heat treated milk; pasteurised, sterilised and ultra-heat treated.

Untreated milk is raw milk, usually bottled on the farm. There is very little of this type of milk available and then only in rural areas. This is not suitable for infant feeding.

Pasteurisation of milk destroys harmful bacteria and prolongs its keeping qualities. Most milk sold today has been through this process which involves heating the milk to 161° F (72° C) for at least 15 seconds. The milk remains fresh for a longer period and the taste is not altered.

Sterilised milk has been taken to a higher temperature, generally about 230–240° F (110–115° C) and held there for approximately 30–40 minutes. This lengthens the keeping quality of the milk, and unopened bottles should keep fresh for at least a week. It has a rich creamy appearance and a slight caramel flavour. Sterilised milk is also homogenised; this is a process that breaks up the fat globules and distributes them evenly through the milk.

Pasteurised milk is also available in the homogenised form.

Ultra-heat treated milk (Long life milk) is the newest type available. It is raised gradually to a high temperature and then flashed momentarily to 275° F (135° C). This milk will keep for several months and tastes very similar to ordinary milk.

Evaporated milk

This is cows' milk that has had two thirds of the water evaporated and vitamin D added. It is sterile and suitable for baby feeding. Generally, by adding one part of milk to two parts of water it can be treated as ordinary cows' milk and modified accordingly.

Powdered milks

Full-cream dried milk is fresh cows' milk from which the water has been evaporated until a powder is formed. This powder is sterile and keeps well providing it is handled carefully, for instance the lid should always be replaced after use. There are two different ways of producing powdered milk, one is by passing it over heated rollers, known as the roller method, and the other is the spray method. It is a popular form of artificial milk and is easily reconstituted by mixing with cooled boiled water.

There are many well-known brands on the market, including National Dried Milk which is made under government licence. Most dried milks are fortified with vitamin D and this must be stated on the tin or packet.

Half-cream dried milk is produced in the same way as full-cream dried milk, but there is a reduction in the fat content and the protein content is modified. It is usually given to babies with a delicate digestion or when there is some difficulty in digesting fat.

Humanised dried milk is dried fresh cows' milk with the protein modified and sugar added, and the content rendered as near as possible to human milk.

The Baby's Requirements

As is the case with breast fed babies the baby is fed in relation to its weight. That is 2½ oz–3 oz per lb of body weight (150 ml per kg) in 24 hours. The strength of the feed may vary but the average normal baby can usually begin with three parts of milk to one of water (see Table IV). Babies who are over-weight may be given slightly less food than their weight indicates, and underweight babies can be given more. The very active baby may be extremely hungry and require more food whereas the placid baby may not need so much. The smaller baby will take a similar amount in 24 hours but may prefer the milk to be less strong, in which case he can be given two parts milk to one part water (see Table V).

Suggested Tables for the Making Up of Feeds

TABLE IV

Using cows' milk – 4 hourly feeding for average babies

Formula: 3 parts milk
1 part water
1 tsp. sugar to every 6 oz

Weight of baby	Cows' milk	Water	Sugar	Amount each feed
8 lb	18 oz	6 oz	4 tsp.	Approx 4½ oz
(3·6 kg)	(540 ml)	(180 ml)		(135 ml)
10 lb	24 oz	8 oz	5 tsp.	5½ oz
(4·5 kg)	(720 ml)	(240 ml)		(165 ml)
12 lb	27 oz	9 oz	6 tsp.	6½ oz
(5·4 kg)	(800 ml)	(270 ml)		(195 ml)

These feeds will be given approximately every four hours. (5 feeds a day).

TABLE V

Using cows' milk – 3 hourly feeding for small babies

Formula: 2 parts milk
1 part water
1 tsp. sugar to every 6 oz

Weight of baby	Cows' milk	Water	Sugar	Amount each feed
6 lb	12 oz	6 oz	3 tsp.	3 oz
(2·7 kg)	(360 ml)	(180 ml)		(90 ml)
7 lb	14 oz	7 oz	3½ tsp.	3½ oz
(3 kg)	(400 ml)	(210 ml)		(100 ml)

TABLE VI

Using unsweetened evaporated full cream milk

Formula: 1 part milk
2 parts water
1 tsp. of sugar to 4 oz (120 ml) of feed

$2\frac{1}{2}$ oz per lb of body weight (150 ml per kg) with $\frac{1}{2}$ oz extra in each feed
These feeds will be given approximately every 4 hours

Weight of baby	Unsweetened evaporated milk	Water	Sugar	Amount each feed	Amount for the day (5 feeds)
6 lb	6 oz	12 oz	3 tsp.	$3\frac{1}{2}$ oz	18 oz
(2·72 kg)	(180 ml)	(360 ml)		(90 ml)	(530 ml)
7 lb	7 oz	14 oz	$3\frac{1}{2}$ tsp.	4 oz	20 oz
(3 kg)	(200 ml)	(400 ml)		(120 ml)	(600 ml)
8 lb	$7\frac{1}{2}$ oz	15 oz	4 ,,	$4\frac{1}{2}$ oz	$22\frac{1}{2}$ oz
(3·6 kg)	(215 ml)	(450 ml)		(135 ml)	(675 ml)
9 lb	9 oz	18 oz	$4\frac{1}{2}$,,	5 oz	25 oz
(4 kg)	(270 ml)	(540 ml)		(150 ml)	(750 ml)
10 lb	10 oz	20 oz	5 ,,	$5\frac{1}{2}$ oz	$27\frac{1}{2}$ oz
(4·5 kg)	(300 ml)	(600 ml)		(165 ml)	(815 ml)
11 lb	10 oz	20 oz	5 ,,	6 oz	30 oz
(5 kg)	(300 ml)	(600 ml)		(180 ml)	(900 ml)
12 lb	11 oz	22 oz	$5\frac{1}{2}$,,	$6\frac{1}{2}$ oz	32 oz
(5·4 kg)	(330 ml)	(660 ml)		(195 ml)	(960 ml)

TABLE VII

Using full cream dried milk

Formula: 1 : 10 or 1 measure of dried milk
to $1\frac{1}{4}$ oz (37 ml) water
1 tsp. sugar to every 4 oz of mixture

$2\frac{1}{2}$ oz per lb of body weight (150 ml per kg) in 24 hours, with $\frac{1}{2}$ oz (15 ml) extra in each bottle

Weight of baby	Full cream Dried milk	Water	Sugar	Amount each feed	Amount for the day (5 feeds)
8 lb	$3\frac{1}{2}$ measures	$4\frac{1}{2}$ oz	1 tsp.	$4\frac{1}{2}$ oz	$22\frac{1}{2}$ oz
(3·6 kg)		(135 ml)		(135 ml)	(675 ml)
9 lb	4 ,,	5 oz	,, ,,	5 oz	25 oz
(4 kg)		(150 ml)		(150 ml)	(750 ml)
10 lb	$4\frac{1}{2}$,,	$5\frac{1}{2}$ oz	,, ,,	$5\frac{1}{2}$ oz	$27\frac{1}{2}$ oz
(4·5 kg)		(160 ml)		(165 ml)	(815 ml)
11 lb	5 ,,	6 oz	1 tsp.	6 oz	30 oz
(5 kg)		(180 ml)		(180 ml)	(900 ml)
12 lb	$5\frac{1}{2}$,,	$6\frac{1}{2}$ oz	,, ,,	$6\frac{1}{2}$ oz	$32\frac{1}{2}$ oz
(5·4 kg)		(190 ml)		(195 ml)	(975 ml)

TABLE VIII

Using full cream dried milk – 3 hourly feeds for smaller babies

Formula: 1 : 12 or 1 measure of dried milk
to 1½ oz (45 ml) water
1 tsp. sugar to every 3 oz mixture
with an additional ½ oz (15 ml) in each bottle

Weight of baby	Full cream dried milk	Water	Sugar	Amount each feed	Amount for the day (6 feeds)
6 lb (2·7 kg)	2 measures	3 oz (90 ml)	1 tsp.	3 oz (90 ml)	18 oz (530 ml)
7 lb (3 kg)	2½ ,,	3½ oz (100 ml)	,, ,,	3½ oz (100 ml)	20½ oz (615 ml)

The metric equivalents given for the above tables are approximate

The Milk Room

In any day or residential nursery where infants are housed, a milk room is of the utmost importance – the chief reason being to avoid any undue risk of infection to the infants. The ideal milk room should have good permanent ventilation which can be obtained by replacing one of the panes of glass with metal gauze, and the window should face north or east. There must be facilities for hand washing, electric or gas stove for boiling milk, a container for sterilisation by the Milton method, a refrigerator and a cupboard for storing the utensils required for infant feeding. All the milk room equipment must be kept solely for use in the milk room.

Strict cleanliness is most important; all clean utensils and milk or foods must be covered and thus protected from contamination by flies and dust, otherwise the value of sterilising or boiling utensils will be lost. The milk room door should be kept closed.

It is advisable for the nurse in the milk room to wear a *gown* which should be kept inside the milk room. The wearing of this gown does not permit her to enter the milk room with a dirty apron or dress.

Care of the gown. After use, it should be placed on a coat-hanger with the inside of the gown still inside. In this way any germs from the nurse's dress will be inside the gown and will not contaminate the feeds when the gown is used again. The gown should never touch the floor.

Masks are frequently advised, but they are not essential unless the worker has a severe cold or chronic catarrh.

The nurse must always wash her hands before starting to do any work in the milk room.

Useful fluid measures for use in the milk room:

60 minims	= 1 fluid drachm	= 1 teaspoonful	= 5 ml (approx.)
8 fluid drachms	= 1 fluid ounce	= 8 teaspoonfuls or 2 tablespoonfuls	= 40 ml ,,
20 fluid ounces	= 1 pint	= 600 ml	
2 pints	= 1 quart	= 1200 ml	

Teaspoons and tablespoons vary in size tremendously, but if the actual measures are not available, these can be satisfactorily improvised if care is taken to find spoons to take the required amounts. It is important that spoons used for this purpose are checked against a true measure.

Care of utensils

Spoons, metal and plastic, should be well washed and sterilised after use. The blades of knives with wooden handles should be scalded before use. Receptacles, such as cups, bowls, plates and trays, should be washed and boiled if possible, otherwise scalded by pouring boiling water over them. Utensils should be boiled preferably just before use or suitable equipment can be sterilised with Milton. All covers of butter muslin or linen, must be washed and boiled after use.

Sweeping and dusting should be discouraged in the milk room but the floor must be washed. The ledges and the shelves should be cleaned with a damp cloth, thus taking up all the dust and avoiding any risk of infection.

Care of feeding bottles

Sterilisation by boiling. After use bottles should be rinsed under the cold tap with the teat on the bottle to remove the milk from the crevices of the rubber. The teat can then be removed and the bottle rinsed in cold water. Using a bottle brush and detergent, wash the bottles very thoroughly inside and outside. Rinse three times in cold running water. Fill bottles with cold water and wrap a little butter muslin round each to prevent cracking, before placing in steriliser or large bowl. Completely cover the bottles with cold water. Bring to the boil and boil for ten minutes with the lid on.

If the bottles are not required immediately, they are best left in the steriliser until they are wanted. Otherwise they can be removed with a boiled or scalded pair of bowl forceps or with a boiled tablespoon. Empty out the water and place a boiled cork or a boiled bottle cap in the neck or over the neck of the bottle to insure that the inside is kept free from dust or germs.

The bottle brush should be boiled daily.

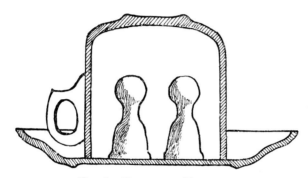

FIG. 62. Teats covered by a cup.

Care of teats

After use and while still on the bottle the teat should be rinsed under the cold tap, then removed and rinsed in cold water. It should then be rubbed inside and out with coarse salt, and water should be squirted through the hole. It is possible to place the teat in a metal container with small holes to allow the boiling water to surround the teat. Drop the container into boiling water for one minute, then remove with sterile forceps allowing the water to drain out. Place the teat in a sterilised container with a lid, or on a boiled saucer as in Fig. 62 and covered with a cup that is boiled at least once a day. Exposure to light and boiling is injurious to rubber.

The Milton method of sterilisation is suitable for glass, china, rubber, polythene and plastic.

The strength of solution required is one tablespoonful of Milton (sodium hypochlorite) to one quart of cold water = 1 in 80 solution.

All articles must be totally submerged and left for $1\frac{1}{2}$ hours or they may be left until next feed. The container must be kept covered. Metal equipment cannot be sterilised in Milton solution.

Feeding bottles are cleaned and rinsed as already described. All air bubbles must be expelled by first filling each bottle with the Milton solution and placing the thumb over the top of the full bottle. The bottles are then immersed in the solution in a plastic, china or earthenware container.

Teats are washed and rinsed as described, then placed in solution with the bulb downwards, and kept completely covered by having a small cup or plastic cover placed over them.

When there are several babies in a nursery, it is better for each child to have his own container in case he has his feed at a different time from the other babies.

Bottles and teats should not be rinsed after sterilising in Milton.

Nobactin method of sterilising – suitable for glass, china, bakelite and rubber. Dissolve *one heaped teaspoonful* of Nobactin to each quart of cold water. Rinse the bottle and teat in cold running water, then quarter fill the bottle with solution and brush thoroughly inside and outside. Clean the teat in the solution. Throw away used solution and now submerge the teat cover with a cup, and bottle (preferably in an upright position to avoid air bubbles); leave until the next feed. Empty the feeding bottle, but do not rinse it.

In emergency Nobactin can be used in the following way. Make up a solution as before. Rinse the teat thoroughly in cold water and clean it with a brush dipped in the solution; squeeze the teat in the solution and leave soaking. Rinse the bottle thoroughly in cold water outside and inside; fill the bottle one-third full with solution and brush it thoroughly inside and outside; empty the bottle. Fill the bottle again one-third full and shake it vigorously; pour away solution, rinse again with the solution, drain thoroughly and fill the bottle with the baby's feed.

In the home, the same scrupulous cleanliness of all utensils, feeding bottles and teats must apply to infant feeding. It would not be practical to suggest that a room be set aside for this purpose, but it can be arranged in every household to keep a special part of the kitchen for all feeding utensils. The feeds can be made up when the kitchen is clean and clear of any other work.

Care of cows' milk

Rules which apply to the care of all milk are to keep it cool, clean and covered. Cows' milk is usually delivered in bottles, which should never be used for any other purpose. When empty they should be rinsed in cold water, then washed and rinsed again and put aside until collected. Milk should not be left standing on the door step as even short periods of exposure to light can reduce its food value. Bottles of milk should first be wiped with a clean cloth and then placed in the refrigerator. This will keep the milk cold but will not kill any germs that may be present.

In very hot weather it is safer to boil milk on arrival and cool quickly and store in a refrigerator if one is available.

All milk receptacles must be clean and boiled or well scalded before the milk is poured into them.

Good personal hygiene of the nurse handling the milk is essential.

Care of dried milk

Any stock of dried milk must be kept in a *cool* and *dry* place. Packets should be placed in an air-tight tin. When using dried milk from a packet or tin, cut away any surplus paper covering the milk in the tin as this may get contaminated each time the tin is opened. It is necessary to use a scalded spoon or scalded measure and to replace the lid or cover immediately after use. The spoon or measure must be sterilised each time it is used, and not kept in the dried milk tin. On packets and tins the latest date when the food is fit for consumption is clearly marked and it is important to note this date.

Preparations. All utensils and receptacles likely to be required must be boiled or sterilised in Milton or Nobactin and covered with clean, boiled muslin. Any metal, for example a knife, should be scalded with boiling water.

Making up cows' milk feeds

Equipment
Enamel tray, approximately 20 × 12 inches.
1 teaspoon
1 straight bladed knife.
2 pint measures – preferably glass.
Milk saucepan.
Kettle with boiling water.
Sugar.
Bottles of milk (number according to requirements).
Feeding bottles for number of feeds to be made up.
Sterilised covers or caps to fit feeding bottles.
General method. Whether one feed is made up or the day's feeds, the method is exactly the same.

Wash hands immediately before making up the feed.

Invert the bottle once or twice to mix in any cream which may have risen to the top.

Place the glass measure on a level surface, and having carefully decided the exact marking which the milk should reach, pour in the milk and read the measure with the eye at the level of the measure. This is very important for accurate measurement.

Pour milk into pan and bring to the boil. In some areas this is not practised. If the milk is pasteurised and handled under aseptic conditions this is not necessary.

Place a scalded spoon in the second glass measure to avoid cracking the measure.

Pour in the required amount of boiled water.

Measure sugar in the teaspoon, level the sugar with the knife.

Put sugar into boiled water and stir till dissolved.

Pour the boiling milk into the boiled water and gently mix.

Pour into feeding bottle or bottles according to the number of feeds being made up.

When the whole day's feeds have been made up, they should be in the refrigerator or in a cool place and covered, until they are required.

The 8-ounce, upright bottle is recommended in preference to the boat-shaped bottle because: (a) it is easier to keep the feed at the right temperature, (b) there is only one teat involved, and (c) it is more practical if all the feeds for the day are to be made up at one time.

Teats. Use a teat with a fairly large bulb and one which is suited to the infant. See Technique of Bottle Feeding (p. 170).

Making up dried milk feeds

Preparations. The same strict cleanliness will apply to dried milk feeds as to fresh cows' milk feeds. It is better to make up dried milk feeds as required.

Hands must be well washed and all utensils boiled or scalded immediately before use.

Equipment

Enamel tray, 20 × 12 inches.

1 measure – for the particular dried milk being used, or a spoon which will take the same amount of dried milk as the measure.

1 knife with a straight blade.

1 teaspoon.

1 glass measure.
Feeding bottle – with teat cover or boiled cap.
Dried milk.
Sugar.
Boiled water.
Some cooled, boiled water.
General method (using cool, boiled water to mix).

Carefully measure the required amount of dried milk – packing the powder into the measure and levelling it with a knife, then place in glass measure. Add sugar which will be dissolved with the cool boiled water.

Mix to a smooth paste with the cooled, boiled water and make up to the required amount of feed with boiled water. *Accuracy* in *measuring is essential.* Pour the feed into the bottle and cover it.

When excess water is added by mistake the feed cannot be adjusted by pouring some of the milk mixture away, as this would also reduce the food value of the feed.

Dried milk feeds may also be prepared by mixing the dried milk with warm, boiled water and sugar, then continue as in the cold, boiled water method.

Making up evaporated milk feeds

Preparations. The same strict cleanliness applies to all equipment and hands.

Equipment
Enamel tray.
1 teaspoon.
1 knife.
1 pint measure, glass preferably.
Sugar.
Evaporated milk in sterile receptacle with cover.
Kettle with hot boiled water.
Feeding bottle.
Cover for top of bottle.

Method
Measure sugar and place in the pint measure.
Pour required amount of milk into the same measure then add boiled water to the required amount and stir well.
Pour feed into bottle and cover the top.

Evaporated milk feeds can be made up separately or for the whole day, providing there is a refrigerator for storage of feeds.

Technique of Bottle Feeding

The baby must be changed and made comfortable, after which the nurse should wash her hands and put on the baby's feeding bib. If this is tied round the neck it should also be fastened round the waist to avoid its being pulled tight round the neck with the possible danger of suffocation. For small babies the bib can just be tucked under the chin.

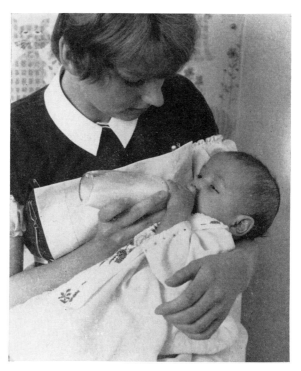

FIG. 63. Good position for bottle feeding.

Preparation of feed tray. Whether in the nursery or in the home – the feed tray is important. It should contain:
Jug of hot water (for heating feed), or
Jug of cold water (for cooling feed).
Dish with the covered teat.

Feeding bottle with prepared feed – with top on the bottle.

Feed thermometer (not essential) in jar of cold, boiled water or Milton solution which is preferable if there is no metal on the thermometer.

Cover for tray of butter muslin or clean, white cloth.

Cod-liver oil and teaspoon (when C.L.O. is due).

Before starting the feed at 10 a.m. and 6 p.m., or at one of these times, give the cod-liver oil in a teaspoon, warmed by dipping into the hot water jug.

Temperature of the feed. If the feed thermometer is used, great care must be taken to keep it clean. It may be placed in a jar of Milton solution before use. Remove the top from the feeding bottle and insert thermometer. It must be read with the bulb of mercury in the feed, as the mercury drops immediately the thermometer is removed. The feed should be given at about 100° F (37.8° C). It is a simple matter to test the temperature of a feed – by allowing a few drops of the feed to drop from the teat on to the back of the hand. It should feel just warm. It is wise to experiment with water which is 100° F to learn the feel of the right temperature for a feed as there is less risk of transmitting infection when testing in this way than when using a feed thermometer.

Putting on the teat. When everything is ready to feed the baby, remove the cap or cover from the bottle, pick up the teat by the base and slip it on to the bottle. Try to avoid touching the bulb of the teat and handle the teat as little as possible. It is very unwise to handle the bulb of the teat, in an attempt to clear a teat which may have become blocked. The milk should drop from the teat when the bottle is held up, at the rate of about twenty drops per minute.

Accurate timing in giving a bottle feed is important. Twenty minutes should be the maximum time allowed. Some babies feed much quicker, taking the feed in 10 to 15 minutes or even less. The hole in the teat should be large enough for the baby to get his feed comfortably without choking.

The base of the bottle should be tilted upwards to avoid air getting into the teat and letting the infant suck wind. There should be a slight tension kept on the teat, which encourages better sucking.

The adult should sit on a low chair in a comfortable position, and hold the baby in a similar position to that for breast feeding. The close contact with the adult helps to give the child a sense of security, a real necessity for a bottle-fed baby. A happy, contented baby will usually show a fair amount of activity and joy during the early part of his feed, and he should be allowed perfect freedom to kick. If his feet are at all cold, a shawl should be wrapped very loosely round them.

It is essential that the baby gets up his wind. This has been described in the technique of breast feeding.

The hungry baby who gulps his feed greedily and has a tendency to sickness when expelling wind, is often helped by being given one or two tablespoonfuls of boiled water before his feed.

Throughout the feeding time, it may be necessary to warm up the feed in the jug of hot water. Cold feeds can easily upset a baby.

When *demand feeding* is not practised it is usual to feed the very young baby three-hourly and when he is doing well, to change gradually to four-hourly feeding. At times it is difficult to establish good feeding habits, and when the child shows signs of real hunger he should be fed and not left to cry until the feed is due 'by the clock'. Within a few weeks the infant becomes more regular in his feeding times. Many children are unable to accept the long interval between 10 p.m. and 6 a.m. Rather than stick rigidly to these times a night feed should be given, or if the baby is sleeping at 10 p.m. that feed can be delayed until he wakes and the 6 a.m. one brought forward. But all babies vary and it is impossible to lay down the same timetable for them all.

The child requires a quiet, peaceful atmosphere during feeds, and the undivided attention of the adult, who is giving the feed. Care must be taken that the baby is not in any way distracted during the feed. After it is finished the baby should be encouraged to get rid of any wind before being settled into his cot, otherwise he will be thoroughly uncomfortable and very restless, and there is a risk of asphyxiation. The adult should talk to the baby, making him feel secure and happy.

If the baby is wet after his feed he must be changed, but great care should be taken to handle him gently, thus avoiding any unnecessary movement, which may cause sickness.

When the feed is not finished after twenty minutes, it should be taken away and the child settled in his cot. Always throw away any part of a feed which is left over, but careful note should be kept of the feed which the infant has taken. If the baby is very hungry for his next feed a little extra can be offered. Babies are like adults, enjoying some meals more than others.

Quite apart from their feeds, babies enjoy *a drink of warm unsweetened boiled water* and this habit should be encouraged in infancy.

Giving the drinks with a teaspoon is a great help in teaching the child to take from a spoon, and in turn will ease the transition period from bottle to mixed feeding.

For dosage volume and body weight conversion tables see the end of the book page 384).

CHAPTER 11

Weaning or Mixed Feeding

The true meaning of the term 'to wean' is to accustom the child to other foods while he is still taking the breast or bottle.

It is usual to start weaning at about two to three months or even earlier. Some doctors suggest that mixed feeding can begin at a few weeks old, but this is not generally practised at the present time. At this early age sucking is still very important and to eliminate sucking too early may have a disturbing influence on the baby's behaviour and growth, and can affect his emotional development. It is obvious that the baby derives much happiness and assurance from sucking and if the mother is also enjoying the experience, her feelings will affect the baby too, giving him a sense of well being.

The first stages

Normally the baby has been given cod liver oil and orange juice from a spoon from the time he is one month old, and this means that being fed with a spoon is not completely unfamiliar. It is important to introduce the spoon gently to avoid discomfort. Some babies do not like the idea at all and it may require a good deal of patience and understanding by the adult before spoon feeds are accepted happily.

Some infants accept new foods with pleasure the first time they are offered, even foods with a definite flavour, such as spinach and eggs. More often, however, the child learns through repeated experimentation to accept the new food. Every new flavour is an important new event in his life, and to get used to it requires time. If a very small amount of a new food is offered at the same time as a familiar taste it may be more acceptable, and with some children the new food is best given early in the meal while the appetite is keen. With many others it may be better to let him satisfy his immediate hunger first, and then introduce the new food when his instincts to attack the food have calmed down. It is advisable to introduce one new food at a time, letting the baby get used to it over several meals, before offering him something else.

The aesthetic appeal of the food has an effect on the appetite of the child and the sight, taste and smell all make a difference to him.

A pleasant experience will help him to venture further and try other new foods, and it is important to remember that not only the flavour but the texture and consistency are also new to the child, and it is these that eventually lead him on to chew.

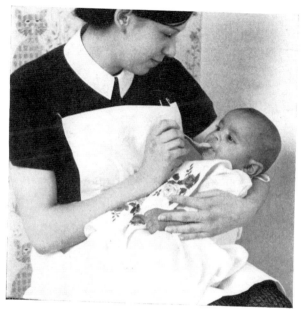

FIG. 64. Spoon feeding – the introduction of solid food.

Naturally some foods will be liked better than others, and a child should never be forced to eat a new food the first time it is served. Quite possibly at a later date he will take it happily. To force a child may make him develop a whole range of dislikes and create feeding problems later in life.

The first solids

The first foods to introduce are yolk of egg, liver, broth, fruit pulp and sieved vegetables.

Yolk of egg may be introduced into the milk mixture, or mixed with sieved vegetables. The egg can be lightly boiled or coddled and given from a spoon. Later it can be given as egg custard or made into sponge cake. Raw yolk can be introduced into milk feeds in the early months as this is a good source of iron. Iron is essential to the baby because the iron with which he was born is soon used up, and milk is deficient in iron; without it there is a danger of nutritional anaemia. Egg is a rich food and must be given in small quantities of not more than half a teaspoonful two or three times a week at first.

Broth may be introduced at an early stage; it can be added to sieved vegetables. Marmite can be given and is easily prepared.

Vegetables can be made into purée by sieving after cooking. Carrots, turnips, parsnips, swedes, tomatoes and all kinds of green vegetables can be given, and fruit pulps, such as apples, bananas, cherries and plums can be offered as an alternative.

Calves' liver should be steamed and sieved, and served with sieved vegetables.

Before the baby can chew he can only take foods which can be swallowed easily, so the food should be very smooth and without lumps.

Puréed fruits, soups and vegetables can be obtained in small tins; they are convenient to use, economical in time and labour and give a good vitamin content in comparison with home cooked foods.

After the introduction of egg, vegetable, fruits and soups, cereals can be added to the diet. Although most babies take these very readily they should not be given in too large quantities as they may make the baby fat. There are many brands available on the market.

Second stage solids

When the baby can chew, a wide variety of foods are available. He can be given white fish (avoiding the bones), meat, minced or cut up finely, steamed liver, a boiled egg, a piece of cheese, non-puréed foods, bacon, raw apple, orange, banana, a crust or hard toast with butter, biscuits, and countless other things. Foods which are easily digested should be chosen avoiding fruits which contain pips and stones. Fried or rich foods should be avoided. Quite possibly some fruits and vegetables will not suit every child, and if this is so they should not be offered.

Once mixed feeding is established, the baby should not have more than one pint of milk a day, as an excess of milk may take away his appetite. Drinks of boiled water may be given between feeding times.

Some babies wake up and appear fretful between meals, because they are thirsty, and a drink of water may soothe them.

The amount of food must be gradually increased to meet each child's needs. When only small quantities of sieved foods are given the full quantity of milk should be offered. If rusks are given at a too early stage there is a danger of the baby biting or softening the rusk so that a piece breaks off in his mouth, which may cause him to choke.

One aim when starting mixed feeding is gradually to adapt the baby to normal meals at normal times. Thus it is usual to offer eggs and cereals in the morning or evening and vegetables, broths and meat and fish at lunch time, but there need be no rigid rules about this.

If a baby goes on for too long having different food at different times from the rest of the family it will be harder for him to come to accept his place as part of the family.

Feeding utensils

The change from bottle to cup

Many babies are very reluctant to give up sucking, and no attempt should be made to force a child to drink from a cup if he is unwilling. To begin with it is probably best to let him begin his drink from a cup, and when he shows signs of frustration let him finish it from a bottle. Many babies who are quite good at drinking from a cup often settle better in the evening if they have their last feed of the day from a bottle.

There are a number of special mugs available which help the change over from bottle to cup. These are a great help to some children, while others have no trouble at all in drinking from an ordinary cup.

Spoon feeding

A small ordinary spoon should be used, and the food put well into the mouth. If it is placed on the tip of the tongue the baby will probably be unable to swallow it and will push it out.

The food should be warm but not hot and should always be tested on the back of the hand before it is offered to the baby.

The type of plate or bowl does not matter until the baby begins to feed himself, then an unbreakable one with straight sides, against which he can push the food, is best. He should be allowed to attempt to feed himself as soon as he shows signs of wanting to, but it is advisable for the adult to have a spoon as well, as to begin with he will get very little food on his own spoon, and what he does get on is as likely to go to his ears or nose as to his mouth!

Some babies seem eager to hold their bottles at a very early stage. If they do this, care should be taken to see that it is well tipped up and that they are not just sucking in air. Even when a baby can hold his bottle quite efficiently, he should never be left with it on his own in a cot or pram as the contact with his mother is vital at feeding times.

By the time a baby is six months old he may be ready to sit in a chair for his meals. But this should be introduced gradually and only if the baby is willing, as the loss of immediate contact with his mother may unsettle him at first. The buffer type of chair with a small tray attached is the best for the early stages.

There is bound to be a mess when children start feeding themselves, and they should not be reprimanded for this. A large bib or feeder which covers most of the child and ties at the waist and neck is most practical, and the surrounding floor should be either washable or well covered.

Planning the weaning diets

A well balanced diet which includes first class protein, minerals and vitamins should gradually be introduced, because at this stage body building foods are of great importance. The usual feed at which to first introduce solids is the midday one, but there is no hard and fast rule about this, it may be more convenient at the morning feed. The time at the breast or the amount of milk in the bottle, can gradually be reduced at this feed. If the baby is taking his solids well he will not need so much milk. Breast feeding should continue to some extent until the baby is eight or nine months old, if the mother is fit and the individual requirements of the home permit her to do so. When ceasing to breast feed, whatever the age of the baby, it is important for the well being of the mother and child that this should be done very gradually, taking at least two weeks, but preferably a month or even longer. Slow changes are not as likely to upset a child as rapid ones, and the mother by gently reducing the stimulation of the breasts, will automatically reduce the milk supply, thus avoiding full and painful breasts. If a baby has been breast fed for nine months it should be unnecessary for him to be introduced to a bottle, as by this stage he should be able to learn to use a cup.

The next feed at which to introduce a new food will be at 10 a.m., then at 6 p.m. Soon the times will be brought into line with the family mealtimes. The 6 a.m. and 10 p.m. feeds will gradually disappear as the baby becomes satisfied with his larger daytime feeds.

Appetites will vary considerably, but the healthy active child usually takes his meals very well.

The length of time taken to wean a baby also varies widely and he should never be hurried or fussed. Most babies are fully weaned by the time they are one year old.

Some general points

Foods should not be sieved for too long, especially when the baby is able to chew. The food should not be all mashed up together, but placed separately on the plate and attractively arranged. Children need to be carefully watched to see that they are chewing and swallowing their food properly.

The young child should never be expected to come to the table and wait for his food. The normal healthy child is full of interest and excitement at what is for dinner and therefore finds difficulty in sitting. If he has to be kept waiting a rusk or crust may keep him happy.

There are occasions when a child may refuse to take his food; this may be because he is teething or thirsty or tired or uncomfortable. There is usually a reason, but if it is not apparent and if patient coaxing fails, no attempt should be made forcefully to feed the baby.

Up to the age of six months it is essential that the equipment used by the baby should be sterile, and after this time it should always be scrupulously clean and should be covered when not in use to prevent flies and dust from settling on it.

G

CHAPTER 12

Mealtimes for the Older Child

By the time children are two their diet can be a normal adult one with slight modifications. Providing they are given the right sort of food, and not a prolonged baby diet, they should be masticating well, and this will encourage good digestion. Water should be available at mealtimes but should not be used to soften the dry food in the mouth. Fluids are very necessary in the diet, and young children should have access to a drink of water during their play hours, and have a drink whenever they feel thirsty.

Sweets. It is unwise to encourage a child to acquire the habit of eating a lot of concentrated sugar, because it becomes a habit and it is not an essential need. It is also very bad for the teeth, and is the chief cause of dental decay in children. If children are to have sweets they should be eaten at the end of a meal, then the child will enjoy them but as he is not hungry he should be less anxious to go on eating. Whenever possible fresh fruit should be given as a substitute for sweets. Sweets given between meals will satisfy hunger and reduce the appetite for the proper meal.

Idiosyncrasies do exist, and they must be considered quite apart from likes and dislikes for certain foods. Three outstanding foods which do sometimes cause marked signs and symptoms of illness are strawberries, shell fish and white of egg. A doctor should be consulted if there is any suspicion of illness after a particular food.

Preparation of the table

Children are usually very interested in helping to lay the table for meals. This should be encouraged both in the home and in the nursery. When a few children are dining together, they are more comfortable seated in small chairs with a proportionately low table. If a young child is eating at the normal table with his family, he should have his chair sufficiently high, so that he can comfortably manipulate his implements.

The majority of children are very proud to be promoted to using a fork and spoon or a fork and knife. Under good supervision, a child can learn to cope with the usual table cutlery and with practice and encouragement he quickly becomes efficient (Fig. 65).

Table-cloths are often a source of worry to the adult, as she fears the child will have a spill and many tables nowadays have a Formica top which does not need covering. If a cloth is necessary it is better to use a coloured plastic one or a plastic mat in the early days when spills are frequent. Later when the child is better able to feed himself he can be taught to appreciate a clean table-cloth, and encouraged to gain confidence in his own behaviour at meals. As soon as the child is really capable of feeding himself well he can take his meals without a feeder. If a small serviette is available, he should be taught to use it.

In a nursery, clean feeders should be used for each meal and unless they are made of plastic should be boiled when they are washed.

Crockery. If the young child is given attractive cups and plates, he will learn to appreciate them and can gradually be taught to treat them with respect. At first, unbreakable cups and plates are advisable.

Meal times in the private household should be happy times, when the parents and child are together, enjoying similar foods and interests, and this provides excellent training for his social development. The mother, although keeping a watchful eye on the child, should never show anxiety over the child's appetite, but simply appear to assume that everyone eats their food at mealtimes, and that it is the right thing to do. Fussing over the child will only lead to more and more difficulties. The child's reactions to food must never be discussed in his presence. It is important that the adults should not make their own particular likes or dislikes too obvious, because this may prejudice the child against certain foods. Any disturbance of the atmosphere between the parents will indirectly affect the child.

In the nursery, meal times should be encouraged to be social events in the routine of each day. It is an excellent plan for a few adults to have their meal with the children, but in doing so their attitude must be a social one, and not one of domination. Children are quick to learn by example from adults they know and trust.

Behaviour at the table should be as calm as possible allowing the child to have conversation as long as this does not interfere with his eating. When a group of adults are lingering over a meal the children should be allowed to get down when they have finished.

FIG. 65. A three year old feeding himself.

If grace is said it should be brief, and as far as possible within the child's comprehension.

Serving meals. There are several points which must be remembered when dishing up food. It should look attractive, be neatly placed on a plate and showing each separate item. The food should not be mashed all together as the meal should look just as appetising for a young child as for an adult. Well served food will stimulate the appetite.

When a hot meal is being served it should reach the child still hot, and not just tepid. On the other hand, if intended to be eaten cold, it must be served as such. Attention to these details add tremendously to the joy of a meal for adults and children alike.

Small helpings should be given, so that the child can ask for more if he needs it rather than giving him too much on his plate at one time. In nurseries there are different ways of serving meals. Probably the best is where the adult serves as the mother does at home in a family group. In residential nurseries a light supper may be given to shorten the gap before breakfast. In this case tea will be a smaller meal and supper a lightly cooked meal just before preparing for bedtime.

Whether in the home or the nursery the child should on occasions see the food being cooked. It is always a thrill to the child to enter the kitchen, and specially so to the child who lives in a residential nursery.

CHAPTER 13

Choosing and Preparation of Food for Children

Intelligent shopping is as essential as good well cooked food and this applies as much in the private home as in the nursery. It is usually more economical to shop once or twice a week in a good supermarket where almost everything can be bought, than to make daily excursions to a series of small shops. However, in some areas individual traders make a real effort to please their customers. They may deliver orders and advise on the best purchases, and this personal touch can be very helpful.

It is a false economy to buy a cheap inferior food simply because it is cheap. A few more pence may purchase something of a much higher quality, which in the long run will prove to be a better buy. Seasonal foods such as soft fruit and vegetables can now be obtained almost all the year round, but they are very expensive out of season, so prices need to be watched carefully. Some frozen foods, particularly peas, which are often cheaper frozen than fresh, give very good value; others are an extravagance. Tinned foods on the whole have a lower food value than fresh or frozen food, and although they are tempting to buy because they are so easily served should not be used too often.

Good shopping can best be learnt by experience, and by a thorough knowledge of local shops.

Hints on buying perishable foods

Meat:	An excessive amount of fat or bone is uneconomical.
Beef	should be a deep red colour. The fat should be pale yellow and not discoloured. It should be firm to the touch and free of any smell.
Veal	is usually expensive. It may be red or very pale,

	the latter being considered the better quality.
Lamb	and mutton, should be firm, the flesh paler than beef and the fat whiter.
Pork	The flesh is paler than lamb, and it too should be firm and free from smell.
Poultry:	Frozen chickens are cheap and readily available, and if cooked with imagination can be very good. Fresh birds have more flavour but are also more expensive.
Fish:	Fresh fish have bright eyes and the flesh is firm and fairly rigid. Strong smelling fish should be avoided.
Vegetables:	
Root Vegetables	such as onions, carrots, turnips, beets, should be firm and the skin not wrinkled.
Green Vegetables	should be crisp and green when purchased.
Peas	should have a full crisp pod. Frozen peas, especially when bought in bulk are often a better buy, and better quality, than fresh ones.
Runner Beans	should be green, tender and firm.
Fruits:	These should be ripe – but sound. Soft fruits, such as raspberries, strawberries, currants, should be dry when purchased. Over-ripe fruits are very wasteful even when bought when their cost is low.

Tinned foods

It is wise to choose well known brands of tinned food. Care should be taken to inspect the tin for any damage in transport, and a tin that bulges at one end should be regarded with suspicion. Once a tin has been opened, the contents should be tipped out and kept in a refrigerator if they are not going to be used immediately.

Cooking

The value of good cooking cannot be overestimated, as it plays a most important part in every child's life. It is fully recognised that good development depends largely on satisfactory nutrition. In Britain the bulk of food in the diet is cooked, and the nutritional value of the food must be retained if the child is to have the maximum benefit from his meals.

To many people, cooking is considered to be just something which has to be done each day, with little thought of the valuable part this work plays in building up healthy children and in maintaining good health throughout life. Cookery has been termed an 'art', and very rightly so. A good knowledge and understanding of nutrition and cooking is necessary for anyone responsible for preparing meals in a nursery or a home. In developing any art one learns by a trial-and-error process, therefore expert tuition is an important factor for anyone who is to be responsible for the feeding and care of children. The importance of serving meals attractively has already been stressed (Chapter 12), but the full value of the meal will only be obtained if the cook has retained the maximum nourishment which the food can supply.

Reasons for cooking foods

Food is cooked for several reasons, the chief being:
(a) To render foods more digestible.
(b) To make mastication easier.
(c) To give variety to the diet.
(d) To make some foods more palatable.
(e) To make some types of food more pleasing to the eye.
(f) To eliminate harmful parasites present in some foods.

Methods of cooking in common use

Steaming is economical and the food retains its full flavour. It is easily digested and very suitable for weaning diets and invalid cookery. A steamer can be used for puddings, but small quantities of fish, or liver, for example, may be steamed by placing it between two plates and laying them on top of a pan with boiling water.

Boiling is a method of cooking meat, fish, vegetables, fruits, etc., by adding boiling water to the food in a pan or adding cold water and bringing it to the boil, then boiling until the food is tender. Once the water has boiled the heat should be lowered and the fluid kept at an even temperature until the food is tender. It must be realised that the temperature of boiling water is the same, whether it is gently boiling or furiously bubbling. When vegetables are boiled there should be a minimum of water used to lessen the loss of vitamin C.

Stewing and casserole cooking. There is usually less liquid used in stewing than in boiling, and stewing is done at a lower temperature and therefore more slowly. It is very suitable for coarse grained meat and, as little heat is necessary, it is economical on fuel. Casserole cooking is a form of stewing which is usually done in a slow oven. This method is particularly good for root vegetables, and if the oven is intelligently filled it is an economical way of cooking.

Baking and roasting. The principles of baking and roasting are the same. Roasting is commonly applied to cuts of meat and baking usually used for cakes, puddings and savouries such as fish pie or cheese pudding.

The food is cooked in a fairly hot oven, so it is more expensive than casserole cookery, but it produces excellent meals. A covered roasting tin reduces the need for basting and prevents the oven getting soiled. Joints for roasting have to be the most tender cuts and so tend to be expensive.

Grilling is a method adopted for the best cuts of steak, cutlets, fish and bacon. It is a quick method of cooking, but is extravagant on fuel. In grilling it is essential to start with a fierce heat, whether from a fire, gas or electricity. Food cooked in this way is appetising and less greasy than fried food.

Frying. This term is applied to cooking food in a shallow pan with a little fat. It is a quick and popular way of cooking, but if badly done can lead to indigestion. To fry correctly, the fat should be at boiling temperature before the food is put into the pan. Fat is not boiling when it bubbles, but later when it gives off a faint blue smoke. This method is not advised for young children.

Deep frying. In this method the food is entirely submerged in boiling fat. It is used mostly for chipped potatoes, fish, doughnuts and fritters. Before submerging the food the fat should be giving off a faint blue smoke, and should be kept at this heat until food is cooked. On removing the food it must be drained of fat.

For some household measures useful in cooking see Table IX, page 188.

Planning the day's meals

The chief aim in planning the day's menu, is to provide good nourishing food in an appetising manner. The cost of the food will play some part in the choice, but it need not mar the attractiveness of the meals. It is usual first to decide on the main course, whether this is to be meat or fish or savoury, and then plan the remainder of the meal around it. For example, stewed steak with suet dumplings would be extremely satisfying and could therefore be followed up with a lighter second course such as fresh fruit or fruit and junket or a blancmange and jelly. On the other hand, if steamed or boiled fish was to be served, then a more solid pudding could follow. Naturally weather conditions will influence the choice of the menu.

In planning for children, the picture of the whole day's food should be considered and the tea-supper can often be used to give some detail to the diet which is obviously missing; perhaps a little more protein in the form of a piece of cheese, or more vitamins and minerals served in a fresh fruit or vegetable salad.

Some of the most popular foods for children are cheap and easy to prepare, and have a good food value providing they are served with other things. Tinned baked beans are almost invariably appreciated, spaghetti is another favourite and so are sausages or frozen fish fingers.

Many children have a marked preference for savoury flavours rather than sweet ones. Savoury spreads, such as yeast extract, cheese or meat spreads often go down better than jam and cakes, and are generally better for the children.

The diet should be varied but children tend to be conservative in their tastes so it is as well to mix new ideas with old favourites as far as possible.

Whatever is arranged, it is highly important to serve all meals to time. Nicely served meals will play a big part in stimulating the appetite. Seasoning of food is important, too little can be as bad as too much. Delicate flavourings are stimulating to the palate, but they should never be very obvious.

TABLE IX

Some useful household measures

Useful household dry measures

1 heaped tablespoon flour	approx. 1 ounce	approx. 28 grams
1 level tablespoon sugar	,, 1 ,,	,, 28 ,,
Fat – the size of a small hen's egg	,, 1 ,,	,, 28 ,,

Fluid Measures

1 small teacupful	approx. $\frac{1}{4}$ pint	5 fluid ounces	150 millilitres
1 breakfastcupful	,, $\frac{1}{2}$,,	10 ,, ,,	300 ,,
1 tumblerful	,, $\frac{1}{2}$,,	10 ,, ,,	300 ,,

Spoons in common use (fluid measure)

2 teaspoonfuls	= 1 dessertspoonful =	8 millilitres
4 ,,	= 1 tablespoonful =	15 ,,
2 tablespoonfuls	= 1 ounce =	30 ,,
20 ounces	= 1 pint =	600 ,,
2 pints	= 1 quart =	1·200 litres

Books for reference and further reading are listed at the end of the book.

PART THREE
Hygiene

CHAPTER 14

General Hygiene

Hygiene is the science of preserving health; it plays an especially important part in the health and welfare of children. Some of the principal factors to be considered are:

(a) fresh air and sunlight
(b) good ventilation
(c) exercise
(d) rest and sleep
(e) warmth and light
(f) good nutrition
(g) personal and general cleanliness of clothing
(h) good sanitation
(i) pure water supply.

All of these are of vital importance and the lack of one or two can considerably minimize the good effects of the others.

Fresh air and sunlight

The air we breathe is a gas and it surrounds the earth. It is invisible and tasteless and when pure is free from smell. To appreciate the part that fresh air plays in our health it is important to understand its composition. It is made up of:

Oxygen – (20 per cent) – essential to human life and the combustion of food. We obtain our supply of oxygen when breathing in. Plants and animals give off oxygen and thus play an important part in maintaining the supply in the atmosphere.

Nitrogen – (78 per cent) This gas plays no part in respiration.

Carbon dioxide is present in very small quantities but is essential for life. The body, by combustion, produces a little carbon dioxide, and a small amount is required by the body to act as a balancing agent in the blood.

Water vapour – (2 per cent) is present in the air; this is produced from various sources, e.g. evaporation from water, also moist surfaces.

Fresh air has a very stimulating effect on the whole system; it promotes a feeling of well-being, and good development in the young child. It stimulates the circulation of the blood in the skin and blood vessels, and ensures healthy lung tissue. It also helps to produce restful sleep and encourages a good appetite. Fresh air passing over the skin surface evaporates the sweat and cools the body in hot weather; in so doing it regulates the body temperature.

Fresh air and sunlight together stimulate the mind and body and produce important effects on the skin, which result in general improvement of body metabolism. They are nature's best aids to the prevention of infection of every kind, as germs thoroughly dislike a clean, cool atmosphere, and the sun's rays also act as a disinfectant.

Hot impure air is usually found in badly ventilated homes and overcrowded halls, and its immediate effect is to produce a tired feeling, with general lassitude. To live and sleep in such conditions will lower the resistance to infections of every kind, including the common cold and other respiratory diseases. Stunted growth, general debility and fainting attacks are all symptoms commonly caused by lack of fresh air. Impure air may be caused by lack of good ventilation, the presence of dust or dirt (inside or outside), or contamination of the atmosphere by insanitary conditions such as defective drains, sewers, uncovered dustbins or dirty roads. Over-crowded, dirty homes or badly kept workplaces will all help to spread infection and cause poor health.

Sunlight is of great importance in building up health. The infra-red rays are felt as heat, which is natural warmth. Ultra-violet rays act on the ergosterol which is a chemical compound found in the fatty substance under the skin, and produces vitamin D, which enables the body to utilize calcium and phosphorus.

With plenty of sunlight the skin becomes thicker and a better protection against infection. Being in the sun is valuable to children and adults. It is important, however, to remember the sun can be very hot, and it is unwise to expose babies or small children to too much of it. The process should be very gradual until the skin becomes accustomed and this will minimize the risk of sunburn. The skin will gradually become 'tanned', then longer periods in the sun can be allowed. Children need to be supervised when playing in the sun and then they can be encouraged not to spend too long in the sun, or in the shade where it may be cold for them. Fair-skinned children usually have very sensitive skins and are more likely to get burned.

Young babies should be exposed for not more than 2 minutes to begin with, then the time can gradually be increased. It is wise at first to have a canopy over the pram (lined with green) which allows free ventilation round the baby.

The eyes, the back of the neck and the spine should be protected from bright sunlight by a sun bonnet and a short sleeveless coat.

Good ventilation

Good ventilation is the means whereby atmospheric conditions which are comfortable and healthful to the body are maintained. The aim of ventilation is to keep the air inside the room as fresh as that outside, therefore it should be continually changing, and the more people there are in the room, using up the oxygen in the air, the more often it will need to be changed. Hot air becomes lighter and automatically rises. To provide adequate ventilation it is necessary to have an inlet and an outlet, the latter being the smaller to help prevent draughts. Natural ventilation takes place through windows, doors, ventilators and fireplaces, and it is helped by the devices used for heating the building. A fireplace is a valuable aid to ventilation, especially when the fire is burning in the grate. It warms the air around, thus causing it to rise, and a great proportion will go up the chimney. Wind passing over the top of the chimney will cause a suction of air from the chimney which will have to be replaced from the room. In this way, a circulation of air is set up in the room, and cool air is drawn in from inlets, which may be an open window, crevices or cracks in the floor boards, or through the door. Cool air entering at a low level will usually pass in a direct current of air to the fireplace, even if there is no fire alight. This draught will make the room very cold to the feet, and a danger to children who may sit or crawl on the floor. Whenever possible the entry of cool air should be encouraged at a fairly high level to avoid draughts.

When there is no adequate outlet for used air, such as a fireplace, most authorities insist on an outlet, which is usually a perforated iron plate let into the outside wall near the ceiling. This is often found in bathrooms and lavatories. Another helpful method where there are sash windows is to insert a three inch wide board between the window sill and the bottom sash. In this way air can enter between the upper and lower sashes, taking an upward course, and so not causing a draught.

As more and more houses are becoming centrally heated, and often no longer have fireplaces, it is particularly important that there should be adequate ventilation. Double glazing is another hindrance to adequate fresh air, and where there is double glazing there should be some sort of mechanical ventilation device.

In large buildings natural methods are inadequate and it is therefore essential to use mechanical methods. In so doing it may be possible to treat the air on the way in, cleaning and filtering it, also warming and moistening it so that it is suitable for the adults and children to breathe.

In Britain it is usual to live in rooms at a temperature of 60° F–70° F (15° C–21° C). But for delicate or premature babies a higher temperature is required.

When a building is specially built for a nursery or a nursery school, it is usually planned to encourage 'cross ventilation', which means that there will be windows on opposite sides of the building above the heads of the occupants to allow a free current of air and ensure against any stagnation of the atmosphere.

Exercise

In order to enjoy good health it is necessary to have exercise throughout life. Activity causes deeper breathing, better expansion of the lungs and thus gives a greater supply of oxygen to the body. Muscles grow and become firmer as is very apparent in a healthy well-developed child. Open air exercise is the best sort because of the action of the air on the skin. It also promotes a healthy appetite and good digestion, and helps to prevent infection.

Quite apart from the physical side, games, rambles and walks have a stimulating effect on a child's mental development. As well as exercising the muscles and limbs a child needs to be encouraged to use and exercise his brain. Games and activities suited to his development will help to create good relations with his contemporaries.

Active open air games or work normally tire the body, but after a good night's sleep the body should be refreshed, otherwise the exercise has been too strenuous. It is important to realize that children vary tremendously in the amount of activity they can take and because of this, the adults in charge must take care to note the child's reaction to games or exercise.

The improved circulation clears the organs of waste products, which are excreted by the kidneys and skin. Peristalsis (the contraction and expansion of the digestive organs) is increased by exercise and constipation is avoided.

There is little danger of the child failing to get sufficient exercise provided he is given adequate facilities. Some over-anxious parents often try to restrict activities to avoid accidents, but the varied equipment available nowadays for young children gives them the opportunity to gain confidence in their actions without harming themselves. Such opportunities should be available in the garden at home as well as in the nursery playground.

The young child is very similar to other young animals, for example the puppy or the kitten. They are playful, then they want a rest period, and this must be borne in mind when arranging their daily activities and routine.

Good posture contributes to physical fitness. It is important to maintain a good posture when walking and sitting. Tables and chairs at school or in the nursery should be comfortable and the correct height, with the back supported and the feet resting on the floor.

Lack of exercise can be harmful, encouraging a poor posture, soft flabby muscles and a general lack of tone to the whole body which will cause poor physical and mental growth.

Rest and sleep

Rest and sleep are essential if the child is to be healthy and happy.

Rest is required as part of the child's routine day. It is needed to counteract fatigue, and is essential after exercise or any activity, when the body can relax and recuperate. The heart and lungs work very hard during games and strenuous exercise and must have the opportunity to recover. It should be remembered that during activity there is a great deal of wear and tear of the whole system, and this tissue has to be built up again. Rest is also needed to allow time for the blood stream to carry oxygen to the tissues and to remove waste. Both physical and mental efforts need to be alternated with rest; this can be achieved by quiet periods and by giving varied interests to encourage relaxation. Every child should be given the opportunity to relax if only for a short time; this can be done by providing a chair, a swing or a rug to lie on. The art of taking rest and relaxing during the day if developed in childhood will prove a great asset later in life.

Sleep is a condition in which the true state of the mind is not known. Normally it occurs rhythmically in every twenty-four hours, when consciousness is lost and the brain rests. This gives the body an excellent opportunity to build up its tissues for good growth and to allow the brain to rest and recuperate. The amount of sleep needed by children and adults varies tremendously; a young baby may require twenty or more hours, a five to six year old, ten to twelve hours, while many adults sleep five to six hours and find this adequate. This is partly governed by the habits and temperament of the individual and possibly by their intelligence. Small children require at least one additional period of sleep during each day, which must be arranged to meet the individual child's needs. The usual time is after the midday meal, but if a child is an early riser, he will often benefit more by having his rest before lunch. Many children under three years of age require the opportunity to rest for about one hour during the morning and again in the afternoon. It is a good plan that these naps should be at approximately the same time every day.

Good sleep habits are essential to all children and can usually be established in the early months. Every effort should be made to ensure that the bedtime is as regular as possible.

Warmth and light

Warmth and light are needed for comfort and health. Warmth is essential for the very young baby because of the tremendous change from his intrauterine existence. The child's relatively large area of skin surface in proportion to his weight makes him more susceptible to chills, and as well as this he has not yet learned to withstand changes of temperature. In cold weather babies can very easily become chilled, and become very seriously ill, requiring admission to hospital.

Warmth is provided in various ways:

1. Regular background heating with additions to provide extra warmth in individual rooms. (It may be necessary to have some form of heating in a baby's bedroom at night during a spell of cold weather). It is very essential that all forms of heating should be guarded in rooms where children play. The guard should be fixed to the wall so that it cannot be pulled over.

2. Clothing will provide warmth for the body and should be light in weight.

Lighting. Under ideal conditions there should be a constant, uniform and adequate supply of light, so arranged that it does not fall directly on the eyes or cast shadows. This is very essential for efficient work and for the maximum enjoyment of leisure. The lighting of buildings may be natural or artificial.

Natural light is obtained by windows, which should be as large as possible. It may be necessary in sunny weather to use sun blinds to avoid the glare.

Artificial lighting. There should be good lighting in all rooms, especially where close work is being done; also in passages and stairs.

Cooling. In very hot weather it may be necessary to cool the air; this can be done by causing greater movement of the air by creating cross draughts or by electric fans.

Blinds can be used to avoid the direct rays of the sun. A room thermometer should be kept as it is often not possible to guess the temperature of a room, which should be 60° F–65° F (15° C–18° C) during the day, though less at night.

Cleanliness

This plays a big part in maintaining a healthy body and also in preventing disease. Personal cleanliness is of the utmost importance to the individual and to all those in contact with him. Dirt, dust, flies and vermin carry the organisms that cause disease and provide a medium for their breeding. It is essential that the skin should be clean, to carry out its function as an excretory gland. It should be a routine procedure to wash the hands before preparing or eating food, and also after using the toilet. Children must be trained to develop this habit, so that it will remain with them throughout life. Epidemics of diarrhoea, food poisoning and other infectious diseases are often due to lack of cleanliness.

It is essential to have the home or nursery cleaned regularly to make them pleasant and happy places to live in. With modern labour saving equipment this is not the laborious business that it was in the past.

Domestic work in the nursery needs to be done efficiently and the dust prevented from rising, because children are very susceptible to infection. The daily work must be well planned to fit into the routine of the day. Floors will need cleaning regularly, according to their type, and there will need to be daily damp dusting. Carpets, rugs and upholstered furniture should be cleaned with a vacuum cleaner to avoid raising dust by brushing. Clean dusters are essential when dusting furniture; modern silicone polishes save labour by making it unnecessary to apply them frequently. If spills do occur on furniture a wash with a detergent will probably be necessary, followed by a rub with polish. High ledges and lampshades must be kept free from dust, and damp dusting or cleaning with a wool mop will pick up the dust without spreading it.

In addition to the daily routine, walls, paintwork, and windows will require regular cleaning, those in large industrial areas needing this at more frequent intervals.

All equipment used must be kept in good condition to ensure that it functions properly.

Furniture must be simple, strong with no sharp corners and washable, with chairs and tables a suitable size for the child's use. Chairs which can be stacked on top of each other are convenient when space is limited. Curtains should be attractive but should not restrict light or air. Children are sensitive to colour and gay schemes should be employed. The playroom in both day and residential nurseries must be made to look like a cosy and friendly home. An armchair or settee can introduce a sense of home and comfort to the child, with attractive rugs or small carpets on the floor. It is good to have a screen in a corner which may suggest a little privacy, if a child wants to be on his own for a time. This creation of atmosphere is necessary in all nurseries and particularly in residential ones. In nurseries low cupboards are nearly always available for play material, but in the home this is frequently not the case. No matter in what type of home the child is living, provision should be made for a small cupboard or box in which he can place his toys when not in use. This encourages tidiness combined with a sense of responsibility.

Suitable lavatories and washing facilities are provided in nurseries, but in the home independence should be encouraged by providing suitable steps or stools to enable the child to reach the adult washhandbasin or towels. Small lavatory seats can now be purchased which can be easily fitted onto the adult lavatory.

A *rest bed* is provided in nurseries and nursery schools for the daytime rest. This should be long enough for the child and be raised about twelve inches from the ground. A blanket should be laid over the stretcher before the child lies down, in addition to the covering blanket. Any chilling during the rest period must be avoided, as this may be responsible for the child bed wetting or developing colds. Resting out of doors is ideal, as it lessens the risk of infection, provided the weather is suitable. In summer the rest period is usually when the sun is very strong, which might cause overheating unless some shade is provided. Cold and windy weather can be very treacherous as the child may become thoroughly chilled.

Play pen. A good type is constructed with a wooden base about 6 inches off the floor, which reduces the risk of floor draughts. Although a play pen is helpful when a child is having kicking practice, learning to crawl or stand, it can become harmful and limit his activity if the child is left in it for too long a period, and it is unwise to put more than two children together. The bars should not be more than three to three and a half inches apart.

Kitchens and larders should be kept scrupulously clean to avoid the danger of food poisoning and prevent the breeding of flies. The larder in the private house or nursery should be conveniently near the kitchen, and well away from the lavatories and the sewage system. The window should be open to allow free ventilation, or if this is not possible an extracting fan can be fitted. A wire gauze can be fitted over the window opening to prevent the entry of flies.

The floors need frequent washing, and all shelves and working surfaces must be kept clean. These can be wiped down with a damp cloth and scrubbed weekly. Walls should be cleaned down regularly, but no food should be exposed; it must be removed or covered over.

A *refrigerator* should be used whenever possible for storing perishable foods such as milk, butter, fish and meat, and these should be wrapped or covered. Food will keep perfectly in the refrigerator, but if the food is taken out and placed in a warmer temperature for a period, and again returned to the refrigerator, there will be more risk of germs. Therefore it is necessary to store the food until it is required, and remove only what is likely to be used at one time. The refrigerator keeps good food safe, but does not improve contaminated food.

The *storeroom* or *food cupboard* should be cool, well-ventilated and dry, with plenty of shelf accommodation. Any boxes on the floor should be raised on slats, so that air can circulate around them. The foods should be used in order of delivery. On arrival, vegetables and fruit should be put into a cool place and inspected daily.

Cleaning and care of the kitchen

There is no place in a home or in a nursery which is more dependent on good organisation than the kitchen. *Cleanliness* and *order* must be the strong key-notes. Whoever is doing the cooking and the work of the kitchen must have her programme for the day thoroughly planned. No kitchen is complete without a clock. A nail brush, toilet soap, and paper towels should be available in every kitchen for thorough and frequent hand washing. It is important that all persons in the home or nursery should appreciate the importance of hygienic methods. Clean overalls should be worn and the hair covered; it is essential that the staff should be healthy.

The cooking stove. Whatever method of cooking is used, the person who is responsible for the meals should understand exactly how to work the particular stove in use. When a solid fuel cooker is used it is important to attend to this first thing in the morning to ensure adequate heat for cooking during the morning. Gas and electric stoves must always be cleaned out regularly. They should be wiped down with a damp cloth immediately the cooking is finished, and thoroughly cleaned once a week. It is important when cooking to avoid pans boiling over, as the gas burners get choked; with an electric stove this spoils the burners. When using a gas cooker it is wasteful to keep the gas burning full on after the pan has boiled.

The electric stove is slower to heat, but it will retain the heat longer than a gas stove. Therefore it is important to understand the management of an electric cooker and also to know what amount of heat is required for the foods to be cooked. Special saucepans should be used for electric cookers.

Kitchen cupboards should contain all the essentials for use in the kitchen. There should be a place for everything and everything should be kept in its place. *Tidiness* in the kitchen will save endless time and also frayed nerves, quite apart from preventing flies and often preventing accidents. All ledges and fixtures must be damp dusted regularly. The kitchen and scullery tables, usually of formica or adhesive plastic, must be washed daily. These are easier to keep clean than wood which can harbour germs in the cracks produced by frequent scrubbing.

It is ideal to have three sinks, one used for the washing of vegetables and the others for washing up. These must be kept scrupulously clean, being washed down after use.

The *kitchen floor* must be kept clean and washed or mopped over once a day and scrubbed once a week. The most practical flooring is linoleum or vynyl tiles. Where a kitchen has a scullery attached, the same cleanliness should apply to the scullery.

The importance of washing up

It will depend on whether the water is hard or soft as to the amount of detergent required. There are many good soap substitutes or detergents on the market which help in eliminating grease from the washing-up water. A mop is extremely useful, enabling hotter water to be used. There should be plenty of hot water available. All dirty dishes and cutlery should be collected together and arranged in groups of glass, china, silver, cutlery and any pans or cooking utensils. Any pieces should be scraped from the plates.

With the hot, soapy water or detergent, first wash the glass and rinse it. Dry as soon as possible.

Next wash the cutlery, taking care never to allow the knives and forks with handles to remain soaking in the hot water as this will in time loosen the handles. Rinse in very hot water and dry.

The china should be well washed and when possible dipped in clean, hot rinsing water. This is necessary when a plate rack is used. Care must be taken to avoid chipping or cracking the china, as such damaged china may become a source of infection and danger.

Where there is any question of infection the utensils should be boiled for five minutes and then dried in the usual way.

Polythene or plastic dishes should be thoroughly washed in hot, soapy water, and these can be soaked in Milton solution (1–80 for $1\frac{1}{2}$ hrs.).

Enamel dishes are now used only for cooking purposes and not for children's meals. These dishes should be cared for in the same way as china.

It is possible to use a heated drying rack which is an excellent method of drying crockery which obviates the use of a drying cloth. Washing-up machines are particularly useful where there are large numbers.

Care of cooking utensils

When cooking it is wise to clear as you go. All utensils and pans should be put into soak immediately after use.

Aluminium pans should be well washed with hot soapy water and dried. Never use soda or wire sponge.

Iron pans or *frying pans* after being well washed must be thoroughly dried to avoid rusting.

Baking tins must be well washed in hot soapy water and dried thoroughly before putting away.

After washing up, the mop and dish cloth must be washed, soaked in Milton solution, rinsed and dried in the open air. Tea towels can also be a source of infection. These must be washed, boiled or sterilised in Milton, rinsed and dried. A specially prepared paper, resistant to water, is obtainable for use as tea cloths and dish cloths, but it is not yet available for general household use.

Bowls and sinks used for washing up must be thoroughly washed after use.

Draining boards should be dried after use and, if wooden, scrubbed once a day.

A *sink basket* is helpful in preventing tea-leaves, peelings, etc., choking up the sink pipe. It is wise to pour some boiling soda water down the sink at least once a day. Boiling soda water should be used with a stout brush to wash round the gully trap outside the kitchen sink. If this is done regularly it will prevent the accumulation of grease and avoid harbouring flies.

Disposal of waste plays a big part in preventing infection in the nursery or home. Left over food suitable for animal feeding, e.g. scrapings from plates, vegetable peelings, etc., should be put into a clean, covered bin or plastic bag and disposed of daily. All bins should be washed out after they are emptied and allowed to dry in the fresh air. The dry waste vegetable material, if not used for chicken or pig feeding, can be put on the garden compost heap, which will prove useful as a fertilizer later on.

Most household refuse is collected in bins made of varied types of material, e.g. galvanised iron, or polythene. They should have a well-fitting lid to keep out flies and cats. Many local authorities now use strong paper or plastic sacks which are waterproofed, and which fit onto a metal frame with a lid. This decreases handling as the sack is placed straight into the refuse vehicle. Bins should be placed well away from windows and from the larder and kitchen.

Flies are a great source of infection, as they frequent dirty places and carry away the germs to wherever they may travel. Milk or food can become contaminated if left uncovered and accessible to flies. Precautions should be taken in the home, especially in the summer, to destroy flies as soon as they appear. It must be remembered that these insects breed very quickly. Wasps, flies, ants and cockroaches and other pests are all injurious to health. Cleanliness plays a big part in preventing their invasion of the home. Kitchens, pantries and store rooms must be kept free from odd scraps of food, e.g. crumbs on the floor, or pieces left in the sink basket at night. Preparations are obtainable to help to clear the house if any pests appear. Action should be taken even if only one appears, as they quickly breed and multiply.

Household sanitation

This is essential in any community because of the large quantity of waste material which accumulates as a result of daily activities. If it is not removed and disposed of efficiently it will soon make any neighbourhood unpleasant and unfit, as well as dangerous, to live in.

There are two types of waste material:

1. *Dry refuse*, consisting of waste material such as ashes, food scraps, paper, wrappings, and metals. These should be wrapped and placed in the dustbin, which should be covered with a good fitting lid to avoid the danger of flies. Local authority refuse lorries collect the refuse at least once a week.

2. *Liquid refuse:*
   (*a*) waste water from sinks and baths is carried through to the waste pipe which empties over a small gully or trap at ground level, usually found outside the kitchen;
   (*b*) human excreta in the form of urine and faeces is carried away by the water carriage system. The pipe leading from the lavatory is known as the soil pipe, which carries the excreta directly to the sewer. This pipe can be seen passing down the outside wall of the building and then underground to the sewer. In every lavatory there is a U-shaped bend which forms a water seal which prevents any foul gases from the sewer entering the building.

Bathroom. Daily care is very important and should never be neglected. This is particularly important when the nursery is used by groups of children. Good ventilation with the necessary warmth must be maintained.

The care of hand wash basins. These must be thoroughly washed with hot soapy water after use, and cleaned thoroughly once a day. First wash or polish taps, then with hot soapy water and a little scouring powder, clean the inside and outside of the basin, paying attention to the overflow opening and the waste pipe. About three times a week use a long stiff brush and pour very hot water containing a detergent or disinfectant of the appropriate strength (see Chapter 23) into the overflow opening and the waste pipe to prevent the formation of scum.

Care of the bath. This must be thoroughly washed out with very hot water and scouring powder after bathing a child. The daily care is the same as that described for the wash hand basin. The bathroom floor must be washed daily.

Thorough regular cleaning of all ledges, walls, paint work and fitments is essential.

Care of hand towels. In day and residential nurseries and in nursery schools these must be marked clearly with the individual child's symbol and hung on the appropriate peg. There must be an adequate distance between each peg to prevent the towels from touching each other, as this will help to prevent the spread of infection.

Bath towels in a residential nursery will require drying facilities and hanging space.

Provision must also be made for the tooth brush and mug of each child to be kept separate and free from dust. The brush and comb in a small bag can hang on the individual towel pegs.

Daily care of the lavatory. It is important that the water forming the seal in the lavatory is always at the correct level, as a faulty seal or trap is extremely dangerous to health. The room in which the lavatory is situated must be well ventilated and easy to keep clean.

The cleaning equipment must be kept solely for this purpose and should consist of a lavatory brush, kept in a container, cleaning cloths, scrubbing brush and a bucket. A disinfectant for the lavatory brush is not recommended for use in a nursery.

Method: First prepare hot detergent in the bucket. With the lavatory cloth and the hot detergent thoroughly wash the outside of the lavatory, the seat and the handle of the chain. It is important to clean under the seat as well as the upper surface, and seats are hinged to enable this to be done. Rinse the cloth and wipe the seat and lavatory dry. Flush the lavatory, and with the lavatory brush, using a scouring powder thoroughly scrub all round the rim inside the lavatory, paying special attention to the trap or water seal. Flush again and add a little disinfectant to the lavatory. Pour the dirty water down the lavatory and flush again. Wash the lavatory floor with fresh detergent. Wash the lavatory brush and dry in the open air. Clean the container and replace the brush when dry. Wash the cleaning cloths and dry them in the open air.

Care of the sluice is the same as that described for a lavatory.

Care of pots. Empty them after use, rinse them using a lavatory brush if necessary, then leave them in hot soda water for a short time. They should then be washed with a lavatory cloth in a detergent and dried.

When there are many children, as in a nursery, it is better if each small child has his own pot. It is a wise precaution to have them boiled each day, or soaked for a few hours at night in strong disinfectant such as Lysol, Izal, or hyperchloride. It is very essential that this should be measured carefully to avoid accidents.

Pure water supply

This is essential for life and therefore the provision of an adequate supply of pure water is one of the most important public services. The provision of water is expensive. The natural sources of water are rain and snow falling on the earth. Some of the moisture evaporates but some forms into river or lakes and part penetrates into the earth and forms springs. When water soaks through the soil it has the power to dissolve some mineral constituents from the rocks and soil. Water containing a high percentage of lime (calcium) or magnesium is termed 'hard' and such water will leave a deposit of salts in the kettle or boiler. It uses more soap to obtain a good lather and is therefore expensive, and it gives poor results when washing clothes, with particularly harmful effects on woollens. It is advisable wherever possible to instal a water softening apparatus in the home to enable all the water to be treated before use. Soft water is kind to the skin, and in the country rain water is often collected from the roof of the house. This water is excellent for household purposes, but unless it is boiled it must not be used for drinking purposes or for bathing young babies, who often put their wet hands in their mouths when in the bath.

Drinking water

Towns are supplied with water which has been treated by the waterworks supplying the area. The water is collected in reservoirs from rivers and sometimes from springs. At the waterworks it is filtered and chlorinated and then stored into a covered service reservoir, from where it is drawn off to supply the town.

Private water supplies, often derived from shallow wells, may be dangerous because of the contamination from the ground where cattle graze, unless it is passed through a satisfactory process of filtration and chlorination. Impure water can lead to epidemics of infectious diseases, and many other unsatisfactory conditions.

An inadequate water supply may cause many difficulties, the chief being the reduced standard of personal cleanliness, more risk of contamination through dirty streets, and sewers not sufficiently flushed to prevent accumulation of germs. Epidemics of diarrhoea and other infectious diseases are more prevalent in a drought.

CHAPTER 15

Materials and Clothing for Children

Clothing is an important aspect of hygiene, for both children and adults. In recent years people have taken far more interest in clothes than they used to, and children's clothes in particular have changed radically, so that as well as being far more attractive they are more comfortable and hygienic too.

Unlike animals our bodies are not covered with a thick coat of fur, so we need clothing to keep us warm, healthy and happy. It maintains the correct body temperature and protects the body from the weather, dirt and injury. Very small babies and older people are unable to keep their bodies warm by exercise, therefore extra care should be taken to make sure that they are properly clothed and that the atmosphere around them is not too cold. Air should be able to get to the skin as it contains oxygen, which helps in the fight against most disease-forming germs.

In *hot weather* heat is lost from the body by sweating; this evaporates and causes the skin to become cooler, and because of this materials worn next to the skin should be absorbent so that excessive heat can be absorbed so that it does not cause chilling.

In *warm weather* light coloured clothing is cooler because it reflects back the rays of the sun, and if less clothing is worn air cannot be trapped between the layers and act as a heat retainer.

In *cold weather* the surface of the skin needs to be kept warm so that proper circulation can be maintained. If the body is not clothed properly shivering, which is an automatic protective mechanism against cold, will take place. This makes children and adults feel uncomfortable and miserable so that they are unable to work properly. It will therefore be necessary for more clothes to be worn so that the heat of the body can be retained and not lost. A layer of trapped air in the clothing can become a form of insulation, so clothing must not be too tight. If darker coloured clothing is worn it will tend to absorb the heat of the sun's rays – if there are any.

Clothes should be comfortable to wear and of an attractive design so that they make the child feel well and happy, and so that he may be complimented on his good appearance. They should give the child confidence at an early age and this will encourage him to take care of them. Most children are very interested in colour or any special point of decoration.

Clothing should be light, absorbent, warm, not tight and easily washed. Materials next to the skin should have a smooth surface and all garments should have suitable neck, and arm openings, which are well-finished and not restrictive or they may damage the skin.

Clothing designs for young children should be simple so that they are easy to wash, and easy for the child to put on himself. They will vary according to the weather and the age of the child and according to what he is doing. Thin children and very small babies need particular attention as they lose heat much more rapidly. Three layers of clothing is usually sufficient for most children when they are indoors; when out of doors they often need a thicker top layer of clothing. The weight and type of material used will vary according to the weather.

Back or front openings may be used provided the garments are comfortable and convenient for slipping on and off. All fastenings should have a good wrap over to prevent any gaping. Hands and feet and ears must be kept warm in cold weather, but opportunity must be provided for the legs and feet to exercise. Hands will feel warmer if the wrists are well covered, but gloves are necessary in cold weather.

Materials used for Clothing

Suitable materials may be wool, cotton, rayon and other man-made fibres, such as nylon, Orlon, Terylene, Tricel – and to a lesser extent, silk and union. These vary considerably in their ability to hold air, to absorb moisture and to allow ventilation. This difference is chiefly brought about by the various types of fibres from which they are composed. It is possible to buy materials and garments which have been treated with Proban, which reduces the flammability and thus makes them safer for children's wear. Proban has little effect on the other qualities of the wool or any other material.

Washing instructions need to be followed closely because with the increasing number of fabrics and fabric mixtures available, it is easy to use the wrong method and spoil the garment.

Wool is warm, porous and absorbent, a bad conductor of heat and light in weight. It is reasonable in cost and because of its ability to hold air in its fibres it acts as an insulator. It is usually a soft material to the touch, and is very suitable for children's under garments worn next to the skin. Wool is obtainable in the form of knitting wool or as a material, and is often mixed with other materials, such as cotton. Viyella and Clydella are a good example of suitable woven fabrics made from wool and cotton.

Woollen fabrics need very careful laundering to prevent them from shrinking and felting; they smoulder rather than flare if they catch fire, so are reasonably safe. Some people, however, have sensitive skins and cannot wear wool next to the skin unless it is mixed with silk or cotton.

Although a material may be labelled 'woollen' this does not necessarily mean that it is 100 per cent wool. It may be a mixture of wool and cotton, or wool and nylon. But most reputable firms state the exact proportions on the garment.

Two layers of fine wool will hold more air than one thick layer, thus giving more warmth.

Cotton is not usually such a warm fabric as wool, but with new methods of spinning, weaving and knitting cotton, warmer varieties, such as corduroy, cellular knit cotton and terry towelling, are appearing on the market. It is a strong fibre which is comparatively cheap to buy. It stands up to very hard wear, and can be easily washed and, in many cases, boiled, making it ideal for napkins. Flannelette and winceyette are also made of cotton, but should not be used for small children's clothes or bedding unless they have been specially treated to make them flameproof. They are made with a fluffy surface which makes them warmer than a smooth fabric.

Silk is very light in weight, washable and allows ventilation, but it is not quite so warm or absorbent as wool. It is less irritating to delicate skin and very useful to wear in hot climates, but it is not really suitable for children's clothes, being rather fragile and very expensive.

Linen is a more expensive material than cotton but has similar qualities. It can be used in this country for outer garments in summer and is very suitable for sunhats. Only linen which has a smooth finish should be used for children's garments. Linen creases and looses its freshness easily.

Rayon can be made to resemble cotton or silk materials and was one of the first synthetic fabrics to be manufactured. It tends to crease easily, and requires very careful washing. If not treated it flares easily when set alight.

Modern man-made fabrics include materials such as nylon, Terylene, Acrilan, Tricel, Orlon, etc. They are hard wearing, warm, soft, and need little or no ironing, and dry very quickly. Unless they are mixed with a natural fibre such as wool or cotton they are non-absorbent and therefore should not be worn next to the skin. If two layers of these fabrics are worn next to each other the friction will create static electricity, making the clothes stick together, and attract dust as well as being uncomfortable. Some children develop allergic rashes when these fabrics have been worn next to the skin.

Care of clothing

Clothing should be made of materials which can be easily cleaned and should be regularly inspected after laundering. Any missing buttons or tapes should be replaced or loops repaired. If thin places or tiny rents are mended as soon as they appear this will lengthen the life of the garment, besides being much easier to mend than a large hole.

For older children it will be necessary to do more repairs and adjustments as they will have harder wear. Often it is labour-saving to strengthen any thin places either in knitted or material garments before actual holes appear. When a few sets of clothes are available they should be worn in rotation, as children grow out of their clothes so quickly. Outdoor clothes which have been wet should be hung up by the shoulders on small coat-hangers and allowed to dry in a moderate temperature. The garments should be shaken and brushed regularly.

Laundry Work

The whole process of washing, drying, ironing and airing is nowadays complicated by the enormous variety of fabrics available, each requiring to be laundered in a different way. Therefore, it is important to have a working knowledge of how to deal with all kinds of washable materials. Babies' and in fact all children's clothing is washed so much that it is essential to have it carefully washed and ironed if the garments are to wear well and look attractive.

In residential nurseries the children's clothing is usually laundered in the nursery. The number of children will influence the facilities required for this purpose. Most nurseries have a laundry and if the water is very hard a *water softener* is usually installed, which gives better results and reduces the heavy expenditure on soaps. Soda is the cheapest water softener, but this can be very unkind to some skins unless the clothing is thoroughly rinsed.

Deep sinks fitted with hot and cold water are useful for many purposes and eliminate the necessity of lifting heavy baths of water.

The *washing machine* is a great asset in the laundry as it saves much time and labour. Many of these machines boil as well as wash which is essential for much of the children's laundry. Each manufacturer supplies full instructions for washing different materials and gives times for boiling. It is important that such directions should be accurately followed.

A *boiler* is necessary if the washing machine does not boil and a *rubber roller* wringer or *spin drier* is a necessity.

Soap, soap flakes, stergene or soap powder can be used, but it is important to use a good quality and never to use too much of it.

Detergents are produced in great varieties and are usually used where the water is hard. Some claim to be valuable for very dirty articles and others for delicate fabrics. If using these, always read the directions on the packet and follow the instructions.

Drying accommodation, whenever possible, should be outside, if the weather is suitable, but in nurseries a large drying cupboard is essential. A spin drier or tumble drier may be used to remove the excess water.

A clothes basket is necessary in which to place the washed articles ready to be taken outside for hanging on the line, and for collecting the dried washing and for collecting clothing for ironing.

Ironing. A table, with a washable top for folding clothes and for ironing on if an ironing board is not available, is needed. The ironing blanket should be double and large enough to cover the table or ironing board, and an ironing sheet should cover the ironing blanket.

Airing facilities are very important and usually a warm cupboard, heated by either the hot water cistern, electricity or gas, is available in most nurseries. In sunny weather, airing can be done very efficiently by hanging articles in the sun.

In a nursery it is necessary to sort out the dirty linen into the following classes: (*a*) white cotton and linen articles, (*b*) coloured cottons, (*c*) woollen garments (knitted or material) and (*d*) synthetic fabrics.

The dirty laundry should be examined for stains and these must be treated, if this has not been done when the stain was made.

Coloured garments in which the colour is likely to run, should be kept quite separate. Babies' napkins must be kept quite separate from the other washing.

Methods of Hand Washing

Woollen material garments. Prepare a soapy lather by dissolving some soap flakes or soap powder or suitable detergent in very hot water, then add cold to reduce the temperature to about 90° F (32.2° C). Be sure the soap is thoroughly dissolved otherwise small pieces of soap may cling to the woollen material and injure it. Never use extremes of very hot or very cold water. Squeeze the garments in the soapy lather, but *do not rub*. Rinse very well in water of the same temperature to get rid of all the soap. Dry fairly quickly, preferably in the open air, or, if indoors, away from the fire or excessive heat. When the garments are almost dry, fold and roll them up ready for ironing. Iron on the wrong side with a cool iron. *Air very thoroughly.* Never soak or leave woollen garments wet any longer than is necessary.

Wool knitted garments. Prepare a soapy water at a temperature of about 90° F (32° C). Knead and squeeze the garments in the water to get the dirt out. Squeeze out the soapy water and rinse in the same temperature of water. Squeeze out as much water as possible and lay flat on a large bath towel – pull into shape and roll up for half an hour. The towel will absorb much of the moisture. The ideal way to dry small knitted garments after being rolled up in a towel, is to place them in position on a flat surface, preferably a string net stretched out rather like a tray which allows ventilation and encourages quicker drying. Do not dry in strong sunshine. If the garments are carefully pulled into shape before being rolled up, they will not be likely to need any further pressing. The white woollens must be washed first and then the coloured ones, leaving any in which the dye may run to the last.

Baby blankets. Prepare some warm soapy water adding one tablespoonful of ammonia to each gallon of water. Shake the blanket thoroughly before submerging in the prepared water. Squeeze and knead the blanket in the water. If very dirty use another washing water. Rinse in warm water, fold, put through the wringer, and hang out in the open air. A sunny day with a little wind is ideal for drying, because it brings up the soft pile of the blanket, and aids the drying. Children's blankets, which have become soiled should have the stain treated as soon as possible and then be washed in the usual way.

White cotton or linen articles. If these are very dirty they should be soaked overnight in a soaking solution, otherwise prepare some very hot soapy water and wash the articles straight away. Dirty marks should be noted before putting them into the water and these can be rubbed between the hands, or with a small scrubbing brush. After washing the clothes, fill the boiler with hot soapy water and add the washed clothes. Boil for twenty minutes. Rinse in at least two waters, first warm and then cold or until the water is clear. If a little blue is added to the last rinsing water it will help to whiten the articles, but the blue block must be wrapped in a small piece of clean rag and squeezed into the water. Only a small amount is required to give the desired result. Blued rinsing water should be well stirred as the blue is not soluble and collects at the bottom of the bath and will stain any clothes it touches. Clothes can be kept a good colour without boiling, but where there is any risk of infection as with young children, then handkerchiefs, feeders, towels, face cloths, sheets and pillow cases should be boiled. In nurseries, tea towels and dishcloths should be washed daily and boiled or sterilized in Deosan (a Milton preparation), one ounce to one gallon of water for one hour, then rinsed.

Coloured cottons or linens. Prepare some warm, soapy water, using only enough detergent or soap, as any excess may be harmful to the colour. Woven colouring may be rubbed but printed materials should be kneaded and squeezed. It is wise to wash coloured articles separately in case of the dye running, and to avoid very hot water. Rinse thoroughly, using clear, warm water and dry in the shade to avoid the sun fading the colours. When the garment is only slightly damp all over, it should be taken in and ironed immediately with a fairly hot iron to avoid damping and rolling as this may cause the colours to run. When ironing anything which is likely to leave a stain, an old ironing sheet should be used. Some colours are temporarily affected by a hot iron. Never boil coloured articles unless the colours are guaranteed as in handkerchiefs.

Starch for washing purposes is particularly useful for cottons and is made by using one tablespoonful of starch powder and mixing it to a paste with tepid water. Boiling water is then added and the mixture stirred until it thickens. Starch must be free from lumps. The average article requires only a thin starch mixture. After rinsing the articles to be starched, they should be dipped, wrung out and dried. When nearly dry, cotton articles should be taken down and rolled up in readiness for ironing. They should be *ironed damp* with a hot iron to give a good smooth and even finish. After ironing, each article must be neatly folded and aired. This is very important if the laundered article is to look attractive and smart.

Artificial silks. These materials are easily damaged when wet and must be handled gently and *never rubbed.* Wash in warm, soapy water and rinse in lukewarm water first, finishing with cool water, which helps to stiffen up the material. Care must be taken to avoid screwing up the garments, as this may cause marks which are difficult to eliminate. Such materials are better dried flat by placing them in position on a large towel and rolling them up for half an hour and then laying them out on a frame to dry. If they have to be hung up the weight must be evenly distributed to avoid undue stretching. Artificial silks vary very considerably in their textures, but they are usually better ironed on the wrong side when fairly dry using a cool iron. If the articles have become too dry, it is better to lay them on a damp towel and roll them up for an hour, rather than sprinkle them with water in an attempt to dampen them.

Silks. These require very careful washing. Use a warm, soapy water, squeeze and knead the garments, but do not rub or twist. Rinse in clear warm water. It will protect the silk if it is placed in a towel before being put through the wringer. Delicate silks can be dried by rolling in a towel and ironed damp with a moderately hot iron. Great care must be taken when ironing, as silks are very easily scorched.

Organdie, which is often used for children's party wear, is washed in a similar way to silk. By ironing it when slightly damp it will regain its stiffness, and starching is unnecessary.

Man-made fibres are produced in great variety today; for example nylon, Orlon, Fibrolane, Acetate, Tricel, Terylene, Acrilan and many others. When buying materials made from these fibres, washing instructions are usually supplied and these should be carefully followed. Many of these materials are used for children's clothing, and will wash well if correctly treated.

Nylon, which is sometimes used for summer and party frocks, should be washed in hot soapy water, rinsed thoroughly and allowed to drip dry. Pressing with a cool iron may be necessary.

Care of napkins

Wet napkins should immediately be placed in a bucket of cold water and covered with the lid. Soiled napkins should be placed in an empty bucket, covered, and sluiced as soon as possible. This is done in a private house over the lavatory, with the seat turned back, or over

H

a sluice in a nursery, by using a sluicing brush with stiff bristles kept separate in disinfectant for this purpose alone. Then the napkin should be soaked in cold water for at least two hours, or longer if time permits.

Boiling method. Wring napkins out of the cold water and wash in hot, soapy water. Prepare another lot of hot soapy water in the boiler and boil the napkins in this for twenty minutes to kill germs and to prevent the spread of infection. Rinse three times, first in warm water, which is very important, because it removes any traces of soap and thus helps to prevent sore buttocks, finishing with two cold rinses. Napkins should be folded, put through the wringer and dried in the open air, preferably in the sun, and thoroughly aired.

Sterilisation by Deosan method (a Milton preparation). Wash napkins as in boiling method, rinse free of soap, then soak for *one hour* in Deosan solution, in a polythene bucket (1 ounce to 1 gallon of water). Rinse thoroughly, fold, put through the wringer and dry, preferably in the open air.

Detergent sterilisation by Napisan. Make up the solution in a two gallon polythene bucket, using $\frac{1}{2}$ ounce or 1 rounded dessertspoonful of Napisan powder, and 1 gallon of cold water. Wet napkins are put into the solution as soon as they are taken off the baby. Soiled napkins are sluiced and then put into the solution. Four hours after the last napkin has been submerged, the napkins can be taken out. The wet or unstained napkins will require three rinses in cold water and can then be dried. Soiled or stained napkins must be washed in hot soapy water or detergent and rinsed, first in hot water followed by two cold rinses and then dried as described in other methods.

Napkins should not be too closely packed in the solution which only requires to be renewed every twenty-four hours.

In nurseries two buckets should be used, one for wet and one for soiled napkins.

Removing stains

Stains should be removed as soon as possible and by the simplest methods. Most stains of tea, coffee, cocoa, fruit or gravy can be removed by soaking immediately in cold water, preferably with the addition of a soaking powder, and then washing in the usual way. Special care is required when treating stains on coloured materials.

Blood stains – soak for 1 hour in lukewarm water and salt, using 1 teaspoonful of salt to each pint of water, then wash in the ordinary way. If the stain is persistent, it should be laid out wet on the grass to bleach in the sun.

Cod liver oil stains – treat the stain with a grease solvent, such as carbon tetrachloride and wash immediately in warm soapy water. Take care not to inhale the fumes of the solvent.

Chocolate, cocoa and coffee stains – if the simple method fails, rub stains with a little glycerine, and then rinse in tepid water.

Egg yolk stains – soak in very hot water with borax. Wash in the usual way.

Fruit stains – rub in powdered starch or salt until the colour is absorbed by the starch or salt. An alternative method is to apply lemon juice with salt. Rinse and wash in the usual way.

Grass stains – if on coloured material, use a little paraffin or glycerin on the stain, and after one hour rinse in warm water, or sponge with water and then hydrogen peroxide.

Grease stains – wash in hot water and borax if the material is suitable or if on white cotton use sodium hypochlorite, 2 tablespoonfuls in 1 pint warm water. For heavy cloth place a piece of brown paper over the stain and iron over the paper with a hot iron. Repeat if necessary.

Ink stains – soak the stain in salt and lemon juice or salts of sorrel. Rinse in cold water.

Milk stains – sponge with warm water and treat as for a grease stain.

Paint stains – rub with turpentine or petrol as soon as possible. Petrol is highly inflammable and must never be used where there is a naked flame.

Rust stains – cover the mark with salts of sorrel, which is a poison, or salt and lemon juice, leave for half an hour, then rinse in a weak solution of ammonia and wash in clear water. Repeat the process if necessary.

Scorch marks – on linen or cotton, if the threads are not damaged rub the place with lemon juice then let it dry in the sun and afterwards wash the article. If on silks or woollens, smear with borax and glycerine, leave for one hour and then wash in the usual way.

Tea stains – if of long standing they may be removed by soaking in borax and water for a few hours.

Tar stains – apply a little paraffin or petrol or benzine with a clean rag.

Suitable Clothing

An outfit for a baby up to 9 months

In planning an outfit for a baby it must be remembered that he usually doubles his birthweight in five to six months, and trebles it in one year. Therefore it is essential that the garments allow for growth, and at the same time give perfect freedom of movement without restriction. Clothes for a young baby can be very simple; they should be soft and non-irritating.

A *vest*, which can easily be slipped on with a front opening or an envelope neck. Whatever type is chosen there must be no gaping over the chest. It should reach well below the thighs and can be turned up a little in the very early stages. Pure soft wool or a wool mixture is suitable. If wool irritates the skin, orlon, a synthetic material, is soft, non-irritating and washes and wears well. A fine cellular cotton vest is sometimes worn under the wool vest. A piece of tape can be sewn inside the bottom of the vest to strengthen the part where the napkin is pinned to it.

Napkins should be soft, absorbent and non-bulky. Two types are in common use, the muslin type and the Turkish towelling type, usually 24 in. × 24 in., which can be boiled. Another type of napkin, the shaped napkin, is becoming increasingly popular as it requires no folding and is considerably less bulky. Although thicker than the towelling square it may not be absorbent enough in all circumstances, particularly overnight. The safety pins used for the napkins should be of the best quality with shielded points and preferably curved. The number of napkins required will be governed by the washing and drying facilities. Many types of soluble napkins are now available and these are useful for travelling. Special types of disposable napkins can be put inside an ordinary napkin; these allow the moisture to pass through so that the baby remains dry. Soiled napkins are made easier to deal with if a disposable paper napkin liner is placed inside the towelling napkin each time it is changed.

From the age of about six weeks or earlier *plastic baby pants* are needed over the napkin, especially when travelling, otherwise a damp nappy will very quickly make all the baby's clothes wet. It is important to see that they allow the air to circulate around the baby's body and to see that they are not tight around the legs. They need to be washed regularly, dried and kept soft.

Dress. It will depend on the time of year when the baby is born as to the type of material chosen. In the cooler months he may wear a woollen dress, or mixture of wool and cotton, such as Viyella or Clydella. In the warmer weather a thinner material such as cotton, silk, Orlon or nylon can be chosen. The dress should be simple and large enough in width and length to last a considerable time. It will help when making to allow for an extra large hem, or to buy a size larger than that actually required. A magyar, or raglan sleeve style is most comfortable. Cotton rompers are useful to protect the clothes when the baby reaches the stage of crawling on the floor, as they are less likely to get in his way.

Nightgown. This should be made of a wool mixture and should be about 24 inches long, with raglan sleeves, rather than set in sleeves. Tucks on the shoulders can be let out as the child grows so that it should last almost to the second birthday. A vest may be required at night until the baby is three to four months' old or a little longer if the weather is very cold, but the same vest should not be worn day and night.

Woolly coats. The dress should be covered by a matinee coat or small cardigan. These can be knitted or made of material. Buttons are a better form of fastening than ribbons, which tend to come undone and frequently end up in the baby's mouth.

A *shawl,* 60 in. × 60 in. or a small blanket is essential for every baby. It can be wrapped around him when being fed, or when going to bed, or when he is in the pram on cool days. If knitted it should be a close pattern so that the child does not get his fingers entangled. To be firmly wrapped in a shawl is comforting to the infant and helps him to settle quickly to sleep.

Sleeping bags. These are usually made of thick wool or Orlon, or other warm synthetic fabric, and give very good protection in cold weather for pram wear and for travelling. They are especially useful when the baby becomes more active.

Leggings, tights or bootees which can be made to stay on are practical in cold weather as they keep the baby covered without restricting movement. Leggings or tights must be long between waist and crutch with plenty of length in the foot. The bootees should be closely knit rather than lacy.

Bibs and feeders. These are made of cotton or terry towelling and also of plastic with an ordinary absorbent material on top. The best shape is one which has a tie at the neck and one at the waist. This keeps it right out of the child's way and at the same time offers good protection to the clothes, especially when the child begins to feed himself. They should be clean for each meal.

Hats or bonnets. These are not necessary except in very cold or windy weather, when a silk lined knitted bonnet is very good because it gives warmth with ventilation. Never use rabbit wool to trim a bonnet round the edge, or make one of rabbit wool, as the fluff may get into the baby's mouth. It is preferable to fasten the bonnet with a button and loop rather than ribbon or Velcro fastening.

Mittens are essential in cold weather; they are best fastened with a woollen cord. Ribbon is often slippery and difficult to keep fastened. They are usually very difficult to keep on and very easily lost, so if they are sewn to a cord which is passed down the sleeves, or sewn to the sleeve of the outer garment, the latter problem at least can be avoided. Wool is better than a synthetic yarn which is very strong and if a thread becomes twisted round the baby's finger it may block the circulation.

Sunsuit. One which is practical and attractive, is a short pair of pants with shoulder straps which form a straight line up the back of the child, in this way protecting the spine. A sleeveless jacket can be worn over the body, with a shady hat or sun bonnet to protect the eyes and the back of the neck.

'Allover' suits. There are several types available. They are usually made of a stretch towelling fabric with long sleeves and leggings, which unfasten between the legs to allow easy nappy changing. They are very easily washed and do away with the need for dresses, leggings and bootees.

Climatic conditions will naturally govern the garments worn both by day and night. In cold weather, three layers are generally necessary and it is important that the child should be evenly clothed. In hot weather the night vest can be discarded but it is a wise precaution to use a fine wool or wool mixture nightgown throughout the year.

Minimum requirements for a baby's first clothes:

> 3 vests
> 3 nightgowns
> 3 dresses *or*
> 3 'allover' suits
> 3 woolly coats
> 3 pairs of leggings or bootees if dresses are worn
> 3 pairs mittens
> 3 bibs

2 shawls
3 pram coats
2 or 3 dozen napkins.

The type and quantity of napkins will be governed by the washing and drying facilities.

Clothing the 9 month to 2 year old child

Much the same type of clothing as described is suitable for this age, but there are additional problems to be considered if the child is to be as comfortable as possible. Crawling must be catered for, by allowing absolute freedom for muscular activity and ensuring that there is no superfluous material, such as loose wide skirts.

During this period the child may be learning to use a pot and by planning garments with the minimum number of fasteners, the adult will be able to help the child quickly when he shows any inclination to use his pot.

The child of this age spends much of his time on the floor, and he must be kept warm; dungarees or allover suits are the most suitable, except in very warm weather. Later, as the child learns more control of his hands, garments should be designed to encourage independence. Good size buttons or a zip which works well are usually the most suitable form of fastening. On seeing the buttons and zip being done up he will become interested, and eventually will attempt to do it himself. Children should be allowed to get dirty, and be suitably dressed for the purpose. It is very frustrating for a child to be reprimanded for getting his clothes dirty. Pretty clothes have their place and even at this early stage children are interested in colour, but they should not be worn all the time. When the child starts walking the garments should hang from the shoulders, giving warmth and freedom to the body and limbs. Towards the end of the second year many children are nearly dry and napkins can be left off during the day and pants worn instead. Pants and rompers must be large enough and should be made to button up at the waist, not in the fork. As boys get older small trousers which have an elasticated waistband are practical, these can be worn with Tee shirts or jerseys.

Vest – as described, adjusted to size.

Pants in a woollen material for cold weather, and a cellular material during hot weather are best. There are towelling pants available which are useful for some children when they are learning to discard nappies.

Rompers are a practical outer garment, made in a woollen or cotton material, with long or short sleeves, according to the season. Two-piece romper suits made with a bodice fastening at the back and the pants part buttoning on to the top are practical. Dresses can often be made into rompers by fixing buttons and buttonholes and threading elastic in each side to go round the legs.

Jerseys or Tee shirts are available in a large range of synthetic fabrics as well as in wool and cotton. The fastening may be in front or on the shoulder. They can have long or short sleeves and the bodice should reach the hip line.

Trousers can be made of wool or cotton or a synthetic material, and can be kept in place by an elasticated band or have shoulder straps attached, sometimes with a bib in front. *Dungarees* can be worn over almost anything and give good protection when the child is playing.

Nightwear. The child may still wear a napkin at night, so that a nightgown may be found to be more practical than pyjamas. As soon as the child is clean, pyjamas will probably keep him better covered. In very cold weather a night vest may be necessary under the night-gown or pyjamas.

Hats are not necessary, unless in cold and windy weather or in strong sunlight when the eyes should be protected. If elastic is attached it is important that it is not too tight.

Coat and leggings are required for wear during cold weather, for sitting in the pram and for walking out. Woolly gloves should be worn long enough to be drawn over the sleeves as warm wrists will help to keep the hands warm.

Clothing the 2–5 year old

The principles for clothing this age group are the same as for younger children. Nappies will have been discarded in most cases and on this account the garments will be much less of a problem. Dressing and undressing is of great interest, and with wise guidance from the adult most children will want to do it themselves and it can be of very real educational value. Therefore, the garments must be planned with simple, spacious front openings and with buttons easy to manipulate, which will enable the child to learn to dress and un-dress himself. For comfort it is important to have plenty of room for bending and no tightness in the crutch or round the limbs.

Colour now becomes of great interest. Children definitely like some colours better than others, and the adult when buying the garments should give some consideration to the child's choice. The joy of having a new dress should be encouraged in a sensible way. Simplicity and practicability should be the keynote of toddlers' garments.

Trousers are best in corduroy or a thick synthetic fabric which needs no ironing. In summer, *jeans* and *cotton shorts* are practical and popular. Braces and shoulder straps are suitable for this age and the front fly may be introduced at about four years, though this is by no means essential as most boys find it much easier to pull their trousers down.

A *pullover* should be worn in cold weather.

Garments for girls: A *pinafore dress* over jumper and tights, which must be the right size, in winter, and over a blouse and socks in warmer weather, is very practical as well as being neat and attractive. *Dresses* should be simple and if possible have a front fastening. *Skirts* should have shoulder straps or a well adjusted waistband. *Trousers*

FIG. 66. Suitable clothing for play.

and jeans are just as suitable for girls as boys, and many girls prefer them to dresses.

Garments useful for playtimes

Overalls with sleeves, which cover all the child's garments, can be attractive and useful in keeping the other garments clean when the child is engaged on some active play such as gardening.

Dungarees in the form of a simple loose pair of trousers with a bib in front and shoulder straps are also useful to slip on the child over his normal garments, when he is revelling in mud pies or some such activity.

Aprons with a bib fitting round the neck and tied at the waist are useful for play and at meal times. The toddler much prefers this to the usual feeder and takes more care of a coloured apron than he would a feeder. *Rubber aprons* are the only effective covering for water play.

Nightwear for older children should supply adequate warmth with freedom of movement and *pyjamas* are usually most satisfactory. The pyjama suit, with the trousers worn over the jacket, will prevent any risk of a gap between the two garments at the waist. In warm weather cellular pyjamas are comfortable and practical.

Dressing gowns. The ideal dressing gown has a closed skirt – a front neck opening approximately ten inches long. It is slipped over the head and should be amply big for the child; it can be closed by a zip fastening.

Outdoor clothes for all toddlers

These must allow perfect freedom of movement and give warmth with the minimum of weight. *Coats* and *leggings* made from a good woollen material give adequate protection in cold windy weather and allow for growth. *Knitted suits*, although made in pure wool, are very chilly in cold weather because the wind blows through the knitting. The one-piece outdoor garment can quickly become too short from the shoulder to the fork of the leg, and this is extremely uncomfortable for the child. An *anorak* is a very suitable garment for outer wear and is easily removed and managed by the child, preferably worn over a pair of trousers.

Judgement must be exercised in the matter of outdoor clothes (see Fig. 67). If the child is going for a walk with an adult he is not likely to be running about very much, and will therefore require warmer clothing than when he is out playing with other children.

Hats are unnecessary, except in cold and windy weather, when the best type is a helmet that covers the neck and ears as well. Sun hats are sometimes needed in very hot weather.

Mackintoshes are useful in wet weather, but if they are rubberized, plastic or PVC they should not be worn for too long at a stretch as the lack of ventilation is unhealthy. A waterproof hat or hood to wear with the coat is useful and practical.

FIG. 67. Sensible clothing for play and weather conditions.

Principles of Footwear

The care of the feet from infancy and throughout life is exceedingly important, if health and happiness are to be maintained. One has only to look around to realize how many people are definitely handicapped both in their work and in their pleasure by painful or deformed feet. The great majority of such conditions could be prevented, if the feet received proper care.

The feet are responsible for carrying the weight of the human body when walking or standing. To do this efficiently it is necessary for the muscles to have freedom and exercise. In the normal foot the whole of the under surface of the foot does not come into contact with the ground. The arch is very slight on the outside of the foot and very marked on the inner side. In walking, the heel of the foot is raised from the ground and the weight of the body is then transferred to the ball of the foot and the toes. The arch helps to give an elasticity to the foot, which is necessary if walking is to be done with the ease and grace which produces a good posture. Anyone who is perpetually conscious of uncomfortable feet, will move in a clumsy and un-attractive way and the earlier this type of habit is formed the harder it is to lose.

The *baby's foot* is usually plump with a good pad of fat under the foot, which does not mean that he is flat footed. As he grows and develops this fat disappears and the arch begins to show itself. As this arch is dependent on good muscle tone, it is important to allow the child to exercise his legs and feet from the very earliest days. A smooth safe surface and *bare feet* will help to strengthen the muscles and give the child confidence when learning to walk. The toes are free to spread themselves and to get a grip on the floor which gives valuable assistance to the problem of keeping upright. In the normal foot of a child or an adult the great toe should lie in a straight line with the inner side of the foot, but unfortunately few adults have retained this shape of foot. The usual cause for this change is badly shaped footwear, which has cramped the toes and distorted them. Very high heels and very pointed toes are also responsible for many malformations.

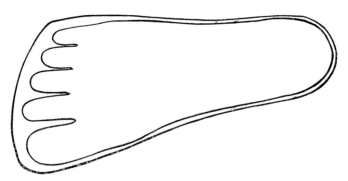

FIG. 68. Diagram showing the shoe following the outline of the child's foot.

It is obvious then that the principles which must apply to all foot coverings are: that they allow perfect freedom, permit ventilation to the skin and that the sock and shoe be designed to follow the line of the foot. Socks and shoes should be wide enough to permit the toes to move freely inside them.

Wool *socks* are more comfortable to wear than cotton socks, and allow ventilation with absorption of perspiration. These should be changed and washed daily. Stretch nylon socks should be avoided as these are not very absorbent and quickly become uncomfortable. Socks which have become felted and tight or badly darned are injurious to the feet. In warm weather babies can remain bare footed, but should have knee length socks or tights in preference to bootees, if they show any sign of chilling in cold weather.

Shoes are unnecessary until about 10 to 12 months, and then a very fine soft leather shoe with a light-weight sole can be provided. As the child learns to walk a slightly stronger shoe will gradually become necessary. At this early age the foot is usually plump and thick, and requires a well cut shoe with sufficient depth to prevent any tightness of bulging over the front of the foot. The shape of the shoe should follow the line of the child's foot and it should be at least half an inch longer than the foot when standing up, as the foot lengthens on standing, and $\frac{1}{8}$ inch wider on each side. It is important that the toes can move freely (see Fig. 68). The shoe should fit snugly round the heel otherwise it will rub and lead to blisters. A tie-up shoe with a flat heel will support the foot well and be comfortable for general outdoor wear. The bar shoe, if well cut, is satisfactory for indoors, but the anklet strapped shoe is *not* recommended.

When purchasing shoes a reliable shop with expert children's fitters should be used and a good make should be chosen with pliable soles and good leather uppers. Sandals of high quality, the correct shape and length, are satisfactory for summer wear. Bedroom slippers are useful for bedroom wear, but not for any other purpose. Shoes with uppers made of plastic material are not satisfactory, since they provide no proper ventilation for the feet. Cheap footwear is often badly cut, which tends towards poor foot development and deformities later in life. Parents, however, must realize that there is a danger in shoes that wear too well as they may become too short for the child before they are worn out. Shoes for children should never be bought without trying them on first. Most children up to the age of seven need a larger size of shoe approximately every five months.

Children wear their shoes in different ways, for example, some may wear down the outer side of the heel, others the inside of the heel, and this should be specially noted, because it will guide the doctor in making a diagnosis of any minor deformities which, if treated early, can be cured. Economic conditions may lead to one child wearing another's cast-off footwear, but if at all possible this should be avoided, as it seldom gives satisfactory results and may be responsible for many unnecessary complications. If possible at least two pairs should be in use at the same time so that the shoes get a rest and keep their shape, and so last much longer. Shoes should not be kept for best.

The foot is part of the human mechanism and is entirely dependent on all the laws of hygiene, including cleanliness, exercise and rest, freedom, good nutrition, fresh air, and ventilation.

Care of footwear

Shoes should be cleaned and polished and the toddler encouraged to take an interest in his footwear and help in the cleaning process when he is old enough. A good polish will nourish the leather and lengthen its life. If shoes are *wet* or *damp*, dry slowly away from the fire. Shoe trees or some newspaper packed into the front of the shoe will help to retain the shape. Careful watch must be kept on the condition of the soles and heels and the necessary repairs carried out. Repairs must be well done, retaining very accurately the original size of the sole and the heel. Extra heavy soles or wedges may lead to abnormalities in walking.

Rubber boots and *winter boots* should be worn outside in wet or snowy weather. Rubber boots prevent ventilation of the feet, so they should be roomy and worn with a thick pair of woollen socks. Care must be taken to see that the leg of the boot is not too long for the child, otherwise it will rub and may cause soreness behind the knee.

Rubber boots when dirty should be washed with warm soapy water, dried and stored in a cool, well ventilated room.

CHAPTER 16

Holidays and Travel with Children

Packing for a holiday

Holidays and journeys with children are much more likely to be happy and relaxed affairs if the packing is carefully and methodically done. It is useful first to make out a full list of garments and articles likely to be required, giving careful thought to probable weather changes and to keeping separate things needed for the actual journey.

Clothing should be carefully folded, the heavier garments being placed in the bottom of the case. Layers of tissue paper between the folds will prevent creasing. Shoes should be wrapped in paper or placed in a shoe bag. The case should be large enough to take all the things required for the child, as additional bags and bundles are difficult to carry and easily left behind.

Medicines or lotions are best packed in a box before being put in the case, in case of breakage or leakage. Travel sickness tablets, if used, are usually taken before setting off, but supplies for the return journey should be included. It is always wise to pack suitable creams or lotions in case of sunburn, and some first aid equipment for cuts and bruises and insect bites. Changed conditions may make a laxative necessary.

The travelling case should have only what is needed for the actual journey or immediately on arrival. The contents of such a case will depend on the age of the child and the type and length of journey. Here is a suggested list which can easily be adjusted to meet the needs of the individual child and the circumstances:

Soap
Face cloth and towel
Brush and comb
Napkins (disposable for travelling)

Plastic bag or newspaper
Change of pants for toddler
Overall for toddler
Some favourite books or toys
Picnic meal if necessary
Barley sugar
Flask for drink, or feeding bottle in bottle flask, according to age
A pot, particularly if the journey is by road
A rug is useful, especially in cold weather.

It is more comfortable for a young baby to travel in a carry cot, and a sleeping bag is useful in cold weather. Luggage must be clearly labelled with name and full address of destination.

Railway journeys

The parent or nurse must realise that the toddler, if unaccustomed to travelling, will possibly be very excited about the whole adventure, and this combined with the unusual movement of the train may upset the child and make him feel sick and uncomfortable. Young babies are not affected by excitement of this kind, although they do sense the nervous tension of the adult. The adult should try to prevent the child becoming too excited before the time, and light, easily digested meals should be given on the previous day.

The baby under six months is comparatively easy to manage; if breast fed the mother can usually arrange to feed the baby quietly in a corner of the carriage, and if artificially fed, the feeds can be mixed ready and kept warm in a vacuum flask. For the older child give a meal of sandwiches, with some plain biscuits or plain, home-made cake, followed by fresh fruit such as an apple or an orange. Boiled milk or fruit juices can be taken for drinks, and it is best to give the food as near as possible to regular meal times, treat it as a picnic meal, and discourage nibbling throughout the journey. A boiled sweet given at the end of a meal is not likely to upset the child, but chocolate is too rich and can also be very messy. Feeders should be provided.

Train accommodation does not give the best facilities for attending to the toilet needs of children, but with care and thoughtfulness things can be done in a satisfactory manner. Soluble napkins are useful for babies as they eliminate the need to carry wet or soiled napkins. A small pot is most helpful to the young toddler. It is impossible to keep children spotlessly clean when travelling, and to avoid heartaches on both sides an overall can be worn over the dress or suit after the outdoor clothes have been removed. After the first excitement of watching out of the windows for trains or animals, the child will just wander aimlessly around or wriggle unceasingly unless play materials have been provided, such as picture books, writing books and pencils, Plasticine, a doll or pet animal. Fellow passengers, even if fond of children, get rather tired of a restless child, and nurses or parents, whilst allowing the child reasonable freedom, must prevent him making a nuisance of himself to other travellers.

If the toddler is accustomed to resting or sleeping after a meal, he should be encouraged to do so on a long journey. This will help to prevent over-tiredness and fretfulness, or irritability in the latter part of the day. The carry cot is an excellent way of travelling with a young baby, as it allows the normal routine of the baby to continue unaltered. It is more comfortable for the baby and much easier for the mother.

Car journeys

The principles given for railway travel will largely apply to motoring, and similar preparations will be required. Whether a picnic meal is possible will depend on the weather and the type of country. A pot is very necessary as toilet facilities are not always available when required. Occupation is much more difficult in the limited space of the car, but if the child is accustomed to motoring he will be more likely to settle down quietly with a favourite animal or doll; being not an entirely new adventure, his reaction will not be so great. The day's routine of rest and sleep should be adhered to if at all possible. Precautions against car sickness, for older children, should be taken if thought to be necessary. Various preparations in the form of tablets are available and it is usually advised that these should be taken at a specified time before the journey begins.

Sea voyages

Again the same principles will apply as for train travel, but with adjustments. The luggage will be increased according to the length of voyage. Babies if breast fed can continue in their normal routine, but if artificially fed, it is necessary to use dried or canned milk which should be introduced very gradually some time before the voyage to avoid sudden changes of food if the baby normally has fresh milk. For the infant the carry cot is ideal, because he can remain undisturbed in the cabin or on the deck. By arrangement with the steward, suitable meals can be obtained for toddlers and dried milk or sterilized milk should also be provided them.

The child's usual routine should be continued, with adequate rest and sleep. The sea air may at the beginning of the voyage make a toddler very tired and his skin will require special care to avoid it becoming dry and rough. He will find life on a ship fascinating with a great number of new interests to explore, which will mean that the adult, whilst allowing him freedom, must give him constant supervision in order to prevent accidents.

The weather can be very changeable necessitating a wide variety of clothing. It is usually colder at sea than on land, and the child is likely to spend much of the day on deck. Wind-proof outer garments will allow perfect freedom and protection. A child will probably find many new and exciting interests as well as a number of friends on board. Under such conditions he will frequently provide his own occupations, but, if not, the adult must see that his needs are provided. On many large ships there are playroom facilities, often with a nurse in charge for part of the day. With careful management the voyage should be fun for all concerned.

Air travel

The airways provide skycots (a hammock type of cot) in plastic $10 \times 16 \times 32$ inches ($25 \times 40 \times 80$ cm). They are fitted with adjustable sides and a safety strap. These cots are clamped securely to luggage racks and babies up to about one year can sleep in perfect safety. These skycots are cleaned and disinfected after use. Infants must be held by the parents during take off and landing. An extra baby blanket should be taken although it is seldom needed. It is important that the baby should not become over-heated at stops en route in tropical countries. Gauze or paper tissue are recommended for napkins. A limited number of disposable napkins are carried on the aircraft.

Privacy for breast feeding is usually provided by curtains. Dried milk feeds can sometimes be made available on request when booking. Cows' milk feeds are a possible danger and are not recommended. Suitable diets are provided for young children on mixed feeding, and facilities for sterilizing feeding bottles are available on the aircraft.

Babies and young children are good air travellers and seldom suffer from sickness. Avoid over-feeding and give frequent drinks of cooled boiled water. Calamine lotion should be taken and used for any heat rash.

Passengers are advised to clear their ears on descent. This is done by pinching the nostrils and blowing gently or by sucking a sweet.

This cannot be done by young children, but they may cry on descent and this helps.

In the interests of all passengers mothers should provide some favourite toy for a child to keep him happily occupied and quiet.

Holidays

It is beneficial for children to have a change of air, and the seaside provides a wonderful background for all sorts of healthy outdoor activities in a clean atmosphere. The type of accommodation should be as good as the family's financial position will allow, because good food and hygienic conditions are essential if the true benefit is to be derived from the holiday. The mother should be free from all catering worries to enable her to enjoy the change of air with the family and to partake in all their activities, which a busy mother has seldom time to do at home.

For young babies it is necessary to ensure that facilities for feeding, bathing and washing will be available. So long as they are fed regularly and cared for in the routine way, babies are little trouble. On the other hand toddlers get excited long before the holiday comes, with the result that they are often tired and out of sorts at the beginning of the holiday. With rest and sound sleep, however, they are soon in bounding spirits again.

The day's activities must be carefully planned to prevent the over-tired child becoming too overwrought to sleep. Exciting events like going to the pictures or side shows should be limited, otherwise excessive stimulation may lead to reactions, such as vomiting, fretfulness, disturbed sleep, fears or night terrors.

Sun bathing, unless the child is used to it, must be taken in small doses to begin with, and increased daily, at the same time protecting the skin by using a little cream at night. Very fair and red head children are particularly susceptible to sunburn. Sea bathing is excellent in many ways and should be encouraged under strict supervision. Babies of six months will sit on the beach beside their mother or nurse and thoroughly enjoy the small waves rolling up their legs but the child should never be forced to enter the water against his will. In time his interest will grow and he will go into the water quite naturally, and have no fear. The adult, however, must closely observe him in case of any unforeseen risks. Fear if allowed to develop in the first few years is difficult to eradicate and in some instances remains for life.

Meals should be nourishing and regular, with not too many of the sea-side extras during the day to spoil the appetite for proper meals.

Children in the tropics

The same care and management of children as that described in previous chapters applies to children in the tropics. There are many additional problems however, such as poor sanitation in some areas, shortage of a good milk supply and fresh vegetables, risk of food- or water-borne infections, and bites from disease-carrying insects. Infectious diseases common in England also affect children in the tropics, but the infectious intestinal diseases, for example, diarrhoea, are more prevalent in hot countries.

The great changes in temperature necessitate careful planning in relation to clothing. It is important to prevent chilling by the use of a cellular cotton vest; see the reference to vests in Chapter 15.

The small baby's day or nightgown should be made of tropical Viyella or cellular cotton. Care must be taken to protect the infant against extreme heats. Sun hats are essential. The child of any age should be guarded against insect bites, for example, malaria-carrying insects, by sleeping under a mosquito net, as these insects are more active at night. The same management in relation to bathing as described in Chapter 6 is essential, but an evening sponge is advisable if there is any tendency to prickly heat.

Breast feeding is very important, and mothers can succeed if they are keen and willing to lead a quiet life. In hot climates it is often found that babies require rather less breast milk to each pound of body weight. Artificial feeding is a problem as there is great difficulty in using cows' milk, because of the risk of contamination and poor keeping properties of milk. Dried or tinned evaporated milk is safer and can be adjusted to meet the child's needs. Usually the fat content of the feed has to be reduced, in comparison to that already described in Infant Feeding (Chapter 10). Adequate boiled water must be given daily.

All babies must have fresh fruit juices and an adequate dosage of vitamin D. Iron deficiency is common and should be given in medicinal form from about three months.

The general principles and management of weaning and the feeding of toddlers are similar to those already stated in Chapters 11 and 12. When vegetables are difficult to obtain, tinned vegetables will be extremely useful in helping to maintain a balanced diet.

Extra care should be taken to keep all utensils and equipment clean, as the water supply, refuse and sewage disposal may not be of the highest standards, particularly away from large centres of population.

CHAPTER 17

Personal Hygiene for the Adult

Health is dependent on good hygiene, and the child will suffer either directly or indirectly through any fault in the adult's personal hygiene. The child learns from the adults around him principally by copying them, therefore it is necessary for the nurse or mother's personal hygiene to be of a high standard. *Cleanliness* must be the keynote. Hand washing before touching foods, before meals and after the toilet is beyond doubt of the utmost importance in preventing the spread of infection.

A daily bath promotes good functioning of the skin and it has a stimulating effect on the whole system. Excessive perspiration and body odours can be counteracted by frequent washing and the use of a good deodorant. *Teeth* should be cleaned at night and in the morning, and the dentist visited regularly whether there is any obvious need or not. *Hair* must be brushed and combed daily and washed once a week or more often if necessary. When working with the children it should be either kept short or neatly arranged to prevent it getting in the way. Hair brushes and combs must be kept clean. *Cosmetics*, if worn, should be well chosen and properly applied, so that the skin simply looks well nourished and healthy giving a well-groomed and attractive appearance. As the texture and the colouring of the skin varies very much in individuals, it is always wise to be guided by an expert on the art of make-up. *Nails* can harbour infection, therefore care must be taken to keep them short and clean. After washing push the cuticle back with the towel but never cut the skin or use sharp-pointed implements, because this may lead to a septic finger. *Nasal hygiene* must be attended to first thing in the morning and before bedtime. Paper handkerchiefs should be used, especially in times of colds, as they are easily disposed of. *Regular bowel action* is essential to everyone and should be encouraged by a good diet, with plenty of fluid and a moderate amount of exercise. The early morning timetable must be planned to avoid rush, as this can easily encourage constipation. Aperients should be used only if the other methods fail. Adequate *sleep, relaxation or rest* and *outdoor exercise* must all form part of the daily routine, remembering that moderation in all work and exercise is essential, otherwise the balance is disturbed and the nervous system will become strained. *Meals* should be regular and consistently good to supply the body's needs. The adolescent will need relatively more food than the adult, because this is a fast-growing period.

Clothing must be clean and the undergarments should be changed twice a week or oftener if necessary. It is important to be neat and tidy in appearance. Well cut, simple garments suited to the individual will give a feeling of confidence and well-being as well as having a good effect on other people.

Footwear should be of good quality and suitable for the purpose required. Well-polished shoes are essential in maintaining a good appearance. Comfortable feet will encourage a good posture and good health.

Recreation, both mental and physical, plays a large part in a person's general well being and attitude to life. No matter how keenly someone is interested in their work there must be periods of rest from that particular line of thought. Social games such as tennis appeal to some people; others prefer walking or gardening. Hobbies are also of great value, and it is usually possible for a person to develop any particular talent or interest which she may possess. Young children benefit tremendously by their contact with the nurse or mother who has many interests outside the nursery or home. The adult who uses her recreation wisely will come back refreshed, and things which looked gloomy before will have taken on a brighter aspect, and a happier atmosphere will result for everyone.

The *menstruation period* should not unduly inconvenience the individual, but at this time rather more rest is required, combined with strict cleanliness. The adult who is responsible for adolescents can do a great deal in helping and guiding them at these times. Any excessive tiredness or depression, excessive loss, or irregularity of the period should be discussed with a doctor. These are abnormal conditions, which should be attended to when they occur and should not be left to chance, in the hope that all will be well.

All women can arrange with their doctor or clinic to have a *cervical smear* test to reveal any indications of cervical cancer which, if recognised early enough in this way, can be treated. Any precaution such as this, on the part of women with children in their care, to maintain their general good health and guard against illness is of vital importance.

Books for reference and further reading are listed at the end of this book.

PART FOUR
Children with Special Needs

CHAPTER 18

The Premature Baby

A premature baby is one born after the twenty-eighth week of pregnancy and before full term which is forty weeks. The calculated date of delivery is often inaccurate, as is usually the case when the baby is born one or two weeks before the expected date but is perfectly normal and well developed. Therefore it is better to assess the child on a combination of the calculated date with the actual stage of development at birth. For example any child weighing $5\frac{1}{2}$ lb (2.50 kg) or under is treated as a premature baby, even if the mother thinks he is a full term baby.

All premature babies must be under medical supervision, and be treated according to their individual needs or stage of development. With good care the premature infant can develop into a healthy well developed child, and be a perfectly normal individual, both mentally and physically.

Causes of prematurity

The reason why a baby is born prematurely is not always known, but it may be due to some illness of the mother, an accident or acute mental shock.

Appearance

The baby's appearance will vary according to the degree of prematurity. The baby will be under weight and usually under 19 inches (47 cm) in length. The face has a wizened appearance, there is a marked absence of fat under the skin, which is covered all over with a soft downy hair, and the fontanelles are large. The baby's cry is feeble and he is generally weak and inactive. The limbs are thin and the abdomen relatively large. Finger nails are short and they are softer than those of a full term baby, not always reaching to the finger tips.

Management of the premature baby

Unless the degree of prematurity is very slight these babies should be nursed in hospital. Three very important factors in their care are to:
(1) Maintain an even temperature and avoid chilling.
(2) Supply nourishment, preferably breast milk.
(3) Avoid all risk of infection.

Warmth is vital to the baby and as his heat regulating system is not fully developed at birth, this has to be provided artificially. Many hospitals today have special premature baby units, equipped with electrically operated incubators in which the babies can be nursed without any clothing but these are not available or suitable for use in the home. Most local authorities have special cots available to meet the needs of the slightly premature baby who is large enough and strong enough to be looked after at home. Such cots usually have a compartment at the bottom, where hot water bottles can be placed to maintain a steady temperature. The cot is deep enough to avoid draughts reaching the baby. The principle is to keep the baby warm and constantly at the right temperature, whilst at the same time allowing ventilation without draughts and the necessary supply of oxygen.

A satisfactory cot can be improvised from a deep basket or clothes basket. This should be well lined with warm material or with brown paper or a layer of each, and should have a foam rubber mattress with a waterproof cover over it. The cot should be made up with an enveloping blanket, which is light weight and of pure wool, and the heat maintained with three or four hot water bottles. Two of these are placed towards the foot of the cot, between the end and the mattress, and one at each side. These bottles need to be changed frequently and in rotation to avoid any marked loss of heat. Some premature babies can be nursed satisfactorily in an ordinary cot providing a screen is used to give protection against draughts. The room should be kept at 70° F (21° C), with a moist atmosphere maintained by keeping a bowl of water near any source of heat.

Clothing

The baby who is not in an incubator should wear a fine soft wool vest, and over this a loose woollen gown which opens all the way down and which can easily be adjusted to meet the infant's needs. The head can be covered by a woollen hood. The clothing will be adapted to the degree of prematurity and to the time of year. A pad of cotton wool can be placed on a napkin under the baby, and tucked round him, but it need not be pinned at this early stage.

Handling

Before attending to the baby all risk of draught must be eliminated. He should be changed in his cot and handled as little as possible. The doctor will say when the infant is fit to be bathed, but until then he should be gently smeared with olive oil. Regular bathing is necessary, but any risk of exposure should be avoided. The weight of the clothing can be assessed and the baby weighed fully dressed.

Feeding

If the infant is sufficiently developed to suck from the breast great care must be taken to keep him warm while feeding. The mother should lie down in bed and the child be well covered with a blanket. Sucking may tire the infant before he has fully taken his feed, or his weak sucking may not stimulate the breast sufficiently to enable the milk supply to become established. Sometimes a breast pump, or in hospital a special machine is used to empty the breast, but most mothers will prefer to express the milk themselves. The milk is then given to the baby in a sterilised spoon or from a special teat and bottle. Failing a supply of breast milk from the mother, efforts should be made to obtain breast milk from another source. In many of the larger cities facilities are available for a supply of milk from a breast milk bank.

As the baby's digestion is not well developed, it is often necessary to dilute the breast milk at first, but the doctor in charge of the baby will decide whether this is necessary. Premature infants require about 3 oz milk to each pound of their body weight (90 ml per 454 g) in twenty-four hours, and this should be given in approximately ten feeds, but again it is up to the doctor to assess the infant's needs and decide accordingly.

Additional vitamins may be prescribed at an early stage. These babies should also be given a little cooled boiled water to drink between feeds. The baby should be disturbed as little as possible when feeding. Arrange to change the baby before his feeds when necessary. The strictest hygiene in relation to feeding is essential.

Infection

The premature baby has little resistance to infection, and colds contracted from adults can lead to serious results. Visitors should not be encouraged, but if permitted they should wear a mask and gown. Everything must be done to prevent any infection reaching the child, either directly or indirectly. Anyone, whether parents or nurse, attending to the premature baby should wear a gown and a mask before touching the baby. The gown must be kept solely for this purpose. There is less risk to the baby if he is only attended to by one or two people.

As the premature baby progresses, his general care is gradually adjusted to that of a normal child, so that he has the opportunity to develop, both mentally and physically as a normal child.

Complications

Cold syndrome. Keep a careful watch for any sign of chilling. The skin may feel cold to the touch, the baby may refuse food, and his hands and feet may appear rather puffy and red, and his cheeks may appear rather flushed. His body temperature will be sub-normal. If any of these symptoms are present medical advice must be obtained immediately. The premature infant is born before he is fully developed to meet the needs of a separate existence, therefore he is more liable to have a tendency to disease and especially to anaemia, rickets, bronchitis and enteritis. Any serious illness in the first few weeks of life is therefore even more dangerous than in a normal new born baby.

CHAPTER 19

The Handicapped Child

This chapter is only a very brief introduction to what is a vast and highly complicated field. The care and treatment of handicapped children has made tremendous advances in recent years, hindered chiefly through insufficient resources, and many of these children are now able to grow up into happy and useful people to an extent that would have seemed impossible only a decade or so ago. Probably even more than with normal children, the experiences and environment of a handicapped child's early years, will play a vital part in his development.

The birth of a handicapped child, or the discovery of a handicap at a slightly later stage, is a terrible shock to the parents and will arouse many varied feelings, particularly if it is their first baby. They may show disappointment, resentment, hate or even anger; on the other hand an excess of pity and sympathy can be just as bad for the infant because it may prevent him ever having the freedom to grow into a happy and independent adult.

The physically handicapped child should never be over protected by any one responsible for his care. His needs in learning to grow up are very similar to those of a normal child. The freedom to explore in his own way and at his own pace, knowing that there is always an adult who will comfort him when he finds life difficult, is essential for his development.

Through his experiences he will gain emotional satisfaction, which in time will enable him to achieve the greater efforts which he will have to make in comparison with those of other children. The young child is not likely to be aware of his defect, and so he will continue to try to learn through trial and error. Even when he is with other children, who are quite normal, he is not likely to compare himself with his playmates. It is good for him to play with other children of about his own age who can stimulate him to more ambitious efforts. If another child notices his defect, for example, a deformed hand, the two children may compare their hands, and perhaps chat about them, and no harm is likely to be done. The more he can associate with normal children, who will quickly learn to accept him without question the less risk there is of his becoming self-conscious. The adult responsible for the handicapped child must never direct his attention to his deformity as this is bound to make him self conscious and will encourage him to become shy and withdrawn.

FIG. 69. A pet will be of interest to
the physically handicapped child.

The physically handicapped child benefits greatly from going to a nursery school or a day nursery or play group, where he will gain much valuable experience. Through the wide variety of play materials he can achieve greater knowledge and skill than would be possible at home, and so become more confident. Under the guidance of an experienced nursery school teacher, or nursery matron he will learn to accept his handicap and do everything he possibly can with the other children. All such training will prepare him for attending a normal school if this is at all possible.

The severely handicapped child

So far we have discussed children with only minor disabilities but severely handicapped children, such as those who are partially or almost totally paralysed, through spina bifida, or some other condition, or those with a severe spastic condition are a much greater problem. There are bound to be severe emotional problems both for the child and his parents, and they will need as much guidance and support as possible from their doctor and social worker, and their friends. If the child can possibly be looked after at home this is usually best for his general well being, but in some cases a hospital may be the only answer.

The deaf or partially deaf child

Any form of deafness can be a great handicap to a child as it is bound to limit his experiences, and make it difficult for him to learn. Any delay in diagnosing this condition may even cause a child to be wrongly classed as mentally subnormal. As a baby normally begins to react to voices and sounds in his early weeks, it is essential that any one caring for a child at this stage should be alert to his reactions, and if in any doubt seek expert advice. Much research has been done in recent years on deafness in young children, and it is now possible to fit a six months old baby with a hearing aid. This early treatment can do much to prevent the child missing out on many of the experiences of other children and make it possible for him to develop at a normal rate.

Special schools are provided by the Department of Education and Science for deaf children, who may be admitted from two years old, and in some instances slightly earlier, and in some ordinary schools special facilities are available for them. If the deaf child can be educated in a normal school this will probably be much better for him. Parents need to be taught carefully about the care of hearing aids, and should see that they are always in good working order.

The blind or partially sighted child

As in any defect the sooner it is diagnosed the better. Defective sight in a young child is extremely serious and will limit his experiences through life. With care and understanding his parents, or whoever is responsible for him, must try to convey to him as much awareness of the world around him as possible, by trying to explain in detail what they see, and by giving him the opportunity to touch and feel whenever possible.

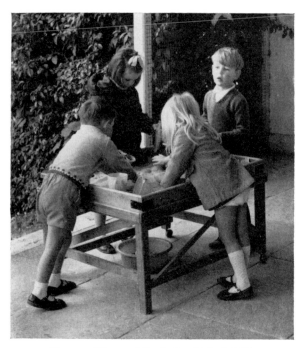

Fig. 70. The partially deaf and blind child
will benefit from his contact with normal children.

Many blind children can be very active in surroundings they know well. If the furniture in the home is kept in the same position the child can move around with reasonable safety, and gradually gain in confidence. And if forethought is given to clothing and general management the child can become reasonably independent. The Department of Education and Science provides special schools for blind children, from five years old, where they are able to follow a normal school curriculum, and begin training in special work suited to their abilities.

The mentally subnormal baby

The degree of subnormality can vary tremendously and it is extremely difficult for the doctor to make a definite diagnosis in the first few weeks. He will almost always seek specialist advice before passing on his suspicions to the parents. When the parents have been told they will need a great deal of help and encouragement but there have been so many advances made in recent years in the treatment of mentally handicapped children that it is often possible to encourage them to look forward to a hopeful future.

One of the many problems of having a defective child in the home arises if the other children in the family do not realise why the parents are so protective to their brother or sister and so become jealous. But wise parents usually manage to overcome this and the handicapped child is generally greatly loved by all his family. If the child needs a great deal of attention it is essential that the parents should have a holiday from time to time, and in some areas there are homes that will take these children for short periods to relieve the parents.

Schools for the educationally subnormal are provided by local authorities and it is only rarely that a child has to be classified as ineducable.

Books for reference and further reading are listed at the end of this book.

I

PART FIVE
Accidents and Their Prevention

CHAPTER 20

Prevention of Accidents in the Home and Nursery

Safety First for the Child

Whenever there are children, precautions must be taken to prevent accidents. Most children have no experience or any idea of danger. At the toddling stage everything is new and interesting and the adult, therefore, must guard the dangers without making unnecessary restrictions. Forethought and tidiness do much to prevent accidents, both indoors and outdoors, and arrangements can be made to reduce the risks to a minimum.

Statistics show a high percentage of accidental deaths in children under two years. Choking and suffocation (asphyxia) are the most frequent in children under one year, and burns and scalds most common amongst young toddlers. Falls and road accidents are also responsible for much loss of life in childhood.

It is essential to protect children, but if over-protected the child will never fend for himself, and will depend on his parents and develop into a very nervous and timid child. Such children are often 'accident prone', meaning that they are more likely to become involved in accidents than other children.

Prevention of asphyxia and sources of danger

1. Care must be taken to prevent a cat suffocating a baby in his pram and a pram net is most useful.

    If a cat is in the house or if there are cats in the neighbourhood this risk to the child should never be neglected.
2. The use of down pillows.
3. Babies sleeping in their parents' bed.
4. Being left in the pram or cot with a feeding bottle or dummy.
5. Not bringing up a baby's wind before going back into his cot.

6. Carelessly arranged bedclothes or unsuitable garments.
7. Plastic bibs.
8. Fluffy toys or toy animals with loose eyes.
9. Garments with draw strings.
10. By drowning, in the young toddler group. Large basins, baths, tubs of water, or ponds, whether deep or shallow, are very dangerous if unguarded, as the child falling face downwards can drown in a few inches of water. At this age if a child overbalances into the water, he cannot save himself.

Small children should only be taken out sailing if they are wearing a life jacket; also as soon as they are old enough they should be taught to swim.

All such accidents can be prevented by careful and wise management.

Burns and scalds

One of the chief dangers is the risk of fire. A child is fascinated by the glow of a fire and longs to poke it, little realizing what will happen if he puts his finger near the flame. Gradually, with careful guidance, he can learn of the dangers of the fire, but by law all fires must have fixed fireguards, preferably one which fits round the fender or hearth and has a closed top. It should be wide enough to prevent a child who touches the guard from being burnt. All gas and electric fires must have fixed guards; this will include hot pipes and radiators.

Children's clothes are often highly inflammable unless made by a reputable manufacturer. It is safer to have materials which have been treated with Proban. They are now obtainable in most stores. Pyjamas are less dangerous than nightgowns for children from 2–5 years old, as they fit much closer and there is less risk of them coming into contact with the fire. A shoelace may trip a child, or a long skirt.

Articles or toys belonging to a child must never be placed on the mantelpiece, particularly if there is a fire.

Matches must be kept out of reach and sight, and parents must never encourage a child to operate a cigarette lighter.

It is important to remember that the danger of burns and scalds may occur to children of all ages and therefore it is essential always to follow safety precautions.

The risk of scalding at the tea-table is obvious; if a tablecloth is overhanging the edge, the child may pull it, and possibly bring the teapot with it on top of himself. The obvious solution is to keep the tiny toddler in the playpen, or not to have a tablecloth which he can pull. Always place the teapot or other vessel containing hot food in the centre of the table.

It is unwise to hold a baby while drinking tea or coffee, as a sudden movement could easily cause a spill and a bad burn.

Electric cables and fitments should, as far as possible, be out of reach and all electric points should have safety plugs, or fitted plugs, when not in use. The electric iron should be carefully guarded.

Portable stoves, whether gas, electric or oil, are a danger; they should always be placed in a fireplace and guarded. Open electric fires must not be used in a bathroom; they should be high up on a wall and operated by a safety flex.

Naked lights must never be allowed near a curtain. Night lights must be carefully guarded.

In the kitchen there are also many risks of scalding and to lessen some of these, pan handles should be turned to the back of the stove, and the kettle should point to the wall. The child must not be left alone in the kitchen with a fire or gas stove alight. Gas taps and electric plugs have a great fascination and should be guarded. It must be remembered that electric stoves remain hot for some while after being switched off, and therefore need to be protected.

Never leave a bucket of very hot water on the floor in the kitchen or elsewhere; it may be knocked over and scald the child.

Hot water bottles should be only half-filled with water, and all air allowed to escape before screwing on the top. A thick cover, big enough to envelop the neck and screw top of the bottle must be used, but it is wiser to heat the bed and remove the bottle before the child goes to bed.

In the bathroom it is safer to run the cold water into the bath first before the hot; this should be the routine training for children when preparing their water for washing hands and face. Never leave a child in the bath; he may turn on the hot tap or he may slip down and drown because he is unable to get up again.

While doing the *laundry* all equipment must be protected when there are small children about; this includes the washing machine (many of which have a safety catch on the door), electric wringers and irons.

Disinfectants and poisons

These should be labelled and kept in a locked cupboard. All medicines, such as sedatives or sleeping tablets, aspirins, and iron pills, should also be locked up. Coloured tablets, often looking like sweets, are attractive to children and are very tempting if left within reach.

Children may also attempt to drink *cleaning fluids* and cosmetics if these are not carefully tidied away.

Before giving medicine to a child the label should always be checked and medicines no longer needed should be thrown away.

Dangers from household equipment

Pins, needles, sharp scissors and knives which toddlers love to play with should be kept out of reach.

The *stairs* may need a gate at the top and bottom to prevent falls. They should also be well lighted. Frayed carpets and loose stair rods are very dangerous. A low handrail will help the child to go up and down stairs. It is also important to see that the child's clothes are of a suitable length, or well tucked up, when going upstairs, otherwise he may trip over; this applies especially to nightclothes. Objects left on the stairs may cause serious accidents.

If children play or sleep in an upstairs room, the *windows* should be guarded by bars, strong netting, or the lowest sash fixed so that it does not open more than a few inches. But the windows should not be barred to such an extent that they cannot be used in case of fire. The bars should not be more than six inches apart because a child often squeezes his head through a wider rail guard.

The *cot* must be safe, with a strong fastening to prevent falls. A cot-stand should be so designed that a carry-cot placed on it is effectively retained in position by a guard rail or rigid stops at all corners, so that it cannot tip over. If a baby is left alone in the garden in his pram it is wise to use a *safety harness* because once he can sit up the baby becomes more active, and he may have a fall by over-balancing the pram.

A well-built *pram* with a good brake is essential.

In the home or nursery garden a child under five years must never be able to get out into the road; there are various devices which can be fitted to gates to prevent children opening them.

Broken bottles, glass or china should be cleared up immediately to avoid the risk of cuts, and children should be trained not to run when carrying anything breakable.

Garden equipment, e.g. spades, forks, lawn mowers, other sharp tools, weed killer, etc., must be kept in a safe place.

Fungi growing in the garden should be removed and children should be taught not to play with them when out for walks. *Poisonous berries* must be explained to children. One of the most common dangers in the garden are laburnum pods, which look just like miniature pea pods.

Swing doors can be a danger, but a soft pad over the edge of the door, tied from the inside handle to the outside handle, can prevent the trapping of fingers.

Outdoor play equipment, such as slides, swings and climbing frames, must be inspected regularly and repaired when necessary.

As soon as they are old enough to understand, children should begin to learn road drill. This can be taught by games but most effectively by the example of adults when they are out with children. It is usually when a child is absorbed in chasing another between 5 and 7 years old, that he suddenly darts into the road, and the only way to prevent this happening is not to let children play on the road or anywhere where access to it is easy.

When children are travelling by car, however short the journey, the doors should always be locked. Toddlers should travel in car seats, and all children should always be in the back seat. If there is a second adult, she should be in the back too if there is room, to see that the children are sitting comfortably and are not too wriggly.

Children's playgrounds are essential in urban areas to keep children off the streets, and where these are lacking local authorities should be urged to do something about it.

The main causes of accidents have been mentioned; there are many others but the most important thing is that those in charge of children should always be alert and aware of dangers. It is difficult to do this without appearing over-anxious or without endlessly forbidding the children to do what they want, but children are much less accident prone when they are relaxed and happy, and their state of mind will be strongly affected by the adults with them.

CHAPTER 21

First Aid to Children

When a child of any age is unfortunate enough to meet with an accident there are two main issues, firstly the *physical injury*, and secondly the *mental strain*. Both conditions must be dealt with in a sympathetic and understanding way. The child who falls and cuts himself will usually react by crying partly because he feels the pain, but also because he is shocked and frightened. This affects the child's whole world for the time being because suddenly his happiness and contentment have been replaced by pain and misery. The child is bewildered by this and feels insecure. In this condition he needs support and comfort from the adult, who must help him to regain control over his feelings by showing sympathy and by keeping calm. Although the adult may be extremely upset over the accident, it is imperative that she should control her emotions as the child is very quick to sense the adult's reaction. Though it is important to know how to give first aid if an accident happens, it is just as important to use the right attitude, in order to give the best care to the child. If the adult feels the incident has been caused through the toddler's disobedience by doing something he should not have done, or by going somewhere he had been told not to go, she will probably feel annoyed. But consideration must first be given to the care of the child, and later the cause of the accident can be discussed.

The adult must always remember that the child's curiosity stimulates him to experiment and although he may have been told not to do something, in exciting circumstances he forgets; he is not being deliberately naughty.

Some people, in their well-meaning efforts to comfort the child, tell him that it is all better now and he must be a brave boy and stop crying, when it is obvious the child is really in pain. Instead, it would be kinder to tell the child you know it hurts, but that he is being very good in trying not to cry too much. On the other hand, a child will often cry from sheer fright after an accident, rather than from actual pain, showing he has had a nasty shock to his nervous system. The adult must recognise this, and treat him accordingly by calming and reassuring him.

Observations of signs and symptoms

The younger the child, the less information he will be likely to give; therefore, observation plays an essential part. The child's general appearance should be noted, whether pale or flushed, if there are any abrasions or cuts showing, if the child cannot walk or use a limb, or if he cries when a limb is moved; such signs all help in diagnosis. All details should be carefully noted; and when sending for a doctor, a brief description of what is wrong should be given. For example – '*John has fallen and cut his leg*,' or '*John has swallowed a pin*,' or '*John has scalded both his legs*.' Such information will save time and enable the doctor to bring essential medicines or equipment.

General principles which apply to all accidents:

1. If in doubt send for a doctor, or it may be more convenient to go to a doctor or to a hospital. Every children's hospital and every casualty department treats children who have had accidents. It is unwise to take unnecessary risks and this specially applies when dealing with children. Some important factor may be missed by an inexperienced person and it is much better to err on the cautious side rather than be too casual.
2. *Treat for shock*, which is present in all accidents in varying degrees of intensity, though it may be delayed.
3. Make the child as comfortable as possible, reassure him, and treat any minor cuts or bruises.
4. *The one who renders first aid must never presume or take the responsibilities of a doctor.*

The first aid box should contain the following:

A few crepe bandages, ranging from 1 to 4 inches wide.
Tubular gauze of different widths and applicator.
One or two triangular bandages.
2 oz packet of cotton wool.
2 oz packet of gauze.
2 oz packet of white lint.
Tin of antiseptic surgical dressings.
Adhesive plaster.

Special non-allergic plaster.
Bottle of antiseptic, for example Savlon.
Bicarbonate of soda.
Calamine lotion.
Castor oil.
Tube of antiseptic cream, for example Savlon.
Surgical spirit.
Small polythene bowl (2).
Small polythene kidney dish.
Scissors and safety pins.
Eye bath.
Eye dropper or pipette.
Tweezers.

This equipment must be *kept in a safe place and out of the child's reach*. Where there are many children, proportionately larger quantities of equipment will be required. With small packets of dressings, there is less risk of infection from previous handling. The hands must always be washed before opening the box, except in very grave emergency, e.g. haemorrhage.

It is essential that all members of the staff should know where to find the key of the first aid box and be familiar with its contents.

Important points to remember when applying a dressing and bandage:

1. *Cleanliness* is of very great importance. The adult should first wash her hands with soap and water.
2. The aim when rendering first aid to a wound should be to cleanse the wound with clean water, boiled if possible, using an antiseptic, and to prevent any further germs from entering the wound by covering it with a sterile dressing.
3. The comfort of the child must be considered by ensuring that the bandage is not too tight which might give rise to serious consequences and that additional pain is not caused by applying an elaborate bandage when a simple type of triangular bandage would suffice.

The purpose of a bandage is to keep the dressing in position, without discomfort to the patient, and unless it fulfils this requirement it is useless.

Antiseptic. This is a chemical substance which will hinder the growth of germs and delay their action, but it does not kill them. A solution strong enough to kill all the germs would damage the body tissues.

Antiseptic lotions in common use:

Milton	use 1 in 40 solution
Dettol	use 1 in 40 solution
Savlon	use 1 in 80 solution
Lysol	use 1 in 80 solution
Gentian violet	1 per cent

Saline – use 1 teaspoonful of common salt to 1 pint of water. Boil and strain. Store in a sterile bottle. (This is not an antiseptic lotion.) Saline tablets are now available and these can be dissolved in boiling water and allowed to cool, a much simpler procedure in an emergency than making normal saline.

First Aid Treatment

Prevention of shock

It is proposed here to discuss the prevention of shock rather than the treatment of serious shock. After almost all accidents there is some degree of shock present and it is important that this should be treated before the injury is dealt with to prevent the development of a more serious condition.

The only exception is haemorrhage, when the injury is treated first. This is because the more bleeding there is the more severe will be the degree of shock. One preliminary measure can be taken which will not waste valuable time, and that is to raise the foot of the bed or stretcher to maintain a good blood supply to the brain.

Place the patient in as comfortable a position as possible, preferably lying down, and undo any tight clothing. Do not undress immediately but encourage him to rest. Keep the patient comfortably warm with blankets. Give warm sweet drinks or warm saline with glucose to drink unless it appears that an anaesthetic may be needed, or the patient is unconscious.

Bruises

Young children are endlessly falling and bruising themselves. There is little to be done except to apply a pad of cotton wool wrung out of cold water. Witch hazel can be applied. The discolouration will gradually disappear. The doctor should be notified if there is any marked swelling.

Superficial cuts

Using some clean cotton wool, first bathe the cut with a warm antiseptic lotion, and then cleanse the surrounding area for about 2 inches (5 cm). Dry with a piece of cotton wool and apply a piece of sterile gauze. Cover with a thin layer of wool and apply a firm bandage, but not a tight one.

As an alternative method if there is any suspicion of infection, after bathing the cut, dry the surrounding area and apply a gauze dressing soaked in antiseptic to the wound and cover with cotton wool and bandage in the usual way or it may be more practical to apply a covering. For small cuts specially prepared antiseptic dressings on elastic adhesive plastic can be bought ready made. All dirty dressings must be burnt.

Deep cuts

These usually give rise to a fair amount of bleeding, in which case, after bathing with an antiseptic, apply a sterile gauze dressing, a pad of cotton wool and a firm bandage. Such wounds may require stitching and a doctor will be required to do this. If a child appears to have fallen on broken glass and cut the palm of his hand, apply a sterile gauze dressing lightly over the wound, cover with cotton wool and avoid any pressure. Place a ring pad round the wound, and apply a firm bandage to try to stop the bleeding. It is for the doctor to decide if there is any glass still remaining in the wound.

To make a ring pad. Wind a bandage several times round your own fingers and then twist the remaining part of the bandage round the circle formed, to create a firm circular pad. The size of pad will be influenced by the extent of the injury.

An *animal bite* or scratch should be treated as a dirty cut and it will be necessary for the child to be seen by the doctor who will decide whether it is essential to give an injection or cauterise the wound (see page 258).

Haemorrhage

With normal blood, there is a tendency for it to clot, which is nature's way of stopping the flow of blood from a wound. Therefore, it is unwise to wash away a clot from a wound. Cover it with a sterile dressing and let the doctor treat it. A rare condition, in which the blood does not clot, is known as haemophilia and occurs only in males.

The treatment for severe bleeding, when there are no complications such as a foreign body or a broken bone is as follows. Lay the child down and only remove any necessary clothing to expose the injured part. Keep the child as warm as possible and send for a doctor. In the meantime apply a sterile gauze dressing with a pad of lint or wool over the gauze and keep up the pressure on the pad with the thumbs. As an alternative method, apply the dressing, placing a thick pad over it and then a firm bandage to maintain the pressure. If the bleeding continues and soaks through, apply another pad with a new bandage on top of the first one. Do not expose the wound again after it has once been covered.

Haemorrhage at the seat of a fracture. Apply a sterile gauze dressing, cotton wool and a loose bandage. Move as little as possible and support the limb to prevent further damage. Get medical aid as quickly as possible.

Haemorrhage with glass present. Cover wound with a sterile gauze dressing and cotton wool, place ring round the wound and apply bandage; in this method there is no pressure on the wound. Send for a doctor. If bleeding is very severe and in grave emergency, a rubber bandage should be applied a few inches higher up the limb. This must be taken off after fifteen minutes and, if bleeding continues, it must be reapplied and taken off at regular intervals of fifteen minutes, to avoid damaging the circulation in the limb.

If the child is bleeding profusely and the doctor is likely to be delayed, treat as suggested and always take a child to the nearest hospital in an ambulance or private conveyance. To delay is dangerous.

Epistaxis. Nose bleeding may happen spontaneously or it may be caused by a blow on the nose. Place the child in a sitting position with the head slightly back and apply pressure by pinching the nose. A cold compress can be applied over the bridge of the nose. Keep the mouth open and encourage breathing through the mouth. Sponge the child's face and hands, change clothing if necessary and possible, and encourage him to sit quietly. Allow a free circulation of fresh air, but keep his body warm. Young children are often frightened by the sight of the blood and, therefore, any stained cloths in use should be covered up.

Nose bleeding may be a symptom of a fractured skull, when the skull would receive first consideration.

Bleeding from the mouth is seldom severe in a child, and it is usually caused by a tooth cutting the tongue or the lip when he has fallen. Give him ice to suck, or give cold water to hold in the mouth. In severe cases, using a piece of gauze, grasp the bleeding part of the tongue between the finger and thumb and apply pressure. *Send for medical aid* if bleeding is severe, or if there is no apparent cause for it.

Extraction of teeth. Bleeding may occur from the socket. Give a cold mouthwash, if necessary place a small gauze pad over the socket and encourage the child to bite on it. If it persists get help from the dentist, but if he is not available consult the doctor.

Coughing up bright, red blood is unusual in children, and denotes a lung injury or disease. The doctor must be notified immediately. If he is delayed the child must be taken to hospital.

Bleeding from the ear may indicate a fractured skull. Apply a light dressing over the ear. *Send for medical aid or in emergency take the child to hospital. Never plug the ear.*

Bleeding from an internal organ is shown by the following signs and symptoms:
1. Pallor.
2. Cold and clammy skin.
3. Giddiness and faintness.

And later by
4. Hurried breathing and weak pulse.
5. Unconsciousness, which may result if bleeding is very severe.

Bleeding in the stomach is shown by vomit resembling coffee grounds.

In all instances send for medical aid at once or take the child to hospital.

Bleeding from the bowel may vary in colour from dark brown to a brighter red depending on which part of the bowel is bleeding. Get medical help at once.

Foreign bodies

Foreign body in the nose

If it is thought or known that the child has pushed a button or some such thing up his nose, encourage him to blow down the affected nostril, but no attempt should be made to remove it by poking. A sniff of pepper may cause a sudden sneeze and so dislodge the object. If not successful then it will be essential to take the child to hospital or to his family doctor.

Foreign body in the ear

If this is an insect, lay the child on the opposite side to the affected ear and pour a little warmed olive into the ear. Heat the oil by pouring it into a warm teaspoon. The insect may float, when it can be removed. Any other type of foreign body must be removed by a doctor. The child must be kept from pushing his finger in the ear. Never syringe or probe the ear, as this may cause deafness.

Foreign body in the eye

Prevent the child from rubbing the eye. Pull down the lower eyelid and if the grit is seen, it can be removed with a very small brush or the corner of a handkerchief. To examine for grit under the upper lid, lift the lid forward and let the lower lid shut up under the upper one. The eyelashes help in sweeping away grit. If the child is old enough to understand, make him try to blink the eye under cold water, or it may be possible for an eye bath to be used. If the foreign body cannot be easily removed, quickly seek the aid of a doctor and in the meantime place a light bandage over the eye to keep the eyelids closed and at rest. Avoid any pressure on the eye.

Foreign body in the eyeball

Place a light bandage over the eye and avoid any pressure. Send immediately for a doctor. Prevent the child from rubbing the eye. Any eye condition must be considered serious and must never be tampered with.

Foreign body in the throat

This may be a fish bone or may be due to the child trying to swallow something which becomes lodged in the larynx or windpipe. The child may cough violently and dislodge it, otherwise bend the head and shoulders forward and thump between the shoulders. If this fails insert a finger into the throat and try to move the article. This acts as an irritant in the throat and will cause further coughing which, in turn, may relieve the condition. If the object is a fish bone a teaspoonful of vinegar may be effective. If this fails get immediate medical aid.

Foreign bodies swallowed

Children sometimes swallow all sorts of things, such as buttons or coins, but unless they have sharp or pointed edges these seldom cause serious trouble, and the child will probably appear perfectly normal. Let the doctor know what has happened and he will advise the necessary treatment and may have the child X-rayed. For the next few days the motions have to be examined to find out when the article has been passed. Do not give an aperient unless ordered by a doctor, who will also advise the diet to be given.

Poisons

If a child swallows some household cleaning agent or chews berries which may be poisonous, the doctor should be notified at once of what has been swallowed. To encourage the child to be sick give a teaspoonful of common salt in a little warm water. Keep the child warm and the doctor will deal with the poison. *If the mouth or lips are burnt do not attempt to give him anything to make him sick*, and if the doctor is not available, get the child to hospital straight away to enable treatment to be given as soon as possible. All poisonous drugs or aspirins, iron pills or sedative tablets and medicines should be kept in a locked cupboard and the key put into a safe place. Cleaning materials and disinfectants used in the bathroom or kitchen must be stored out of the child's reach. Weed killers or any chemicals used for the garden should be kept in a locked cupboard.

Burns and scalds

A burn is caused by a dry heat such as fire, electricity or lightning.

A scald is caused by moist heat such as steam from a kettle, boiling water or boiling oil.

The chief principles which apply in burns or scalds are:

1. Treat for shock – keep patient warm and give warm sweetened drinks.
2. Exclude the air from the affected place by using one of the following methods:
   (a) Cover the area with lint or gauze and a bandage if medical aid is available, *or*
   (b) Apply smooth side of lint or clean smooth cloth soaked in sterile water or warm normal saline.
3. Do not break blisters.
4. The simplest first aid treatment must be given, as the doctor will have to examine the condition, and this will necessitate another dressing and a good deal of discomfort and further shock to the child.

The younger the child the more serious the burn or scald is likely to be, and a superficial burn over a large area, for example, both legs, may be more serious because of a greater degree of shock, than a deeper burn over a small area. *Get medical aid immediately or take the child to hospital without delay if a doctor is not available.*

Clothing on fire

If a child's clothing is on fire, quickly wrap a thick hearth rug, blanket or coat round the child and lay him on the floor, being careful not to allow your own clothing to ignite. After extinguishing the flames, apply the necessary immediate treatment. Shock is likely to be severe. Send for the doctor at once or take the child to hospital if a doctor is not available.

Stings and bites

Stings or bites from insects

These can be particularly troublesome to some children, causing great irritation. Apply undiluted Milton or Dettol. If this is not available bathe with an antiseptic solution. Get medical advice if the skin becomes red or swollen.

Bee stings

First remove the sting, which is like a short fine hair, with a sterile needle or tweezers. Apply undiluted Milton, Dettol or spirit to the punctured wound. Failing these apply bicarbonate of soda solution or the wet blue bag. Get medical aid immediately if there is any sign of inflammation.

Jelly fish sting

This can be treated by vinegar or olive oil. If swelling occurs it will be necessary to get advice from the doctor.

Dog bites

In England today, because of the quarantine rules for dogs entering the country, *mad dogs* (affected with rabies) are very rare. The bite of any dog should be treated by encouraging bleeding, then bathe the wound, and apply an antiseptic dressing and bandage. In all cases seek medical aid. Signs of *rabies* are nervousness, shivering, salivation, with a high pitched, yelping bark, and a bite from such an affected dog must receive medical treatment at the earliest possible moment.

Heat stroke

This may happen if the child is allowed to have his head and spine exposed to the rays of the sun in very hot weather, or humid weather, for long periods without any protection. The child feels faint and giddy. He may be sick and his skin feels dry. Give a cool bath and keep the child in bed in a darkened room; give fluids and consult a doctor.

Head injuries

These may be caused by something falling on the head, by a blow, or by the child falling down.

Concussion

This is a condition which may result from a fall and in which the functioning of the brain is upset.

Signs and symptoms. The child becomes unconscious, or goes into a stupor which may be only for a moment, or may last for some time. The child is pale and there may be severe shock present. Pupils of the eyes are equal and dilated. In a child this is a serious condition.

Treatment. Send for the doctor and put the child to bed with a raised pillow and in a darkened room, and apply cold compress to the head. Keep him warm with blankets. Drinks must *not* be given until consciousness returns.

Fracture of the skull

This may be the result of a blow or a fall. The condition is not so common in young children because of the softness of the bones of the skull in the early years.

Signs and Symptoms. Concussion, signs of injury, such as a scalp wound or depression of the skull. In a fracture of the base of the skull there may be no apparent injury to the skull. Bleeding may be present from the nose, the ear or the mouth. Paralysis may be present or may develop. Pupils are unequal.

Treatment. Send for a doctor and treat as for concussion. Apply a gauze antiseptic dressing to any wound, but avoid pressure on the injury. *No drinks* should be given.

Compression

This is a condition caused by a blood clot forming due to haemorrhage in the brain. The blood clot sets up pressure on the brain, and this condition is very serious. *Treat as for concussion* and send for medical aid at once.

Fractures

These may be caused by a fall or by a direct blow. There are several types of fractures and these are divided into two main groups – *simple*, when the skin is not broken, and *open* or *compound* when there is a wound. The latter is the more serious because of the risk of infection. In childhood, as the bones are still soft, there is often a condition known as a *greenstick* fracture, which is, as the name implies, really a bending or splintering rather than a clear break. In a *comminuted* fracture the bone is broken in several pieces and in an *impacted* fracture one end of the broken bone becomes impacted in the other end. Any simple fracture can be made compound by careless handling.

Signs an 1 Symptoms:

Pain and swelling at the seat of the injury.

Loss of power in the limb.

Unnatural position of the limb.

Alteration of the outline of the limb.

Crepitus, when the ends of the bone can be felt rubbing against each other. *This test must never be attempted by a first aider.*

Treatment. Send for a doctor. Do not allow a simple fracture to become compound by careless handling. Only move the patient after the limb has been supported on a splint or by hand. When fixing the temporary splint keep the limb or bones as straight as possible until the leg is bandaged to the splint above and below the fracture, thus preventing all movement of the injured bone. Apply an antiseptic gauze dressing to any wound. Never attempt to set a fracture. Keep the child warm, give a small sweet drink, and try to reassure him. As an anaesthetic may be necessary to set the limb, it is unwise to give food or milk before the doctor has seen the child.

Spinal injuries

Any injury to the back which shows loss of power in the limbs must be treated as very serious. Keep the patient lying on his back and move him as little as possible. Try to encourage the child to keep still, and tie the legs and feet together. Get medical aid quickly and treat for shock.

Only the broad principles of fractures have been outlined, but naturally fractures of the different bones require varied treatments, although the general principles remain the same.

Sprains

This condition is caused by a sudden wrench or twist injuring the ligaments around a joint.

Signs and symptoms:
Pain in the joint.
Difficulty in using the joint.
Swelling.
Discolouration later.
Treatment. Apply a cold compress as soon as possible. Send for a doctor. If in any doubt about the condition, keep the limb rested and apply a firm bandage over the compress.

Dislocations

Dislocation is a term used to describe the displacement of the parts of the bones which form a joint.

The most common dislocations are those of the shoulder, elbow, thumb, fingers, and lower jaw.

Signs and symptoms:
Severe pain at the joint.
Unusual position of the limb.
Inability to move the joint in the usual way.
Treatment. Send for a doctor. Make the patient as comfortable as possible. Apply a cold compress on the injured joint. Make no attempt to alter the position of the limb.

Drowning

Drowning produces a condition of *asphyxia* or *suffocation*, which means that breathing is interfered with, thus causing a lack of oxygen and eventual death.

When rescued after a drowning accident the child will appear limp, cold, bluish, and the nasal passages and the mouth may be blocked. Even if the breathing has stopped it is important to make efforts to get this established again by applying artificial respiration.

Treatment. Send for a doctor, and *immediately try to clear the mouth and nasal passages*, as there may be leaves or weeds present. Try to get the child warm, loosen clothing, and if it is possible remove wet clothing and wrap in warm blankets.

Artificial Respiration

Mouth-to-mouth breathing

In this method of artificial respiration the rescuer introduces oxygen by breathing into the child's lungs. The procedure is simple:

extend the child's neck so that the head is tilted backwards and close the child's nostrils; take a deep breath and, making an airtight seal with your mouth over the child's mouth, breathe into the lungs of the child. Watch the child's chest rise; if it does not, there cannot be a clear airway and this must be rectified. Remove the mouth after each breath to allow the child to exhale and the rescuer to inhale. Repeat these deep breaths about twelve times a minute until spontaneous breathing recommences.

Schäfer's method

The child should be placed chest downwards with his head turned to one side and arms stretched forwards with the head resting on one hand. Kneel by his side near the hips, and facing his head. Place the hands flat over the small of his back with the thumbs almost touching each other. Keep the fingers close together. Gently swing the body forwards from the hips, keeping the arms straight and press downwards. This movement forces the diaphragm upwards, driving air and water out of the lungs. Now straighten the body and relax pressure. Repeat these swaying movements about twelve to fourteen times a minute until the doctor arrives even if the pulse cannot be felt. It has been known for breathing to be started after two to three hours.

After breathing is established and the patient is conscious give warm sweetened drinks.

Other methods of applying artificial respiration are described in first aid manuals, but it is important to realise certain factors before attempting this treatment.

1. *The air passages must be clear.*
2. *Less pressure is used when giving artificial respiration to young children than when dealing with an adult.*
3. *The head should be placed in a position, possibly on one side, to enable a free passage of air.*
4. *Clothing must be loose round the neck and chest.*

This treatment must be performed with a regular rhythmic movement in accordance with what should be the normal respirations of the individual.

Electrocution

Electrocution is caused by a current of electricity passing through the body. This may be due to lightning or to contact with an electric cable or an exposed live wire. In all instances the patient may suffer from *asphyxia, shock* and *burns*. This accident can happen to children in the home if the electric wires or plugs are faulty and unguarded.

If the child is in contact with an electric cable, the *first thing that the adult must do is to try to turn off the power* and then attempt to help the child. Failing this, she must first protect herself by using thick dry rubber gloves or a thick woollen blanket folded to several thicknesses. If these things are not available then the child could be pushed to safety by using a long brush or a piece of dry wood, remembering that it is dangerous to use anything with metal attachments or to be in contact with any dampness.

Treatment. Send at once for a doctor. If the child has stopped breathing start artificial respiration at once.

The child should be treated for shock. Put him into a warm bed. Cover any burns which may be present. The doctor will prescribe all necessary treatment.

Books for reference and further reading are listed at the end of the book.

PART SIX
Medical Conditions

CHAPTER 22

Medical Conditions and their Prevention

The child who has good care, plenty of fresh air and sunlight, and good nutrition, will be much less likely to contract disease of any kind than the neglected and malnourished child.

Children cannot accurately describe how they feel but their behaviour will indicate their feelings. Therefore, by keen observation of any minor signs of illness, it is possible sometimes to prevent serious conditions from developing. It is very important for the mother or nurse to recognise any deviation from the normal, but it is for the doctor to diagnose and treat. Friends and neighbours often give advice which, although it is well meant, may, through ignorance, cause a good deal of unnecessary suffering to the child and worry to anxious parents.

The purpose of this chapter is to encourage the recognition of the early symptoms of disease, and only briefly to mention treatments. For convenience the conditions are arranged in alphabetical order.

Abnormal stools

The following are types of stools which vary from the normal and which are mostly caused by digestive disturbances, but in some instances by infection and chills.

Green coloured stools are due to a quick passage of the faeces through the intestines, and the colour is due to pigments. Some medicines may also cause green stools.

Loose green stools are frequently caused by an excess of sugar in the baby's diet; they give rise to sore buttocks.

Frothy stools, usually of acid reaction, are due to too much sugar.

Large, white curds in the stools are due to too much protein or to inability to digest the protein of cows' milk. They are more usual with artificially fed babies.

Very offensive stools are often associated with a diet too rich in protein.

Large copious stools, yellow in colour, with fat curds which glisten in the stool, are signs of overfeeding which, if continued for a long period, will eventually lead to green, watery stools and loss of weight in the child.

Small, rather dark, hard stools are caused by under-feeding.

Crumbly, pale and rather glistening stools indicate inability to digest the normal fat content of the feed.

Watery or green watery stools, usually containing mucus, and sometimes with streaks of blood, are a symptom of infectious diarrhoea (Chapter 29).

Very dark stools are usually caused by the administration of iron, bismuth or other medicines.

Blood in the stool is a serious condition calling for medical advice. It may be almost black or bright red mixed with mucus depending on the cause (see p. 338).

Appendicitis

This is usually more common in the older child. There may be a rise in temperature, vomiting with generalised pain in the abdomen which gradually becomes more localised low down in the right side. The child may be constipated, but no aperient or heat treatment should be given until the doctor has diagnosed the condition. Never delay in calling the doctor.

Asthma

This is thought to be an allergic condition; it is not usually seen before two years and often follows infantile eczema. There may be a sensitivity to pollen, feathers, dust or other substances; on the other hand the nervous child through excitement or overtiredness may develop asthma. Attacks may come on at any time, day or night, with spasms of difficult breathing and marked wheezing when exhaling. There are no feverish symptoms unless associated with bronchitis.

Good health, good open-air life, and a happy home environment can help a great deal. It is wise to consult a doctor, who can prescribe treatment to relieve the distress.

Boils

These are not very common in young children. They usually affect the child who is badly nourished and generally in a poor state of health. When there is any sign of a boil developing, a doctor should be consulted, who may be able to control it provided the pus in the middle has not formed. If the area has become inflamed, with a yellow centre, then the doctor will prescribe the treatment. Protect the surrounding area from infection by wiping with spirit and apply a dry dressing to encourage healing. Never attempt to squeeze out the pus or discharge from a boil.

Bronchitis

This is an inflammation of the bronchial tubes, and is very common in young children who are badly nourished or who lack sunlight, fresh air, and good care. Over-crowded sleeping conditions predispose to bronchitis, which may become chronic.

Some infants, when cutting teeth, have attacks which pass off in about a week. If a child has little resistance to disease the condition will get a hold and is liable to develop into bronchial pneumonia, which is very serious. Immediate medical attention is essential. The child must be kept in bed in a warm room with good ventilation but free from draughts.

Chilblains

There is redness of the skin with swelling and marked itching, which may be caused by poor circulation, lack of calcium and vitamin D in the diet, or exposure to extreme cold without adequate protection.

It is best to prevent this condition by giving good nutrition with plenty of open-air exercise. The limbs should be protected against chilling, gloves and footwear should be warm, but these must allow for freedom of movement, and this particularly applies to very young toddlers who cannot explain how they feel. It is unwise to come in and sit in front of a hot fire if the hands or feet are chilled. A soothing lotion is comforting and a little lanolin well rubbed into the skin before going into the cold air helps to prevent any further development. Broken chilblains should have a soothing antiseptic cream applied and should be kept covered. Protective treatments have recently been used with some success. It is wise to seek medical advice for this condition.

Colds

These are caused by bacteria infecting the mucous membrane of the nose and throat. In the acute stage colds are very infectious, the germs being spread by coughing and sneezing or by secretions from the nose or throat and by soiled handkerchiefs. Although only a slight disturbance, colds must be treated with care to avoid serious respiratory complications such as pneumonia or bronchitis, and ear infections. Any suggestion of a sore throat should be reported to a doctor as this may be an indication of an infectious disease. The nasal catarrh is often extremely difficult to clear up and may become chronic, resulting in the dirty noses so often seen in children and especially in those who do not get good care.

Predisposing causes are malnutrition, with lowered vitality, lack of fresh air and sunlight, rickets and infected adenoids.

Treatment should aim at preventing the spread of the infection to others and also at avoiding the development of serious complications. It is wise to keep the child in bed in a well ventilated, sunny room for one or two days, giving a light diet with extra fluids and a mild laxative if required. If there is a rise in temperature, the child should be kept in bed and the doctor should be called in. A teaspoonful of honey and glycerine in equal parts will often relieve a tickling cough. Give plenty of fluids.

Colds can be prevented by a good diet, rich in vitamin A, fresh air, sunlight and exercise, with good clothing and suitable warm footwear. The child must be taught to blow his nose and to use paper handkerchiefs when he sneezes. Crowded places and contact with infected persons should be avoided whenever possible.

Croup

This may follow a heavy cold or occur suddenly. There is a hoarseness accompanied by a noise in the throat on breathing in and out. The respirations appear laboured and it will be noticed that the lower part of the chest is drawn in as the child breathes. The doctor should be called but in the meantime hot steam inhalations may give relief. He will badly need comfort and reassurance as this is an extremely alarming condition for the child.

Colic

This gives rise to acute spasms of pain in the intestines and the young baby usually lies with his legs drawn up and screams. This condition may be caused by a chill, diarrhoea, constipation or wrong technique in feeding, for example, giving too cold feeds, allowing too long a sucking period, over-feeding, or the wrong proportions of food. At the same time it is important to realise that colic may also be a symptom of a more serious condition, therefore medical advice is necessary if these attacks are very acute and prolonged.

Treat by applying warmth to the abdomen and giving warm drinks of boiled water. Try to encourage the child to expel wind. Note any signs of a rise in temperature.

Constipation

Constipation is descriptive of the consistency of the motion, rather than the number of stools; a child having two or three small hard stools each day would be constipated, whilst another child having one normally formed bowel action on alternate days would not be constipated.

The constipated child may also have headaches, abdominal pains, furred tongue and be very listless and fretful.

The *chief causes* of constipation are:
1. Lack of sufficient fluid in the diet.
2. An unbalanced diet which is lacking in vegetables and fruits, or poor in foods rich in vitamin B.
3. Too much milk taken to the exclusion of other essentials in the diet of the toddler.
4. Lack of opportunity for exercise.
5. Faulty management and training in habit formation.
6. Poor muscular tone of the intestines.
7. Aperients given too often or regularly.
8. Hard and painful motions which will further complicate the condition.
9. Emotional or nervous strain.

The *treatment* will be to trace the cause of the trouble and attend to it. In dealing with children of all ages it must be remembered that alterations in routine and diet should be instituted gradually, otherwise a sudden adjustment may lead to further difficulties. Sympathetic encouragement can be given in habit formation and, according to the adult's approach and manner, the child will feel secure or the reverse. If he is happy and fond of his mother or nurse, he is likely to establish good habits very quickly. The nervous mother, by showing her anxiety to the child, may do much more harm than good by fussing with him. Many children dislike using a pot if there are other people present. This feeling should be considered and respected. This may arise with children on entering nurseries, when they are most likely to be emotionally disturbed.

Constipation should be prevented from the very earliest days by:

1. Good management.
2. Balanced diet with adequate roughage.
3. Adequate fluid intake.
4. Exercise and fresh air.
5. No regular aperients.
6. Showing no disappointment when lapses occur in training, as these are bound to happen.

Laxatives, if necessary, should be used with the idea of educating the bowel rather than to ensure a motion. To do this, reduce the dosage very, very slightly, until it can be omitted. Liquid paraffin or paraffin preparations are safe, but should be used only when necessary.

Castor oil must *never* be used for constipation.

Convulsions

These are more common in young babies than in older children, due to the lack of stability of the nervous system at this age. There are many predisposing causes such as malnutrition, rickets, digestive upsets, teething or an acute infection. Convulsions may occur at the onset of whooping cough and in brain diseases. In a typical convulsion the baby quite suddenly becomes stiff in the limbs, the eyes stare, the face looks bluish, respiration stops and unconsciousness ensues, followed by twitching movements of the limbs and the eyes. The duration of the attack varies with the severity of the convulsion. Breathing usually starts again in a few seconds with a grunting noise, and consciousness returns, but the child appears very limp and thoroughly exhausted. *The general principles of treatment are to keep the body warm and the head cool. Never leave the child alone during the convulsion as the tongue may go back and so block the air passage.* A warm bath, temperature 105°–110° F (40°–43° C), is sometimes advised, with cold cloths on the head, but this must be done at once to be of any use and it requires the help of another adult. It is usually just as effective to keep the infant warm in blankets and apply a cold compress to the head.

No matter how slight the attack it is essential to consult a doctor so that the cause can be thoroughly investigated and treated.

Dandruff

Fine scales, sometimes seen on the scalp, are possibly due to a very dry skin. It causes irritation, which, if the child is allowed to scratch, may lead to inflamed sores. Applying liquid paraffin freely some hours before washing the head with a little soap and with very

thorough rinsing, will usually clear up this condition. Advice should
be sought if the condition persists, and good hygiene must be
practised.

Diarrhoea

This may be caused by:
1. Over-feeding or inability to digest the food, or an excess of
   sugar.
2. A chill.
3. Excessive heat.
4. Other illness, such as rickets, and respiratory infections.
5. Bacteria, causing a very serious inflammation in the intestines,
   which is highly infectious (see Chapter 29). This has often been
   referred to in the past as summer diarrhoea.

Diarrhoea in young children, no matter what the cause, is serious,
and must always be treated immediately. In the mild form it is most
commonly caused by digestive upsets, when vomiting, colic and loose
or watery stools are the chief symptoms, but this can quickly develop
into the more serious infectious type if carelessly handled.

Prevention of any form of diarrhoea is very important and every
precaution must be taken to avoid it spreading wherever there are
children grouped together.
1. All milk for children must be pasteurised or boiled.
2. Contamination of boiled milk by dust or flies must be guarded
   against.
3. Strict cleanliness in all feeding equipment, including bottles
   and teats, both for breast and bottle feeding.
4. Suitable feeds for each individual child.
5. Good hygiene is essential and hand washing by the mother or
   nurse after attending to the child or using the toilet, and before
   making up feeds or handling any food.
6. Dummies should be avoided.
7. Children should never be exposed to infection.

Treatment consists in righting any errors in diet under expert
advice. The condition of infants can change very rapidly, therefore
a delay in consulting a doctor may prove very serious or even fatal.
Treat all diarrhoea as highly infectious until it is proved to be
otherwise.

Stop all milk food. As diarrhoea causes a loss of weight and dehydration of the tissues it is necessary to give frequent drinks and
the doctor will usually prescribe half-strength normal saline ($\frac{1}{2}$ tea-

spoonful salt in 20 ounces of water, boiled and allowed to cool) or half-strength normal saline and glucose. This feed should be given approximately every 2–3 hours if there is no vomiting. The aim is to give 2½ ounces to each pound of the normal weight of the baby. Keep the child warm in bed in a well ventilated room. Diluted skimmed milk or a weak solution of half-cream dried milk may be ordered by the doctor when the loose stools have stopped. Good hygiene and good nursing care are essential.

Discharging ear

This is a serious condition and if untreated may cause permanent deafness. It is usually caused by infection spreading from inflamed nasal passages into the Eustachian tubes leading to the middle ear, causing *otitis media*, (inflammation of the middle ear). An abscess may develop giving rise to severe pain and pressure on the ear drum, which may burst and cause deafness. In the early stage the child will be restless or crying and possibly rolling his head from side to side. *A doctor should immediately be consulted* and he may be able to prevent damage to the drum, and so safeguard the child's hearing. Never syringe an ear unless on medical advice and this must be done by a doctor or a trained nurse. Any discharge from the ear is infectious.

Discharging eyes

These are caused by inflammation of the mucous membrane of the eye and eyelids. This condition is known as *conjunctivitis* and is often referred to as 'pink eye'. It can be extremely serious and may cause blindness. Sometimes a 'sticky eye' develops when a child has a cold, and this should be treated to avoid the infection becoming purulent. If only one eye is affected care must be taken to avoid the spread of infection to the other eye. When the baby is placed in his cot always lie him on the side of the infected eye. Even when the eyes are healthy each should be cleaned with a separate swab, and in cases of infection this is of even greater importance. All types of conjunctivitis are infectious and any case must be isolated. (See also p. 296.)

Treating the eye is a highly skilled art, especially with young children. Any purulent discharge should be immediately reported to the doctor who will advise on what treatment is required.

Eczema

This is a non-infectious skin disorder of which there are many varieties. It is an inflammation of the skin, accompanied by severe irritation. The condition is found in young, well-nourished babies, whether breast fed or bottle fed, and it is not uncommon to find this condition when one parent or member of the family has had asthma, hay fever or eczema. It usually appears first on the cheeks as red patches, spreading over the face and head, in the crevices, and is found less frequently on the body. The affected areas become moist and crusts are formed. With good care the skin is undamaged after the condition has cleared up, although this may take six to eighteen months. All babies with the *slightest tendency to eczema should be kept under medical supervision.*

Treatment. Much research has been done in recent years on this condition and is still being done. There are a variety of treatments which the doctor may prescribe.

General care. The child must never be allowed to become over-heated, and a thin fine cotton or silk vest will avoid any irritation to the skin. His finger nails must be kept short, smooth and clean. He should not be exposed to strong sunlight or strong winds.

Care must be taken to give the child the maximum freedom for play at the same time as preventing skin irritation. If necessary cardboard splints can be applied to his elbows, which though restricting his movements, will still leave him freedom to reach and handle his play materials, thus supplying the very necessary interests and stimulation so vital to his mental and physical growth. Periods of complete freedom under close supervision will be most beneficial to him.

Epilepsy

This may show at an early age, by the child becoming very pale and losing consciousness for a little time. This condition is known as 'petit mal' which may be very slight and in some instances may be almost overlooked. It is, however, very important for a doctor to examine the child.

Feverishness

This frequently occurs in children of all ages. It is a symptom of many diseases, and care should be taken when a child appears flushed, has a rise in temperature, complains of, or shows signs of, headache, and appears to be generally out of sorts. He should be put to bed in a well-ventilated room, and given a light diet with plenty of fluids. The bowels are often quite loose. Feverishness is the beginning of many children's ailments and infectious diseases, therefore a careful watch should be kept for any rash or any specific symptom and medical advice sought.

Hiccough

This is caused by a spasm of the respiratory muscles involving the diaphragm. It usually occurs after a meal and indicates that the baby has slight indigestion, but if the condition persists consult a doctor.

In normal health it is nothing to worry about. Give a little warm boiled water and hold the baby in the same position as for 'getting up his wind'.

Impetigo

This is a very contagious skin disease, and is spread by the child scratching himself and by direct contact with an infected child. It first appears as a small red spot, which becomes moist, and a characteristic yellow crust forms over the spot. It frequently appears on the face or behind the ears and is often a complication of pediculosis or head lice, and is more commonly found in dirty home conditions.

Treatment consists of cleansing the skin with warm water and if the hard crusts have formed, soften these with warmed oil to remove the crusts, then a starch poultice may be applied. The doctor will probably recommend an antibiotic cream such as chloromycetin, or the use of Betnovate-C cream. Whenever possible it is better to leave the skin uncovered, but scratching must be prevented and nails must be kept clean and short. Where there are many children strict hygiene precautions must be taken, particularly in relation to towels, to stop the disease spreading.

Intussusception

This is a very acute and serious condition in young babies caused by a part of the bowel becoming interlocked or wedged within another part of the bowel causing a complete obstruction. Vomiting may occur and the abdomen becomes distended with severe spasms of pain and tenderness. A stool may be passed but soon blood and mucus will be passed which must be kept for medical inspection. Any delay in calling the doctor could be extremely dangerous. Treatment will necessitate surgery.

Mastitis

This is an inflammation in the baby's breasts which may occur in the first month; in the majority of cases there is no redness. If this does develop a doctor must be consulted. Never massage the breasts. The only care necessary is to cover them with a little cotton wool and apply a fairly firm bandage.

Napkin rash

This is commonly caused by badly washed napkins or faulty washing and drying of the skin each time the napkin is changed. For care, see sore buttocks (see p. 277).

Ophthalmia neonatorum

This refers to any discharge from the eyes of a baby in the first three weeks of life. There may be a watery discharge which is often referred to as 'sticky eye' and no matter how slight this is, it must be reported to the doctor and treated. Any yellow discharge can be due to a staphylococcal infection of the anus. This condition must be notified and treated immediately as it can cause blindness. Any persistant watery discharge may be caused by a blocked tear duct.

Pediculosis

A verminous condition when lice infest the human body. There are three varieties of lice, the first being found on the hair of the head, the second on the body and a third on the hair of the body in adolescents and in adults. Lice or pediculi live on the blood of the human body, causing a severe itching, and irritation. Verminous conditions are spread by contact with infected people and aggravated by bad hygiene and dirty living conditions.

The *head louse* inhabits the hair of the head (*Pediculosis capitis*) and the eggs or nits adhere to the hair quite close to the scalp. These nits are minute, greyish in colour, and hatch in about 8 to 10 days. Within two weeks the young louse is ready to reproduce. The lice are quite visible on the scalp and also the nits on the hair. Other children can easily become infected by contact, and by using infected brushes or combs or by trying on each other's hats.

The condition is shown by severe scratching, commonly behind the ears and at the back of the head. This causes a secondary infection and sometimes impetigo, or the glands in the area may become swollen and inflamed.

Treatment consists in cleansing the head as described in Chapter 6, and this condition can also be treated at a cleansing station.

Body lice live on the body, and inhabit the folds or seams of clothing. General cleanliness will quickly clear up the condition, but the seams of woollen garments should be ironed to kill any lice or their eggs which may be adherent. Bed and bedding must be inspected and, if necessary, disinfected by the local authority. Cleanliness is the only cure.

Lice infecting the hair of the body cause extreme itching and should be treated in the same way as body lice by inducing general cleanliness.

Pink disease

This disease occurs from about four months to three years and the cause is not definitely known. The onset may be of a mild feverish nature, with some digestive upsets accompanied by marked restlessness, irritability, sleeplessness, and poor appetite. The hands, feet, nose and ears appear red, although they feel cold to the touch. The child dislikes the light and tries to burrow under the bedclothes and there may be irritation of the skin. Early medical advice is very important as the condition may be quite serious and take many months to clear up. This condition has often to be treated in hospital, as the day and night care may become too much for the mother.

Rectal prolapse

The bowel protrudes as a red mass after a stool has been passed. This may be due to many causes such as constipation, being left too long on the chamber, worms, coughing or debility with poor muscle tone, and sometimes there is no apparent cause. The over anxious adult may even stimulate the child to produce the prolapse.

Treatment. Gently push back the bowel with an oiled finger preferably with the child lying down; afterwards he should remain on his bed for a short time. Constipation must be avoided by giving a mild aperient such as liquid paraffin. Any special treatment will be advised by the doctor. The adult must never encourage the child to concentrate on the condition.

Pyloric stenosis

This is caused by thickening of the pyloric sphincter muscle at the outlet of the stomach. This prevents the food passing freely out into the duodenum and much depends on the degree of the defect. The stomach attempts to force the food through the exit but fails and the result is a swift return of the food through the mouth producing what is termed *projectile vomiting*. The baby takes his food in the normal way but does not benefit from it. He fails to gain weight and

K

will have small constipated stools. This type of vomiting shows soon after birth and no time must be lost in getting expert advice because much can be done to rectify this condition.

Rheumatism

Rheumatism is a very serious disease in children, appearing at about 3 years and throughout childhood. In the acute form of rheumatic fever there is a grave risk of the heart becoming affected. In a mild form there are pains in the muscles or joints, which in the past were often referred to as *growing pains* and more or less taken for granted. This causes much restlessness and sleeplessness at night. It is a great mistake to treat any form of rheumatism too lightly, because even in the mild form the heart can be damaged. Dampness and inheritance are both factors which predispose to rheumatism; *tonsillitis* and upper respiratory infections are often associated with this condition. Chorea (St. Vitus' dance) is a form of rheumatism affecting the brain.

Treatment must aim at building up good health by fresh air, good food, and good environment, and any infection of the nose, ear or throat must be treated and cleared up. Any type of rheumatism should be kept under medical supervision.

Ringworm

This is caused by a fungus and it is very contagious. It is usually seen in the scalp, but it can affect the skin of the body as well. It appears as a circular patch with horny scales. When on the scalp, the hair thins and the area becomes bald. It is spread by direct contact and in children this occurs by trying on each other's hats or by indiscriminate use of brushes and combs or from animals, e.g. dogs or cats. If there is any suspicion of ringworm, a doctor should be consulted and the child kept away from other children. The condition is much less common than it was some years ago, partly because of better hygiene and partly on account of the more effective treatment now available. All cases of ringworm should be kept under medical supervision.

Rumination

After swallowing his food the older baby may return it to his mouth and appear to chew it again, which is often referred to as 'chewing the cud'. By giving a fluid diet for a time, the condition or habit should quickly clear up. The child shows no sign of illness.

Scabies

This is caused by a parasite, almost invisible to the naked eye, which burrows between the layers of the skin. The female lays her eggs in the follicles of the skin, and these hatch and mature in a few weeks. This causes a rash round the areas, giving rise to intense irritation, especially in bed. Because of the child scratching himself secondary infection is very likely to occur. This condition is found chiefly between the fingers and the toes, on the wrists, the forearms, in the armpits and in the groins, but it does not affect the face.

Treatment consists of a hot bath and thorough washing. After drying, the whole body is painted with an emulsion of benzyl benzoate and an entirely clean set of clothing put on. The treatment should be repeated after two days. All clothing and bedding should be disinfected. Treatment and disinfection can be carried out at the cleansing station belonging to the local authority (Chapter 31) and all infected members of the family must be treated, otherwise there will be continual reinfection. Treatment must be prescribed by a doctor.

Scurf or seborrhoea

This is a common condition found on the heads and particularly over the anterior fontanelle of young babies. It is a yellowish crust which forms, due partly to the mother's fear of thoroughly washing over the fontanelle. It can easily be treated by using a little liquid paraffin, baby oil or petroleum jelly. This should be applied overnight, then the head washed the next morning. Care must be taken to avoid making a sore on the scalp in the process. Wash the head daily in the normal way, care being taken very thoroughly to rinse off the soap.

Sore buttocks

There are many degrees of sore buttocks, varying from a dry and slightly red skin to septic sores.

The *chief causes* are:
1. Infrequent changing of wet or soiled napkins.
2. Lack of attention to washing and drying the skin each time a child is wet or soiled.
3. Coarse, rough napkins or badly washed napkins.
4. Irritation from loose stools, green stools or diarrhoea.
5. Irritation due to very acid or alkaline urine.
6. Always laying a baby down in the same position.

7. Lowered vitality of the child.
8. Incorrect diet.
9. Diarrhoea.

The *treatment* must be concentrated on removing the cause of the trouble. If the motion is abnormal, the digestive condition must be corrected. Too much sugar will frequently lead to a loose acid stool. Should the urine smell of ammonia, give some boiled water to drink to which a pinch of bicarbonate of soda has been added. Allow the buttocks to be exposed to the air for short periods and if the skin appears to be dry apply a cream. Wash the buttocks thoroughly with soap and water when changing napkins and massage the buttocks with a circular movement which encourages a better circulation to the area. Use an antiseptic cream or zinc and castor oil cream whenever the slightest sign of redness appears. If the buttocks are very sore, a few drops of tincture of benzoin may be added to an ounce of the cream, which should be spread on white lint and a fresh piece applied whenever the baby is changed. If the skin is broken, do not wash, but cleanse the skin with warm baby oil or baby lotion and use the cream. Some doctors recommend gentian violet.

Sore throat and tonsillitis

These are vague terms used when the throat feels painful. It is usually due to swollen and inflamed tonsils, the condition referred to as tonsillitis. The child is feverish, with a headache, and refuses to eat. This condition is infectious and the child should be isolated. All discharges must be treated as highly infectious. Any form of sore throat should be reported to a doctor, as it may be the onset of an infectious disease. The function of the tonsils is to prevent the spread of infection into the body. Although they do at times become enlarged, it is not necessary to have them removed unless they are unhealthy or septic (see also p. 330).

Sleeplessness

Sleeplessness in children may lead to serious consequences if not adequately treated. It may be due to any of the following reasons:
1. Too much excitement before going to bed, e.g. unsuitable stories.
2. Fear of the dark, or of shadows from a small light.
3. Any emotional upset.
4. A parent or nurse who fails to give security.
5. Hunger or thirst.

6. Illness causing pain or irritation.
7. Uncomfortable clothing, too heavy or too light bedclothes, overheating or chilling, e.g. cold feet.
8. Lack of good ventilation and fresh air.
9. Badly planned routine and lack of outdoor exercise.
10. Overtiredness or fatigue.

Treatment required will be to rectify the cause, which must be done quickly, otherwise a habit of sleeplessness becomes established which will be exceedingly difficult to eradicate in later life. Sedatives must never be encouraged except on medical instructions.

Snuffles

This is a term which denotes noisy breathing caused by some form of nasal obstruction, for example catarrh. It is often present with infected adenoids, and is sometimes found in mongols. It is often caused by bad hygiene, germs may be transmitted from the mother or nurse through lack of hand washing and thus give rise to staphylococcal infection. Medical advice should be sought.

Stomatitis

This is an inflammation of the mucous membrane of the gums and the mouth and in some forms tiny blisters occur, which break causing small ulcers. It is commonly found in young children when teething, and especially in those in poor health. The infection is caused by dirty teats or dummies or by rough cleaning of the mouth. Strict cleanliness and gentle handling are essential, and the mouth may be carefully swabbed out with 0.5 per cent gentian violet. Feeding may be difficult but try to give plenty of fluids. A doctor should be consulted and care taken to avoid spreading the infection.

Styes

These are small abscesses formed at the root of an eyelash. They usually affect children in poor health and a doctor should examine the child. Relief is obtained by frequent bathing with warm saline lotion or sterile water and for older children an eye bath may be used and the condition treated as infectious.

Teething troubles

Teething may cause slight disturbances, but it is certainly not at the root of all the child's ailments up to two years of age. Before the teeth are cut, the gums may be red and inflamed and a little swollen, and the child may be feverish, fretful and restless and refuse his food and be generally out of sorts. There is usually an increased flow of saliva, causing the characteristic dribbling. As the teeth are cut, the condition quickly passes. During teething habits may relax but if the child is simply treated with kindness the problem will right itself in a short time. Some children cut their teeth almost unnoticed. In many instances serious symptoms such as earache or diarrhoea are blamed on teething, and because of this the child is left without any proper treatment, which, may lead to very serious consequences.

Treatment should consist of helping the child by building up his health, keeping a regular daily bowel action, giving extra fluids, but never forcing food. Strict cleanliness must be used to prevent any bacteria infecting the mouth. Hard crusts or a stout boiled bone to bite on may give some comfort. A mild sedative, ordered by a doctor, is useful in cases where the child has much pain and is restless at night.

Thrush

Thrush appears as little white patches on the tongue and in the mouth. This is an infectious condition caused by a fungus and usually attacks the malnourished baby. It can be introduced by neglected nipples, dirty teats, dummies, dirty fingers, or cleaning the mouth, thus leaving the delicate mucous membrane open to invasion by the fungus. Thrush may be accompanied by loose stools.

In severe cases ulceration occurs which may spread into the throat. The child is fretful, feels ill, and will often refuse his food. A doctor should be consulted and may prescribe the following treatment.

Treatment. Gently swab out the mouth with an aqueous solution of 0.5 per cent gentian violet after a feed. All used swabs must be burnt. The strictest cleanliness must be applied to the care of the teats, or anything coming into contact with the mouth. In a nursery the child must be isolated and everything used for him must be boiled or disinfected and kept separate in his own room.

Tight foreskin (see Chapter 3)

Tuberculosis

This is nowadays a rare condition and is most often found amongst recent immigrants. Although tuberculosis is not inherited, a child living in a home with an infected person runs the risk of catching the disease because of the continual contact with it. All such children should be given BCG vaccine as early as possible (see Chapter 28).

Bovine tuberculosis, affecting glands, bones and joints, was once commonly found in young children, but the danger of developing this is now virtually eliminated as all milk is pasteurised or sterilised. Although pasteurised milk is reasonably safe, it is wise to *boil all milk* for children under five years because it may contain other harmful bacteria.

Young children affected with tuberculosis may not show any marked symptoms, although there may be poor growth. An attack of whooping cough may not clear up, causing the child to be listless and pale with a poor appetite. Always consult a doctor if the child is not making steady progress.

Umbilicus (or navel) moist or discharging

Known as pemphigus this is a highly infectious condition in the new-born baby caused by a staphylococcal infection. This may cause a bulbous rash on any part of the body except the palms of the hands and soles of the feet. The navel must be kept dry after birth and powdered with chlorhexedine powder. Do not allow the cord to be pulled or caught up in the napkin. Under normal conditions it should be healed by the seventh day.

Urticaria

Often termed 'nettle rash', this may occur in several forms. It is usually caused through indigestion, due to errors in diet, or by an idiosyncrasy to a particular fruit, fish or drug. During teething it is quite common and appears as papules or heat lumps on various parts of the body. At night these give rise to intense irritation and scratching may lead to secondary infection. In other varieties the typical wheals or blotches appear.

Treatment. The cause should be investigated. Reduce starch and sugar in the diet and try to allay the irritation by applying calamine lotion or an antiseptic cream. Keep the nails short and clean; in severe instances some restriction may be necessary to prevent scratching at night. A saline bath (1 tablespoonful common salt to 1 gallon of water) can be given night and morning.

Vaginitis

This is a condition occasionally found in little girls. It shows itself as a purulent discharge from the vagina. This may prove to be a serious infectious condition and must have medical treatment (Chapter 29).

Vomiting

Occurring with little effort immediately after a feed, the food being almost unchanged, this is often referred to as possetting, and may be caused by the baby swallowing air, by too much bulk in the feed or by wrong technique in feeding the baby. The only treatment required is to correct the cause, possibly to give a more concentrated feed. Care must be taken to avoid the habit of vomiting being formed. Vomiting from half an hour to one hour after a feed is often due to the infant's inability to cope with the fat in the feed. Too strong a feed may also cause the child to vomit (see Chapter 10). In toddlers also it may be due to excessive fat in the diet. Another cause may be an idiosyncrasy to certain foods such as egg. Again, the cause must be diagnosed and the necessary adjustments made.

Vomiting may also be associated with some infectious conditions or fevers, when there is usually a rise in temperature, rapid pulse and restlessness. The doctor should be called and, after diagnosing the cause of vomiting, will order treatment (see Chapter 29).

Vomiting is also associated with many intestinal infections and with diarrhoea. Food poisoning will cause a child to vomit, he will at first feel sick with abdominal pain and will be pale and exhausted. Medical advice must be obtained without delay.

Vomiting attacks which occur at intervals, particularly prevalent in the rather nervous child or in one who is influenced by a highly strung mother, are caused by an upset to the chemical balance of the body and are commonly associated with *acidosis*. The child appears listless, fretful, with a furred tongue and offensive and pale or undigested motions. This condition frequently occurs with any great excitement, such as parties, holidays, etc., or it may be due entirely to over-feeding with too rich foods.

Treatment will possibly necessitate a diet of diluted milk or glucose and water for 24 hours. A light diet can then be gradually introduced. Milk of magnesia is a good aperient to use if necessary. A rest in bed with no excitement may help; if not consult a doctor.

Vomiting is a symptom in many *abdominal conditions*. In such cases retching is usually severe and the child appears really ill. No time must be lost in seeking medical advice.

Worms

These infest the intestines of young children. They cause indigestion, irritability, restlessness, hunger and night terrors. There is often irritation round the anus, but the only sure symptom is when the worms are actually seen in the stool. Medical advice must be obtained.

Thread worms are about $\frac{1}{4}$ inch (6 mm) long, like small pieces of white thread, and can be seen wriggling about in the faeces. Children will frequently reinfect themselves through scratching the anus and getting the eggs under the finger nails, from which they are transferred to the food. The child must be kept from reinfecting himself or anyone sleeping with him by the strictest hygiene, with special attention to short finger nails and the use of pyjamas for night wear. The sheets should be carefully inspected for the presence of eggs, as the child may easily pick these up in the finger nails. It is quite possible for the whole family to become infected. All vegetables must be well washed as they may be a source of infection. The general health of the child must be improved by good diet, rest, sleep, fresh air and good hygiene. Medical advice is essential and the doctor will prescribe the necessary treatment.

Round worms are almost white in colour and are very like an earth worm in size and formation. Again the definite symptom is actually seeing the worm or part of it in the stool. There are usually only one or two worms present. Similar precautions to those against thread worms are necessary and medical advice is essential.

Tape worms consist of many segments, which are passed in the faeces, but until the head has been passed there is no likelihood of clearing up the condition. All segments must be kept for inspection by the doctor, who will give detailed advice, as to what medicines and purgatives to give and when to give them. The intensity of the treatment will naturally be influenced by the child's condition. Infected meat is the chief cause of this condition, and there are strict controls on the import of meat in order to guard against it.

CHAPTER 23

Home Nursing

When a child is seriously ill he is usually nursed either in a hospital where his mother may be allowed to stay with him or to visit him frequently, or at home if conditions are suitable and there are adequate home nursing facilities. In many instances, however, the child although not acutely ill requires simple home nursing. The child in the early years cannot understand why he must remain in bed or stay in one room, when he thinks he could enjoy running round or playing with toys, and a great deal of skill and patience is needed to persuade him otherwise. It is wise for the adult, whenever possible, to explain what is going to be done and so win the child's confidence. If there is a mystery about any treatment the child will automatically become suspicious, and then difficulties will arise.

The young child cannot explain his condition or the type of pain he may have, therefore it is only by keen observation of every detail that the adult can really help the child when he is not well. The experienced nurse can recognise signs and symptoms, but the untrained adult who knows the child in health can sometimes more easily note any changes and report these to the doctor. What appear to be trifling factors may be of great value in diagnosis. In the home neighbours often give very useful help in times of illness, but any advice from such friends must be used with discretion, and never as a substitute for calling in the doctor.

The Sick Room

The modern home does not give much choice in rooms. The ideal sick room should have a southern aspect, which will allow the maximum amount of sun, and windows which open, allowing plenty of fresh air. A fireplace helps to promote good ventilation.

Cleanliness of the sick room is of the greatest importance. Care must be taken to avoid raising dust, and the floor should be cleaned with a vacuum cleaner. A damp or oiled duster is useful when dusting. *Never use a feather duster* as this will spread dust and germs.

Coal fires are valuable but unfortunately they create dust, and are seldom found in the modern home. Adequate warmth can be provided in the sick room by electric, gas or oil heating, which must be protected adequately.

A wall thermometer is necessary to record the temperature of the room. This should be hung on the wall at a convenient height for the adult to read, and away from the fire. The temperature normally should be 55° F to 60° F (13° C–15.5° C) but 60° F to 70° F (15.5° C–21° C) in all respiratory conditions. The room should be thoroughly aired during the day.

The cot or bed should be placed in a position to get the maximum fresh air, but out of draughts, and preferably not facing the window. *Safety measures* are important in the sick room. The window must be guarded if the child is old enough to reach it. Safety straps for the young child are necessary if he is to be left alone in the room. Medicines, or any dangerous poisons such as lotions, must be stored outside the room in a locked cupboard and the key kept out of reach.

There are times when a child must be kept warm although it is not necessary for him to remain in bed. In such cases, it is good for the child to have a change of surroundings, and at the same time this eases the work of the household.

Early signs of illness. Any change from the child's normal behaviour, such as sleeplessness, lack of interest in his surroundings or no desire to play, fretfulness or irritability, may be the early symptoms of an illness. He may just sit about and do nothing and there may be a general lassitude frequently accompanied by a poor appetite. Sickness is often a warning of a coming illness.

Definite signs are a rise in temperature shown by flushed cheeks, hot dry skin, a dirty tongue, sore throat, skin rash, sickness, constipation or diarrhoea.

Chief factors in home nursing

(a) *Good hygiene.* This must include strict personal cleanliness of the adult with special attention to *hand washing* before preparing meals, after attending to the child, and after any toilet hygiene for the adult or the patient.

(b) *Comfort.* This is of the utmost importance for any sick person, and the adult should as far as possible anticipate the child's needs.

(c) *Observation.* In any illness, but particularly with young children, every detail must be noted in relation to the condition, whether improvement or otherwise.

(d) *Doctor's instructions.* These must be accurately and intelligently noted, and if the condition of the patient changes the doctor should be consulted before carrying out any further treatment.

(e) *Accurate records.* Never trust to memory, but record temperatures, type of stool, urine, feeds taken, nature of pain, restlessness and hours of sleep. Any new symptoms should be noted and reported.

The home nursing care should, as far as possible, follow the usual routine to which the child is accustomed. Lapses of good habits may occur and must be dealt with sympathetically. When attending to the child it is important for the adult to appreciate just how he feels and handle him accordingly. The daily care will naturally vary with the type of illness and the age of the child.

As the temperature, pulse and respiration form a valuable guide to the child's condition, it is important to record these before bathing or making the bed in the morning.

Clinical thermometers vary in the time they take to register, but each is clearly marked, thirty seconds, one minute or two minutes. A few seconds longer than the time stated should be allowed. All thermometers are numbered, ranging from 95° F to 110° F (or 35° C–43° C) and on a Fahrenheit thermometer each space is divided into five smaller spaces by four lines, each being .2 of a degree. The normal temperature is 98.4° F (or 37° C). The mercury in the thermometer registers the temperature and if the mercury rises to the first line after 99° F that temperature would be 99.2° F, second line 99.4° F or the third, 99.6° F. Magnifying thermometers which are easier to read can be obtained.

Temperature

A child under 2 years of age usually has his temperature taken in the groin, or the rectum, when it is necessary to use a special rectal thermometer, with a round bulb.

Method for axilla and groin. Prepare a tray with cotton wool swabs, receiver, thermometer, and receptacle with disinfectant for the thermometer after use. This should be dry and must not register above 96° F when put into position. Wipe the skin with cotton wool before placing the mercury bulb end of the thermometer in the axilla or groin. Care must be taken to avoid clothing lying between the skin and the thermometer as this will prevent the true temperature being registered. Hold the thermometer in position for the necessary period if the child is restless or fretful; he will often remain quiet if he is seated comfortably on the adult's knee, well wrapped up in a warm blanket. Remove the thermometer, cover up the child, read and record the temperature. Shake the thermometer down and place it in a bowl of disinfectant, one teaspoonful Dettol to 5 ounces of water, for a few minutes, then dry and return the thermometer to its case or, if it is likely to be used again, leave it in the lotion.

Method for rectum. Prepare a tray, add petroleum jelly and a rectal thermometer. With the child lying on the bed or on your knee, smear the round bulb with the jelly and insert it very gently about $1-1\frac{1}{2}$ inches. Hold the thermometer in the rectum to avoid any risk of breaking. After two minutes remove it and record the temperature, then put it into a disinfectant for at least half an hour. Some children find this method very upsetting. After two years of age the temperature should be taken in the axilla or in the groin but with small children *never in the mouth.*

(For temperature conversion tables see Tables 14 and 15 at the end of the book).

Pulse

The child's pulse is usually taken at the wrist on the thumb side, or at the temple, by placing the end of the first and second fingers over the artery. The beat can be felt and should be counted for at least half a minute, but preferably for one minute. Apart from counting the pulse beats, the rhythm of the pulse should be noted, for example, if the beats are regular and of the same volume. Crying or any emotional upset can affect the pulse quite apart from physical causes, therefore the pulse should be taken when the child is quiet, to obtain an accurate record. For pulse rates, see Chapter 3.

Respiration

Like the pulse rate this is also disturbed by excitement or any upsets. If possible, it is best to count the respirations for one minute without the child knowing, by simply watching the rise and fall of the chest wall or by placing the fingers lightly on the chest. For respiration rates, see Chapter 3.

A morning and evening record of temperature, pulse and respiration should be kept, and in acute illness it is advisable to keep a four-hourly chart. The whole procedure, if done efficiently, should not disturb the child.

The morning toilet

In the home, much depends on the condition of the child and if he has slept soundly throughout the night. Sleep is a wonderful tonic and it is often wiser to let the child sleep rather than waken him just because it happens to be the routine time for getting up. This procedure may not always be possible in a residential nursery, but the importance of sleep must always be remembered. Before disturbing the child it is important to get everything ready that is likely to be required. This should include:

Towels (as described for bathing in Chapter 6).
Soap.
Tooth brush, mug and small bowl (according to age).
Brush and comb.
Change of clothing (well aired).
Clean bed linen (if necessary).
Pot with cover.
Two blankets for bed bathing.
Essentials for any dressing to be done (on a covered tray).

Arrange the room in the most convenient manner. The temperature should be 60° F to 65° F (15.5° C–18° C), with suitable heating, and windows closed to avoid draughts.

The child will possibly like a little drink when he wakes up and before he is washed.

Encourage him to use the pot either sitting on the bed or near the fire. Place a blanket round the child thus avoiding chilling. It is advisable for the adult to have a bowl, soap, nail brush, water and a towel for hand washing after cleaning the child and before proceeding with the remainder of the toilet. Nasal hygiene must be encouraged (see Chapter 6).

The older child can have his teeth cleaned and should gargle if possible. If the child's temperature is over 100° F (37.8° C) he should be bed bathed.

Bed bath

Throughout this procedure the child should be exposed as little as possible. Remove the bed cover and top blanket. Lay one warmed bathing blanket over the remaining bed clothes, then gently remove these, leaving the child covered with the blanket. Roll or lift the child and place the other warmed bathing blanket underneath him. First wash and dry the face, ears and neck. Remove the clothing and proceed to wash and dry the arms, trunk and legs, under the blanket. Roll the patient over and wash the back and genital organs. Note any skin conditions or discharges and after thorough drying apply any necessary treatment; then put on clean garments and wrap the child in a warm dry blanket. If he is well enough it is easiest to lift him on to a comfortable chair and then make the bed. Soiled or dirty linen should be placed in a bucket or receiver. Clean linen must be used when required.

When returning the child to bed it is important to see that he is warm and comfortable. If the child is anxious to sit up in bed he must wear a warm bed jacket in addition to his usual garments for bed wear. Before brushing and combing the hair place a small cape or towel round the child's shoulders.

Throughout the day, if the child is restless or fretful because he does not feel well, he may need a good deal of care and attention from the adult, who by understanding and sympathy can reassure him. Frequent drinks should be offered as a young child cannot explain what he wants.

The evening toilet should follow the same routine as the morning toilet, except that only the hands and face are washed instead of a bed bath being given.

In all cases of illness it is essential to settle the patient comfortably for the night and with a child this should be at his normal bed time or earlier if he seems tired, after using a pot. It is quite useless to insist on a child lying in a certain position in bed, therefore the nurse must cooperate with the patient and ensure that the child is warm and happy. Such conditions are conducive to good sound sleep, which is vital to a child.

The child should not be disturbed or wakened in the night unless he is wet, or if the doctor has ordered him to be roused for medicine or treatment. When attending a sick child the nurse or mother must note if he sleeps peacefully and breathes regularly. A child may become cold during the night, due to tight clothes or insufficient clothing, or simply because he becomes uncovered. Warm pyjamas are best for the child over eighteen months as they help to prevent chilling if he is restless. When a child is feverish he will very possibly require his clothing changed on account of perspiration. There should be a shaded light to enable the adult to observe the child without disturbing him.

Using the pot

Care must be taken when seating the child to keep him warm by tucking an extra blanket round him. In the night, if a child has to be raised, he should not be talked to as this wakes him up very thoroughly, and it may be difficult for him to settle down again.

The pot or bed pan must be emptied, rinsed after use, and well washed in soapy water, rinsed again and dried with a special lavatory towel. These must be disinfected if there is any risk of infection (p. 300).

The stool. If this should be in any way abnormal, it is wise to keep it for the doctor's inspection. Leave it in a pot and cover this with a lid or lavatory cloth and place in the lavatory.

The urine. The doctor frequently asks for a specimen of urine to be saved, and the younger the child the more difficult it is to obtain this. After washing the chamber, rinse it in clean water, dry it, and encourage the child to pass urine when the bladder is likely to be full, for example, in the early morning. Pour the urine into a clean bottle and label it immediately with the child's name, date and the time it was passed.

Sputum

The young child may cough and produce a little sputum, but he usually swallows it.

Hot water bottles

When filling a hot water bottle it must be remembered that hot air expands and increases in volume; therefore, to avoid accidents it is necessary to allow the steam to escape before screwing up the cork. A rubber hot water bottle is commonly used and it must be carefully handled. To fill, remove the stopper, place the bottle flat on a table, hold the neck up in the left hand and pour in hot, but not boiling water, until the bottle is half full. Help the steam to escape by slight pressure on the bottle, then immediately screw in the top. Turn the bottle upside down to ensure there is no leakage. *The hot water bottle must be completely wrapped in a thick bag and the end securely fastened with ties.* There must always be a blanket between the child and the hot water bottle, even when it is covered by a bag.

Diet

The diet in sickness and in convalescence is a very important part of the treatment, and it must be considered in relation to the condition of the individual child. The digestive system is often rather disturbed, calling for great care if the patient is to get his maximum nutritional needs. It is often wiser to give small meals more frequently rather than maintain the three meals a day basis.

Before a meal is prepared, the content must be planned to meet the child's needs. When fat tolerance is difficult, the palatability of the food will be reduced unless great ingenuity is exercised to produce an appetising meal. The diet, even if ordered by the doctor when the child is ill, requires much skill if it is to be acceptable, for example, he may suggest giving a light diet of milk foods and white fish, but this must not be taken to mean only milk puddings and steamed fish. With imagination it is possible to present the same foods in a variety of ways and, by so doing, help to stimulate a poor appetite. Colour is a great attraction to a child, for example, if a fillet of steamed fish is served with potatoes it is uninteresting, but if some green vegetable or tomato purée is added the whole effect is changed. The same applies to milk puddings or stewed apple, a little colouring can make a tremendous difference. Food is frequently refused after one or two mouthfuls, because it has not been sufficiently seasoned to be palatable. Food should be tasted before serving it to a child, who may not be able to explain why he dislikes it so much.

Serving meals

Before serving food to a child in bed he should be made thoroughly comfortable. If he can sit up, he must be supported with pillows and a warm jacket put on over his pyjamas. In all degrees of illness the child at any age is likely to be difficult about feeding, simply because he has no appetite. Sometimes, with minor illnesses, parents are apt to spoil the child by fussing him too much. At the same time it is essential to realise that though there may be little desire for food, with careful handling and persuasion he will take some of his meal. Therefore it is important that small quantities of nourishing food should be attractively served on a little tray with pleasant china, serviette and perhaps a few tiny flowers. The fact of having a lovely tray like mummy's or daddy's is often a great thrill and a stimulant to the appetite (Fig. 71). *Thirst is common with children in bed* and must be catered for by giving frequent drinks, and the greater the variety the better.

When foods or drinks are served in the sick room, they should be either cold or warm and not tepid. Care must be taken to ensure that the flavour of the food or drink is palatable, and when possible the child should be allowed to choose what he would like.

FIG. 71. I am enjoying my meal in bed.

When the child has to be fed this must be done slowly, allowing time for mastication. A little gentle persuasion works wonders, but it requires discretion and patience.

If he shows a dislike of food which he has previously enjoyed it is really nothing to worry about. Attempting to force food when the child may feel sick will thoroughly upset him.

Spills and accidents are bound to happen with the younger child, and to avoid dirtying the sheet, it can be covered with an attractive plastic tablecloth, which prevents the adult being over anxious in case of accidents.

Occupation

This is just as necessary to the child in bed as it is to the one who is well. If he has something to do which is interesting, when he sits up, he is less likely to attempt or want to get out of bed or to be difficult, and if he stays in bed until he is really fit, complications are less likely to occur. Although the child is unwell, his mind may be very active, and he must be given scope to exercise his brain by the use of play material, which should be carefully chosen to meet the particular condition of the child, for example, if his eyes show any sign of inflammation he must not be given picture books, small puzzles or anything which may strain his eyes.

FIG. 72. A child in bed needs occupation.

Unless a child is very ill he will soon become bored without some form of occupation. He will tend to be irritable and tire easily and it will need real patience and ingenuity to keep him quietly occupied. During the period when he is lying in bed he can be given picture books which are light to hold to look at, or some small soft toys to play with, e.g. a favourite doll or animal which the child could pretend was ill in bed with him. For short periods he could listen to the radio programmes, e.g. Listen with Mother, or one or two of his favourite gramophone records could be played. The adult should arrange her routine so that she has time to sit down by the bedside and read or tell stories. When he is able to sit up a large tray can be used on which to keep his playthings. Now he will be able to play with Plasticine, crayons, drawing books, bricks, puzzles, have beads to thread, or blunt scissors so that he can cut out pictures from magazines and make up a scrap book. The tray can be lifted off the bed intact saving clearing up every time and disarranging what the child is doing. Although the older child should be encouraged to keep his playthings reasonably tidy, it is far more important at this stage to have a contented patient than a scrupulously tidy room.

In some cases it might be possible to have a bird table near the window so that the child can watch the birds or some fish in a tank where they can be seen. Flowers add an interest and pictures should be placed where they can be enjoyed. A sick child will not concentrate for as long as a healthy one.

The child under 2 years old is likely to throw his material on the floor if there is someone to pick it up for him; in fact he makes a lovely game for himself. Therefore it is wisest to give him things which can be tied to his cot and to give simple playthings for short periods if he is capable of using them, such as a string of large beads. He will spend a long time opening and closing lids, looking at coloured cards and so on. A large bag with all sorts of junk, or even an old handbag with contents like mummy's is just wonderful. The child who has already learnt to play contentedly on his own will probably be much less of a problem than one who has not.

Medicines

The administration of medicines or drugs of any kind must be strictly according to the doctor's instructions.

The following rules are important:
        Read the label on the bottle very carefully.
        Use a graduated medicine glass.

Measure accurately – holding glass at eye level.

Give the dose regularly.

Note any reaction to the medicine.

Keep medicine out of the child's reach.

When giving a dose of medicine, first read the label, shake the bottle before taking out the cork, and then measure, pouring out from the opposite side to that of the label. Replace the cork immediately, and wipe the neck of the bottle before putting it away.

Tonics are usually given after a meal, medicine to help digestion before meals, and aperients or sedatives at night or as prescribed.

The following abbreviations may be found on medicine bottles:

t.d.s. meaning three times a day.

b.d.s.   „   twice daily.

a.c.   „   before meals.

p.c.   „   after meals.

Sedatives or sleeping draughts must be administered only on a doctor's prescription, and after the child has been comfortably settled for the night, otherwise they are useless.

Capsules, if ordered by the doctor, must be emptied of their contents and given on a spoon with jam.

Tablets can be crushed in a spoon, and given with a little drink of fruit juice, water or milk. The older child will be able to swallow tablets quite easily.

It is a bad principle to try to cover the taste of medicine in a valuable food such as milk, as it may lead to a permanent dislike of that particular food. A small sweet or drink will help to take away the taste of the medicine.

Medicine cupboard

This must be kept locked and the key placed in a safe place. All bottles or containers of stock medicines such as aperients, tonics, cough mixtures or sedatives must be clearly labelled with dosage, to avoid accidents.

Any medicine prescribed for a child should have his name distinctly written on the label on the bottle.

As a safety measure it is important to keep any dangerous drugs locked in a separate cupboard. Poisons and lotions must be stored in dark green ribbed bottles as a safety measure and clearly labelled. Medicines specially prescribed for a particular child must be thrown away when they are no longer needed.

Treatments

Care of the eyes

Any *purulent discharge* must be immediately reported to a doctor who would prescribe and advise on treatment. If slight stickiness of an eye is present care must be taken to avoid spreading the infection to the other eye.

Method. First wash the hands thoroughly and boil any bowls or utensils required. Prepare a tray, with a jar of cotton wool swabs, a receiver for dirty swabs, and lotion. Use normal saline, temperature 100° F (37.8° C), and swab the eyelids from the nose side outwards using a clean swab for each stroke. When treating the right eye lay the child down and turn the head slightly over to the right. *To put drops into the eye* draw the lower lid slightly down and allow the drop to fall on the inside of the eyelid. *Never allow the dropper to touch the eye.* Burn all used swabs and wash the hands after giving treatment.

Antiphlogistine and kaolin

These preparations which are used as poultices are bought in tins and have the advantage of keeping hot for at least ten hours. Open the tin and place it in boiling water until it is hot. Then spread the paste, about $\frac{1}{4}$-inch thick, on a piece of clean cotton or linen sufficiently large to cover the affected area. Then cover the poultice with gauze and turn in the edges of the cotton. Test on the forearm and, if not too hot, apply to the part requiring treatment. Cover with wool, and bandage. On removing the application wash and powder the skin, then apply wool and a bandage for at least another twenty-four hours.

Starch poultice

This may be used to help to remove persistent scabs due to impetigo or eczema. Prepare a tray with the following articles:

Starch (powdered).
Piece of thin cotton large enough to cover the affected area.
Boiling water.
Mixing bowl and wooden spoon.

Method. Measure two tablespoonfuls of powdered starch into the mixing bowl, then add some boiling water, stirring well, until the mixture is of a thick, jelly-like consistency. Cool slightly and spread about $\frac{1}{4}$-inch thick on the piece of cotton, and apply the poultice to the crusts. This softens the scabs and eases their removal.

Cold compress

This is applied to relieve pain due to a sprain.

Use a piece of lint or cotton material large enough to be used double to cover the affected area. Dip in cold water and wring out, and place over the part. Cover with cotton wool and bandage if necessary. Change at least every 2 hours or oftener if required, the principle being to keep the application cold.

Saline compress

This is used sometimes to help to remove the crusts found in eczema. Use normal saline and prepare as described for a cold compress.

Evaporating lotion

Known as lead lotion, this is used for the same purpose as a cold compress. Dip a piece of lint in the lotion and apply to the painful area, leave it uncovered and re-apply frequently to keep the lint moist.

Inhalations

These are valuable in cases of respiratory disease, such as bronchitis or asthma.

Steam tent and steam kettle

An improvised tent can be made at home by placing two large clothes horses round the cot and arranging sheets on these and over the top of the cot.

The steam kettle has a long spout carrying the steam into the tent. It must be placed well out of the child's reach. Such kettles can be hired for private houses but it is much more usual for a child requiring this type of treatment to be admitted to hospital.

Maw's inhaler

This is an earthenware jug with a narrow type of spout. Pour one pint of boiling water into the inhaler and add one teaspoonful of Friar's Balsam or any other drug the doctor may advise. Wrap a large towel round the jug and encourage the child to inhale the vapour. *The adult must support the inhaler and never leave the child during the treatment in case of an accident.*

Care of equipment

Care of dressing bowls. These must be scrupulously clean, and should be scalded before use. After use they must be thoroughly washed with soap and water and scalded with boiling water; if there is any risk of infection, allow them to soak for one to two hours in lysol, one teaspoonful to one pint of water, or boil them for ten minutes.

Forceps and probes used for dressings must be boiled for ten minutes and removed by other forceps, which have previously been boiled and kept in a jar of lysol for this purpose. The sterile forceps should be placed in a boiled or scalded bowl, either dry or in boiled water, or in spirit.

Sterile is a term used to describe the condition of an article which by boiling or by other methods has been rendered entirely free from germs. Immediately any sterile article has been touched by hand or by something not sterile, then it cannot be classed as sterile. Dust or flies will easily undo all the good which has been done by boiling. Therefore it is important to cover any sterile article with a plate or bowl, which has also been boiled, to be kept clean and free from germs.

Care of an Infectious Child in the Home or in a Nursery

A child who is suffering from a mild form of infectious disease will be nursed at home, for example in the case of influenza, measles, German measles (rubella), mumps or chicken pox. Unless special precautions are taken, according to the particular type of illness, there will be a grave risk of spreading the disease throughout the family and possibly to outside people as well. Although good hygiene is essential in all nursing, there are additional measures which should be taken in all cases of infection.

Isolation in the residential home or in the nursery means that a child is nursed in a room by himself and only the person who is nursing him is allowed into the bedroom. Visitors, if permitted by the doctor, should take the same precautions as the person nursing the child. The room should, if possible, be sunny, and conveniently near a lavatory or bathroom. There should be some form of heating in the room, except in very hot weather. Furnishings such as curtains, cushions and rugs must be reduced to a minimum. There must be a nail brush, soap, towels and a hand basin for hand washing, and also a bowl of disinfectant for rinsing the hands after washing, for example, Dettol (2 teaspoonfuls to 1 pint).

All feeding utensils and crockery must be kept solely for the child's use and these should be washed up, dried on a special tea towel and kept in the room on a covered tray.

The child's towels and toilet utensils should be kept in the room, and all his play materials must remain in his bedroom for as long as he is isolated.

All equipment necessary for any treatment which has to be given must be kept in the isolation room, for example, the thermometer, the medicine glass, blankets, etc. There should be a bucket for soiled linen, and another receptacle for dirty dressings, which should be burnt.

A *gown* must be worn in the sick room to prevent the spread of infection. After attending to the child the nurse must thoroughly wash her hands. Then she should unfasten the gown, take the coat hanger in one hand, slip one arm out, place the hanger in position, remove the other arm and hang up the gown inside the room near the door. The hands should be washed again before leaving the room. When using the gown next time, the nurse should lift the coat hanger off the peg, insert one arm into the sleeve, remove the hanger and finish putting on the gown, touching the outside as little as possible. By this method, only the clean side (inside) of the gown contacts the nurse's dress, and therefore she does not carry germs on her clothing when she goes out of the sick room.

Mask. This should be worn by the nurse if she has a cold and is attending to the child. When leaving the room the mask must be placed in disinfectant to soak and should be washed later.

Sunlight is a most valuable agent in killing germs, therefore it is important to admit the sun's rays, preferably through the open window. Fresh air and good ventilation are essential.

Antiseptics prevent the growth of germs and these can be used for dressings as they are not harmful to the skin but prevent the growth of germs (see Chapter 21).

Disinfectants are often necessary, but the use of a nail brush with soap and water must never be neglected when cleansing any article. It is important to appreciate that disinfectants require time in which to act, if they are to fulfil their purpose to kill germs. Carelessly used, they can do more harm than good by giving a false sense of security. The weaker the solution used, the more time it will take to act. Therefore it is most important to know exactly what strength is necessary and how long the infected article must be soaked.

The strength of a disinfectant is described, e.g. as 1 in 20, and this means that one part is disinfectant and nineteen parts are water, therefore to make up one pint of the solution, use one ounce of disinfectant and nineteen ounces of water.

In a private home such precautions are rarely necessary, and it is often more convenient for all the children in the family to contract the disease at roughly the same time, so that it is over and done with. But it is important not to have visitors unless they have already had the disease, and not to allow the affected child or children out and about until the doctor has said they are no longer infectious.

Disinfection of equipment

This can be done by *boiling* (heat) or by *using chemicals*. The latter method may be used when boiling would harm the article in question.

The following methods may be used:

Glass or china	Boil for 10 minutes *or* soak in Milton 1 in 80 for $1\frac{1}{2}$ hours.
Plastics	Soak in Milton 1 in 80 for $1\frac{1}{2}$ hours.
Metal spoons	Boil for 10 minutes.
Metal cutlery	Boil for 10 minutes.
Thermometer	Soak in Dettol 1 in 40 for $\frac{1}{2}$ an hour *or* Milton 1 in 80 for $1\frac{1}{2}$ hours.
Infected linen and napkins	Soak in Izal 1 in 20 for 2 hours, or in Napisan.
Soft toys	Wash and soak in Dettol 1 in 40 for 1 hour. Dry in open air.
Wooden toys	Wash and soak in Dettol 1 in 40 for 1 hour. Dry in open air *or* send to cleansing station (see Chapter 31).
Books	Send to cleansing station (see Chapter 31).
Mattress	Send to cleansing station (see Chapter 31).

CHAPTER 24

Convalescence

Convalescence, a time that is often almost ignored, is a period, especially with children, which requires very careful management.

When the child reaches the convalescent stage he is on his way to health, but he is not yet back to normal, nor should he be regarded as a completely healthy child. Every illness is a strain on a growing child and the longer the illness the greater the strain, and the longer the time which must be allowed for recuperation. It is necessary for the adult to ensure that the child maintains his progress until recovery is complete and he is able to take his place once more in the normal home or nursery life. During this period of convalescence the child needs to 'go slow', having extra rest during the day and getting up later and going to bed earlier.

The child must never be allowed to get up until the doctor says he may do so, and then if he has been seriously ill he should be allowed to sit up for a short time only at first, getting up for longer periods each day. He must not be allowed to overtax his strength during this time, and all manner of ingenuity will probably be needed to prevent him from doing too much. The child is more restless when he is getting better and will need a great variety of things to keep him occupied. He will tire quickly and possibly be fretful and badly behaved when he finds he cannot do all that he wants to do.

Suitable activities during convalescence

In bed:
    Reading and looking at books.
    Imaginative games with soft toys, e.g. hospitals or schools.
    Drawing and colouring with crayons.
    Making up stories and poems.

Cutting up paper.
Knitting or French knitting, or sewing.
Toy cars.
Threading beads.
Jigsaw puzzles.
Watching television.

When allowed up:

Painting.
Modelling with Plasticine or clay.
Making models out of cardboard boxes, the inside of toilet rolls and other household things.
Playing with almost any toys, providing they do not cause too much excitement, or need much exertion.

When he is able to get up he will have much more scope for his play and when he is allowed to go out of doors he will be able to play for short periods in the garden or go for short walks. The latter must not be overdone, because if he has been in bed for any length of time his muscles will have become weak and lost some of their tone, and this is very noticeable in the child's feet. Simple exercises in the form of a game can help when the child begins to sit up in a chair. For example, picking up a pencil with the toes, resting the foot on the heel and then on the toes, or placing the foot flat on the floor and then trying to lift up the arch of the foot. If a child does too much walking before his muscles are properly toned up it may predispose him to flat feet, which could later be a serious handicap. Growth of the feet continues during an illness and after a few weeks in bed the feet are sometimes considerably longer, a fact which has to be considered in relation to footwear. It is false economy to use shoes which hinder the normal development of the foot.

Interesting, quite occupations requiring little energy, must take a prominent place in the day's routine, especially in the early days of convalescence. However, during this time the child requires as much fresh air and sunshine as possible with good nourishing food and as much individual care and affection as possible. The adult, through her own experience, must try to appreciate just how the child feels, his desire to be active beyond his present strength and his great disappointment in his lack of ability. The child's mental development may not have reached the stage of understanding why he cannot do what he wants, and all types of difficulties may arise if his management is at fault. The burden of a long illness falls heavily on the mind as on the body and he may fall back into habits long outgrown, e.g. bed-wetting and thumbsucking. In cases of long or serious illness the child may even forget how to talk or walk and learning to acquire these skills may take many weeks, so that the child can be set back quite considerably in his development. The child may suffer from being allowed to take part in the activities of his companions before he is really fit to do so, and he will need that little extra care which will enable him to catch up with the others, both mentally and physically, without undue strain.

Companionship is necessary, otherwise the child may become reluctant and afraid to mix with others. Visitors must be carefully chosen to avoid too much excitement and boisterousness.

The diet

This is a very important part of the treatment, and must be considered in relation to the individual child. The digestive system is often disturbed, calling for great care if the patient is to get his maximum nutritional needs. The diet must be nourishing, interesting, easily digested and attractively served. Appetites are fickle and small helpings are essential, but with patience this becomes better as the health improves.

The approach to the child is important. It should never be hurried or impatient, but the adult needs to show an interest in the food the child is going to have and should never compel the child to eat more than he feels able to.

The diet during convalescence should be light and as varied as possible. It can include jellies, plain or milk, milk puddings, egg custard, or eggs poached, coddled or boiled. Steamed fish, white meats, fruit purées, fingers of bread and butter and sponge cake. Then as progress continues the child is gradually returned to all the foods suitable and necessary for his growth and development.

The stage of building up health again can be very irksome and disappointing to the child, but it can be made far less trying by a cheerful and imaginative adult.

Complications may set in quite a time after the acute illness, and this fact must never be forgotten. In illness the child's resistance is lowered and because of this, during convalescence, he should if possible be kept away from contact with any infectious disease. He is also more susceptible to respiratory conditions, especially colds.

A secondary infection could prove serious and greatly retard his progress to complete recovery.

When practical, a change of air may prove a great tonic and restorative. A child who attends a nursery or a nursery school is often sent back long before he is really well. Care must be taken that such a child has individual care, with extra rest and sleep, otherwise the strain of coping with normal healthy children may make him ill again.

Exactly the same principles apply to the convalescence of adolescents and adults. They, unlike the young child, can understand why they are not fit to do a normal day's work, but even so they are very apt to be extremely depressed and emotional. Good food, the maximum amount of fresh air, sunshine, rest and sleep, with some hobby or occupation to claim their interests are just as important as they are for children.

CHAPTER 25

Remediable Physical Defects

Advice should be obtained at the local child welfare centre, or from the family doctor if there is any sign of abnormality in a child's development. The following are some of the more common abnormalities which may be present at birth.

Adenoids

These are growths of lymphoid tissue on the soft palate at the back of the throat, near the entry of the nasal passages into the throat. They may become infected and enlarged and partially block the nasal and ear passages. When this happens the child becomes a mouth breather, giving him rather a vacant expression, he suffers from frequent colds, has a poor appetite and is generally pale and listless. Such a child is prone to infectious diseases. If it is necessary the adenoids can be removed by an operation, which is usually very successful, though the child may require encouragement in learning to breathe through his nostrils.

Birth marks

These are caused by some abnormal development of the tissues. Disfiguring marks can be treated and it is better to have advice about these when the child is still young. Many of these can be reduced if not completely cured. 'Old wives' tales' about the cause of birth marks are quite unfounded and should never be repeated.

Bowed legs or knock knees

These often show themselves when the child starts walking. Careful note should be made of how the child wears his shoes, as knock knees cause extra wear on the inner side of the sole and heel and bowing of the legs affects the outer edge of the shoe. Regular medical examination at the child welfare centre will enable these early symptoms to be treated as soon as they appear, and usually to be corrected. It is a fallacy to say that these defects are inherited, the only relation being that possibly both the parent and the child have been malnourished and have not been treated by a specialist, who can correct or at least reduce the condition.

Malnutrition, rickets, and bad hygiene, often due to ignorance, all predispose to such physical defects.

Flat feet

This is a condition caused by poor development of the arches of the feet, which in turn is due to poor muscular tone. The condition does not show until the child starts walking and running at about two to three years when the foot has become longer and more shapely. The same procedure should be followed as already described for bowed legs.

Hare lips

This is caused by a cleft or split in the upper jaw, which involves the soft tissues of the upper lip and sometimes also the nostril. It is a congenital deformity. The child is unable to suck properly and spoon or pipette feeding is necessary. An operation is required to repair the split. This is usually done if the child is healthy at about eight weeks, with little or no disfigurement resulting. In some instances speech therapy may be necessary to encourage good speech.

Cleft palate

A congenital deformity which may occur alone or with a hare lip. It is a fissure in the roof of the mouth, which varies in size and gives rise to great difficulty in sucking. In some instances a dental plate has been used to enable the baby to suck. The opening in the palate is closed by operation at about fifteen months, and speech training is essential in the aftercare of such conditions.

Hernia or rupture

In the abdominal region this is a protrusion of part of the abdominal contents (usually the small intestine) through a gap in the muscle fibres. This appears as a swelling and varies in size according to the severity. Always consult a doctor. A protrusion at the umbilicus is fairly common in infants, and usually can be reduced and cured if early treatment is applied.

Squint

A squint may appear in a baby who has not yet learned to use his eyes together. If anything is held near to his eyes he is likely to squint. After a few months the baby learns to control the muscles of the eyes and he learns to use them together. Failure to control these movements which may be for a variety of reasons will cause a permanent squint if left untreated, meaning that one of the eyes is not functioning properly and this will cause poor vision or loss of sight in that eye. As soon as the defect is noticed, a doctor should be consulted. It is now possible to correct a squint by exercises, or by covering the good eye continuously for at least three months; or by an operation.

Tight foreskin

If the foreskin appears tight and the baby cries on passing urine it is necessary to consult the doctor. Stretching may be possible, which may right the condition, otherwise an operation (*circumcision*) will be necessary. There must be no delay in getting advice if in any doubt about the condition.

Tongue tie

This is caused by a tightness of the membrane stretching from under the tip of the tongue to the floor of the mouth. This is a rare condition and it is seldom that it interferes with sucking. The membrane usually stretches with use.

Torticollis

Wry neck, as this condition is called, may be present at birth (congenital) or it may develop after birth (acquired). The child holds the head on one side and this becomes more noticeable as the neck grows. In some instances, the physiotherapist will try to develop the short muscle in the neck, by giving stretching exercises and will teach the mother how to continue these at home. Severe conditions may require surgical treatment to rectify them.

Dislocated hip

This condition may be present at birth and is due to the head of the femur not fitting correctly into the socket in the pelvis. Examination of the baby will enable early diagnosis to be made, the chief signs being *shortening of the leg* with *limited movement*, and *the leg out of*

L

alignment. Much can be done at the present time to rectify this condition, and thus prevent a permanent disability.

The adult responsible for the care of the child must realise the importance of any deviation from normal physical development being recognised as early as possible and should seek expert advice if she is at all worried. Much can be done to prevent or lessen physical disabilities if the defect is recognised at an early stage.

CHAPTER 26

Deficiency Diseases

Diet deficiency may exist in varying degrees, giving rise to subnormal health in the individual, although no acute symptoms may be present. Lack of sufficient complete protein, vitamins or mineral salts will retard the normal growth of the child and affect his general health. Lowered resistance to infection may indicate some deficiency, whilst poor appetite, indigestion, constipation, skin irritations, tiredness or general debility are a few conditions which may be due to an inadequate diet. Such symptoms are often rather taken for granted and the cause is not investigated. Metabolism, the way in which the body digests and uses the food must be considered. Any defect in the functioning of the digestive organs may affect the well-being of the child. Therefore any lack of response to a good, well-balanced diet should be carefully investigated.

Night blindness

A deficiency of vitamin A causes this condition and the individual cannot adapt his vision from a bright light to a dim one. *Vitamin A, moreover, is also responsible for maintaining healthy mucous membranes* and any deficiency may give rise to *conjunctivitis, respiratory tract or digestive tract infections.*

Treatment. This must include adequate amounts of vitamin A, e.g. by giving cod liver oil and a balanced diet. Medical advice is necessary to ensure that the right care is given.

Beri-beri

This is caused by a deficiency of vitamin B_1, but is seldom seen in Britain. This condition produces general debility and in *severe infections leads to deterioration of nerves and muscles, causing paralysis. Mental conditions* may also occur in some cases.

Treatment. This is by means of providing a well planned and adequate diet.

Pellagra

A deficiency of the B_2 group of vitamins causes this. Dermatitis or nervous conditions will develop which are capable of being influenced by other deficiencies in the diet. Medical advice is essential.

Scurvy

This is a rare disease, except amongst immigrants, and is caused by deficiency of vitamin C in the diet and if allowed to develop can be extremely serious. Anaemia and local haemorrhages in the muscles give rise to great tenderness, appearance of bruising and pain. The gums become spongy and the bleeding from capillaries under the skin discolours the gums. The baby is pale, under weight and fretful. Fortunately, this is now a rare condition because it has become routine treatment to give orange juice to all babies. Slight reactions may be present if vitamin C is not administered regularly, for example, the growth will be slow and the appetite poor.

Treatment consists of ensuring that the child under 2 years has a full dose of vitamin C daily, and a good diet. For the older age groups, a good diet should supply all the necessary vitamin C.

Rickets

This is a deficiency disease caused by the lack of vitamin D and calcium and stimulated by lack of fresh air and sunlight. This condition affects:

1. The bone structure, preventing the normal growth of strong healthy bones and teeth.
2. The mucous membranes, predisposing to catarrh and respiratory infections.
3. The nervous system, predisposing to convulsions.

The first signs may appear as early as four months, or not until two or three years of age. An excess of starch or sugar will hinder the process of absorption of vitamins and minerals, thus making the right quantity of these protective agents in the food inadequate. Digestive upsets, anaemia and respiratory infections all predispose to rickets, and are all liable to occur in the child who has rickets.

Signs and Symptoms. Irritability, restlessness at night with head sweats, paleness and poor muscular tone causing late development. Tendency to digestive upsets and diarrhoea, bronchitis and catarrh.

Dentition is slow and the condition known as dental caries (decaying teeth) is very common.

The growth of the bones is seriously affected and a thickening occurs at the ends of the long bones, noticeably in the wrist of the child, and on the ends of the ribs. The bones are soft, and bow legs or knock knees are common deformities. The true formation of the chest is impaired, producing the typical 'pigeon chest'. The pelvis is often flattened – a serious complication in a girl as this will affect her in childbirth. In marked rickets the child first walks with a characteristic gait, and has a very large abdomen and a marked inward curve in the back. The head assumes a square appearance, there is late closing of the anterior fontanelle and growth is stunted.

At the slightest sign of any of these symptoms, expert advice must be taken. Early treatment will do much to prevent permanent deformities and to build up health.

Rickets can be prevented by giving a well-balanced diet, rich in vitamin D, with a liberal allowance of calcium and phosphorus, combined with fresh air, exercise, rest and sleep. All children should regularly have cod liver oil or its equivalent. The expectant mother must have the necessary diet, with sunlight and fresh air, if the baby is to be given a good start in life. Good general care, and helping to build up the child's resistance to disease will help a great deal.

Medical advice is essential, either from the family doctor or from the child welfare centre.

It is essential to give only the prescribed dose of vitamin D. The Ministry of Health as it was then known, issued a direction that the vitamin D content of cod liver oil was to be reduced in order to provide only the required amount. Hypercalcaemia, a medical condition recognised a few years ago, was thought to be associated with too much vitamin D in the diet. This condition disturbed the normal process of ossification and, in some instances, affected the kidneys. This disease is still being investigated.

Anaemia

This is caused by the lack of iron in the red cells of the blood if the diet is deficient in iron, when it is considered as a nutritional disorder and a deficient disease. When such a condition exists growth cannot be normal and the health is affected.

Signs of anaemia. Paleness of the mucous membrane lining the mouth and the eyelids, general pallor of the skin, tiredness with loss of appetite, irritability, frequent colds, respiratory disorders and fainting.

312

MEDICAL CONDITIONS

Causes of anaemia in the baby. (1) If the diet of the expectant mother is deficient in iron. (2) Haemorrhage from the umbilicus (very unusual).

Causes found in children over four months:
1. Diet deficient in iron-containing foods.
2. Poor living conditions, especially in towns.
3. Accidents with loss of blood.
4. Illness and lowered vitality.
5. Diseases of the spleen and liver.

It is important to concentrate on the prevention of anaemia rather than the cure.

Prevention of nutritional anaemia:
1. Balanced diet with adequate iron for expectant mothers.
2. Early mixed feeding (including foods rich in iron), e.g. liver, egg yolk, greens and medicinal iron if prescribed by the doctor.
3. Balanced meals for the older child.
4. Fresh air and sunlight, adequate ventilation, rest, sleep and exercise.
5. Regular medical examination which should prevent this deficiency disease developing.

Babies of four to nine months often show slight signs of anaemia, as this period includes a change over to solid foods, started in small quantities, which may prove inadequate in their iron content. Children from three months should be given additional iron in a medicinal form, under medical instructions, whether they are breast fed or artificially fed, to tide them over the period when the diet is most likely to be deficient in iron.

Iodine deficiency

This influences the functioning of the *thyroid gland.* Under-secretion in babies causes the condition called *cretinism,* and, if not diagnosed in time, produces *mental deficiency* and *dwarfism.* The face is broad with wide nostrils, the mouth is large and the tongue appears to be large and often protrudes. The appearance of the patient can easily be confused with that of a *mongol,* a mentally defective child. The cretin child *must be treated with regular doses of thyroid extract,* a treatment that must be started as early as possible in order to ensure good mental and physical development. He will require this treatment throughout his life. Iodine deficiency in the adult causes goitre, which is seen as a marked swelling in the front of the neck. This condition was common in some districts where iodine was lacking in the soil. The risk of deficiency has been reduced by using iodised salt.

Kwashiorkor

This is caused by *lack of protein*. The growth of the child is seriously retarded and death may occur. This disease is not found in Britain, but it is very common in the under-developed countries and it has been given much publicity in recent years.

CHAPTER 27

Diseases Caused by Defective Metabolism

In recent years much research has been done on infants who have not responded to normal diets, and this has enabled some defects to be diagnosed in the first few weeks of life. Early treatment is necessary in order to prevent serious complications from developing, for these may prove fatal. It is possible that some of these conditions may be inherited.

Phenylketonuria

Phenylalanine is an important amino-acid which is found in relatively large amounts in an average diet; it is essential for good growth. This amino-acid must be changed into *tyrosine* by the action of an enzyme, and this enables it to complete all its functions within the body. Deficiency or complete lack of this enzyme will result in the accumulation of phenylalanine in the body and this will lead to serious damage to the tissues. The condition is confirmed by means of a simple urine test. Early diagnosis is essential.

Signs. These consist of poor growth rate, skin conditions, irritability and poor mental and physical development.

Treatment. Diet is all-important and must be very specialised. The foods will be prescribed by the doctor or a trained dietitian and will consist largely of vegetables, fruit and special bread. Protein is reduced to a minimum. Special foods for infants are now on the market, but individual tests have to be made on each baby in order to ensure that he has the correct diet to meet his nutritional needs.

Galactosaemia

Galactosaemia is a serious condition caused by the lack of an enzyme in the liver which converts galactose into glucose for use in the body. Because of this defect galactose accumulates in the body and is finally excreted in the urine. Early recognition of this condition is essential if serious damage is to be prevented. It is nowadays a routine practice to test the urine of all babies within the first month of life. This is commonly known as the *napkin test*.

Symptoms. These occur if treatment is delayed. Growth is poor, and vomiting, jaundice and enlargement of the liver are seen, together with mental retardation in severe cases. The condition may prove fatal.

Treatment. Since milk contains *lactose*, this must be eliminated from the diet. Milk substitutes are now available for infant feeding and are produced by several dried milk firms. Naturally the doctor or trained dietitian will prescribe the food and the amount to be given. Careful supervision must continue when mixed feeding is introduced. Milk in any form and all foods containing milk, for example cakes, puddings and chocolate, must be avoided in order to ensure that the child's normal development is maintained. The content of any addition to the diet must be scrutinised by the doctor before it is given to the child.

Coeliac disease

Coeliac disease is caused by the child's extreme sensitivity to *gluten*, a protein found in wheat, which begins to show when flour or bread is introduced into the diet.

Signs. Growth is retarded. The stools are pale, offensive and large, giving rise to diarrhoea. This causes poor absorption of food in the small intestine (see p. 145). Because of this there are marked deficiencies of fat, carbohydrates, mineral salts and vitamins.

Treatment. This consists of giving a gluten-free diet, which will be prescribed by the doctor. Gluten-free flour and bread are now available. The condition usually improves and very gradually a normal diet may be tolerated as the child grows older.

As medical research advances, it is possible that more causes of illness in young children may be traced to defective metabolism.

PART SEVEN
Infection

CHAPTER 28

The Cause of Infection and its Prevention

Bacteria and other microorganisms were discovered in the seventeenth century by a Dutchman named Leeuwenhoek. These living organisms are invisible to the naked eye and have to be magnified hundreds of times before they can be recognised. They multiply by dividing and sub-dividing and thousands can be reproduced in a few hours. The bacteriologists in the laboratory, by supplying these germs with favourable conditions for growth, which are warmth, food and moisture, can cultivate them and, in this way gain much information about them, for example, their shape, size, habits and characteristics. This knowledge gives valuable help in the prevention, diagnosis and cure of infectious diseases. Local authorities make this laboratory service available to doctors, to enable specimens of any suspected infected material such as faeces, sputum, or discharges to be examined and the cause of illness to be confirmed or diagnosed.

In considering these minute forces of life it must be appreciated that a large proportion of them are not harmful to human beings, and fulfil essential purposes. For example some aid in the decomposition of dead organic matter, and in fertilisation of the soil. Others live naturally in the body, inhabiting the bowel, and are harmless so long as they remain there.

Many of the classes of bacteria are named after the bacteriologists who discovered them.

Bacteria are minute and can be seen only with the aid of a microscope. One measuring only one eight-thousandth of a millimetre may be termed a large one. They vary very much in shape, some round, others rod-like, long and thin and some short and thick. Bacteria can be divided into two main classes, namely the cocci and the bacilli.

Cocci, round in shape, appear in clusters, in pairs or in a chain-like formation. Varieties are the streptococci, the staphylococci and the diplococci. They are commonly associated with the formation of pus, as in an abscess, boil, or stye.

Bacilli are rod-shaped, and some have spores which make them more resistant to ordinary methods of sterilisation. Examples of diseases caused by this type of bacteria are diphtheria, tuberculosis and tetanus.

Viruses form another group of microorganism and are so small that they cannot be seen through an ordinary microscope. They can pass through the finest filter. Measles, rubella, chickenpox, smallpox, influenza and poliomyelitis are caused by viruses.

Protozoa and *fungi* are two more groups of microorganism, their structure being much more complicated than the cocci and bacilli types. Protozoa cause malaria, and examples of diseases caused by fungi are thrush and ringworm.

Pathogenic is a term used to denote a harmful germ which causes disease. *Pyogenic* germs cause sepsis.

Bacteria may enter the body:

1. Through the *respiratory tract* (by inhaling).
2. Through the *mouth* (by sucking).
3. Through the *skin*, if damaged by a pin prick, cut or scratch.

How Infection is Spread

An infectious person may give off germs in several ways depending on the type of disease.

Germs may be expelled in droplets by coughing, sneezing or talking. These may be inhaled by someone near at hand or they may drop on anything in the surrounding area, such as furniture, toys or floor and may remain alive for many days or even weeks, as for example the tuberculosis bacillus.

Germs may also be excreted in the stools or in any abnormal discharges, for example from the ear, nose or eyes; they may be transmitted to the mouth by hands.

Direct infection is conveyed by contact with an infected person, for example by kissing. When in close proximity to someone who has pathogenic bacteria lurking in their air passages it is quite possible for another to become infected by inhaling the germs as they are breathed out. Babies can get colds from adults in this way and by being kissed. Mouth breathers are very liable to respiratory infections.

Indirect infection means that germs are conveyed from the seat of infection through infected articles, clothing, towels, bedding, crockery, cutlery, toys or dressings. Other sources of infection may be contaminated food, milk or water, excreta (stools), dust, flies and other insects. Bad hygiene is responsible for spreading infection, for example *failure to wash hands after using the toilet or before meals.*

A carrier is a person capable of carrying pathogenic bacteria in his body, but who shows no sign of the disease, appears to be in normal good health and is often quite unaware of the germs he gives off. The way in which these are excreted will depend on the particular infection, for example the germs of Sonne dysentery will be in the faeces, therefore bad hygiene can easily cause the spread of this infection.

The result of bacteria entering the body will vary very much, depending on the number of germs, whether only a few or a large number, on the virulence of the germ, and on the resistance of the individual who is attacked. A person in good health is more likely to resist infection than someone in poor health. Children, and particularly babies under one year, are usually very susceptible to germs because of their lack of resistance.

How Bacteria Act in the Body

Germs which have found their way into the body rapidly increase in numbers and produce toxins (or poisons) which are liberated into the body through the blood stream; the bacteria may actually circulate in the same way, and then invade a particular part of the body.

Germs may enter the body in small numbers, giving little evidence of their presence but large numbers may cause severe illness and the result will depend on the ability of the body's mechanism to overcome the bacteria. The same type of germ may vary very much in its virulence which is why an infectious disease may take a more severe form in one epidemic than in a previous one. The term communicable disease means any disease or condition which can be communicated from one person to another. But speaking generally the term infectious disease is reserved for the description of those diseases which are notifiable diseases, and if allowed to spread may give rise to epidemics and seriously affect the health of the community.

The body's defence mechanism

The entrance of bacteria into the body will have the effect of stimulating the production of suitable antibodies to attack the invading germs. This is mainly achieved by antitoxins being created to neutralise the toxins and by the leucocytes or white blood corpuscles being rapidly increased to attack and devour the germs. The defeat of the bacteria will be dependent on the body's ability to overpower them. Once these antibodies are produced they can have a lasting effect in giving resistance and thus preventing another attack of the same disease.

Immunity

Immunity is a term used to express the individual's resistance to infection.

Natural immunity

This is an inherited immunity. Some races have a degree of immunity to certain diseases and there are some people who seem to resist infection much better than others, which may be largely due to very good functioning of their defence mechanisms and also to good health. The infant may be born with an antitoxin in his blood, which he has inherited from his mother, giving him resistance but as he grows this will gradually be reduced and his resistance lowered.

Acquired immunity

This may be active or passive.

Active immunity can be developed by having a disease so that antibodies are formed giving adequate protection against any further attack. This procedure takes place with most of the common infectious diseases. Active immunity can also be developed as a result of small doses of bacteria entering the body at different times, never enough to cause illness, but sufficient to stimulate the body to produce resistance.

Artificially acquired active immunity. This is achieved by the introduction of modified or inactivated organisms through injection, or orally which stimulate the body to produce antibodies thus giving similar protection to that obtained by having the disease. Artificial immunisation takes some weeks to establish resistance. In England, Wales and Northern Ireland *The Department of Health and Social Security* issue directions to local health authorities on immunisation and vaccination. *The Scottish Home and Health Department* also advise in similar ways. These directives from the Ministries suggest a scheme of how all the vaccinations and immunisations can be fitted into the first five years and continue through school life. To put this treatment off because the parents think the child is not likely to meet such infections or because they do not wish to cause him any discomfort is simply courting disaster.

Passive immunity is used as an emergency measure and is obtained by the injection of serum containing suitable antitoxin, which takes effect immediately. This lessens the severity of an infectious disease, for example in whooping cough, diphtheria, or tetanus (from an infected wound). Passive immunity can be given to a delicate child who has been in contact with measles, to give immediate protection: this type of immunity lasts from two to four weeks, and active immunity cannot be given until after this four weeks' period.

Prevention of Infectious Diseases by Active Immunity

Vaccination

At the beginning of the nineteenth century, when smallpox was rife in this country, it was noted that milkers who developed sores on their hands from coming in contact with a cow suffering from ulcers on the udders or teats, a condition known as cowpox, never developed smallpox. It was then realised that an acquired immunity to cowpox gave resistance to smallpox. This brought vaccination into being for the prevention of smallpox. The early methods of vaccination left much to be desired and produced a good deal of criticism. Now the lymph used in this country is pure and is not likely to cause any harmful results. Vaccination is the only way of preventing smallpox and thus reducing the recurrence of the disease. It is advisable to have *healthy* children vaccinated against smallpox, preferably during their second year, and further vaccination at school, but the doctor in the child welfare centre or the general practitioner will give advice about when this should be done. Protection lasts for eight to ten years and after this period the child should be revaccinated. If the vaccination does not take, the doctor will advise about further treatments. It is dangerous to conclude that a child is immune because there is no obvious reaction. Reports are forwarded to the school health authority and the child will be revaccinated in his school years. Vaccination is not compulsory, but can be done by the private doctor or by the health authority. Vaccination should be postponed if the child is not in good health.

Method of vaccination. The area chosen, especially in girls, is usually the thigh or leg, and the procedure is very simple. The skin in the area to be used is cleaned with spirit. The Department of Health and Social Security now recommend vaccination by a series of multiple punctures of the skin. In about four days a small red papule or pimple appears, and about the eighth day a pustule is formed with some inflammation round the area. Gradually a crust forms and this should be kept dry, using clean dressings until it dries up and drops off at the end of fourteen days. The child may be a little restless because of the possible irritation, but no further complications should occur. Any unusual symptoms must be immediately reported to the doctor.

Adults vaccinated for the first time or even revaccinated sometimes show a very marked reaction with general symptoms of fever as well as local reaction in the area of vaccination. This is seldom serious but it is advisable to consult the doctor.

Diphtheria immunisation

Diphtheria is a very serious infectious disease, which is preventable, and if all children in this country were immunised the condition would become very rare. In Canada and America where immunisation has been used extensively the number of cases is extremely low, as also in this country, where the number of cases has decreased dramatically. The first few hours of the illness are vital and neglect through ignorance at this time may result in loss of life. Even if the child recovers there are great risks of grave complications.

The *Schick test* is a simple skin test which gives a red reaction in three to four days if the child is susceptible to diphtheria. Children may be born with an immunity from the mother, but this passes off, and the child may be affected if he is unfortunate enough to contact this particular bacteria. Therefore the only way to guard the child against this danger is to have him immunised at a child welfare centre, or by the family doctor.

Immunisation is almost painless, consisting usually of two or three injections of detoxinated toxin or toxoid, in the upper arm, at specified intervals (this is a toxin rendered non-poisonous). There is no feeling of general illness and rarely any reaction at the seat of the injection. Immunity is established about six to ten weeks after the treatment. Records of this treatment are kept on each child and these are passed on to the School Health Department who give further immunisation during school years.

Whooping cough immunisation

As whooping cough is extremely dangerous under one year it is wise to take advantage of the precautionary measures when the child is about six months old. Although the result of this vaccine is not a sure prevention of whooping cough it has reduced the incidence of the disease and the severity of the attack, which is of great value in the early months. 'Combined immunisation' when a triple antigen is used is explained below.

Typhoid immunisation

This gives an immunity against a group of closely allied diseases, often termed *enteric fevers* and known as typhoid, paratyphoid A and paratyphoid B. Protection against these infections is obtained by the administering of a mixed vaccine containing all these types of bacteria. This treatment consists of injecting two doses of this mixed vaccine into the muscle of the upper arm with an interval of seven to ten days between each injection. Very often after the inoculation there may be a slight rise of temperature with a feeling of tiredness and a local reaction at the site of the injection, of redness, swelling and stiffness. The immunity resulting from the inoculations usually becomes effective soon after the last injection, and lasts for two years. A single dose annually thereafter will ensure a high level of protection. This is a wise precaution for children who are going to countries where such diseases are prevalent.

Tetanus is a serious and sometimes fatal disease affecting the nervous system, which is caused by infected cuts and bites. It can be prevented by immunisation.

Triple vaccine

Diphtheria, whooping cough (pertussis) and tetanus can all be guarded against by triple vaccine. This is normally given in three doses at monthly intervals beginning at approximately six months and a fourth booster dose is given when the child starts school.

Poliomyelitis This vaccine is normally given in an oral form when the child is about six months old. This is followed by a booster dose six months later, and another when the child starts school.

Measles immunisation

This is of comparatively recent origin and is normally performed when the child is about fifteen months of age.

Tuberculosis immunisation

Babies born to tuberculous mothers and young children in contact with tuberculosis in the home should be protected as soon as possible. Before immunisation the child must be tested for negative or positive reaction. Immunity is given to all who are negative by injecting BCG vaccine, which is a vaccine of attenuated live tubercle bacilli. The bacteria being thus weakened are not virulent but are capable of stimulating a resistance to tuberculosis. Tuberculin testing of children entering school is proving to be very valuable. Adolescents are tested and immunised if necessary, and also people who are likely to be in contact with tuberculosis.

The effects of vaccination and immunisation have been carefully studied and the results have shown a remarkable reduction in the incidence of these infectious diseases, combined with a very marked reduction in the death rate. Because the effects of vaccination and immunisation have been so effective, the diseases they prevent have become very rare, and the danger that people will become lax about their administration must be guarded against. There are many parts of the world where these conditions are still endemic and any relaxation of protective measures could be disastrous.

TABLE X

Suggested timetable for immunisation and vaccination

Age	Vaccine	
New born baby	Tuberculosis	
6 months	Diphtheria, pertussis and tetanus	Oral poliomyelitis
8 months	,, ,, ,,	,, ,,
14 months	Diphtheria and tetanus	,, ,,
15 months	Measles	
1–2 years	Smallpox	
4–5 years	Booster dose against diphtheria and tetanus	Booster against poliomyelitis
Over 12 years	Tuberculosis	

Terms used:

Epidemic – when an outbreak of infection involves a number of people.

Sporadic – when individual cases occur in many areas.

Endemic – when a disease is found constantly in one place.

Pandemic – when an outbreak occurs throughout many countries.

Incubation and Quarantine

Incubation period

This is the time between the entry of the bacteria into the body, and the appearance of the first symptoms of the disease. Germs vary very considerably in the time they require to develop and each infectious disease has its own incubation period. It is most helpful, particularly in nursery work, to have some idea of these, and they can be classed into three groups namely:

Short – an incubation period under one week.

Medium – an incubation period from one to two weeks.

Long – an incubation period over two weeks. Some diseases take as long as four weeks and poliomyelitis possibly five weeks (see Table XI).

TABLE XI

Incubation periods

Short	*Medium*	*Long*
Influenza	Measles	Whooping Cough or Pertussis
Diphtheria	Smallpox	Chickenpox
Diarrhoea		German Measles or Rubella
Gastro-enteritis		Catarrhal Jaundice
Scarlet Fever		Enteric Fevers or Typhoid
Tonsillitis		Infantile Paralysis or Poliomyelitis
Dysentery		Mumps

The actual incubation period is very difficult to assess, but each disease is usually fairly consistent; when in doubt consult the doctor or the local Medical Officer of Health.

The patient is infectious during the incubation period.

Isolation

This means that the infectious person must be kept apart, in a separate room, until he is no longer a source of infection to others. It is the doctor's responsibility to say when isolation can be discontinued.

Quarantine

This is the term used to describe the period of time, when a person who has been in contact with an infectious disease should keep herself apart to help to prevent the spread of infection. This period is usually slightly longer than the maximum incubation period.

In nurseries, or in a home where there are other children, if it is known that a child has been in contact with an infectious disease it is wise to keep a very careful watch on him during this period, and if there is any sign that he is at all unwell he should be kept away from other children until he either contracts the disease, or is clearly not going to do so.

Disinfection is the method of killing germs, which can be done in several ways, for details see Chapters 23 and 31.

Notification of infectious diseases (see Chapter 30).

Prevention of Infection within the Nursery

The following precautions will do much in preventing infectious conditions in children:

1. Provide the maximum of *fresh air* and avoid chilling.
2. Encourage *open-air exercise.*
3. Ensure adequate *rest* and *sleep* in the open air or in well-ventilated rooms.
4. Allow *sunlight* to enter the building wherever possible because the *sun is nature's enemy of germs.*
5. Give a *well-balanced diet* including adequate vitamins and mineral salts.
6. *Boil all milk* (including pasteurised milk) for children under two years.
7. See that *good general hygiene* is practised by the nursery staff, the cook and the domestic staff, and the children.
8. Provide convenient *hand washing* facilities.
9. Provide adequate *hot water for washing up* and clean dishcloths and tea towels.
10. Protect all food from *dust and flies.*
11. Ensure a clean *water supply* and *good sanitation.*
12. Avoid *overcrowding.*
13. *Avoid contact* with *infectious persons.*
14. *Isolate* all suspicious cases of infection.
15. Ensure that the staff *immediately reports* any illness to the matron.
16. Encourage *immunisation* and *vaccination.*
17. When in doubt *consult a doctor.*

The same precautions for maintaining good health also apply to the child's own home.

Health and Welfare Services

Steady progress and development of the health services have done a great deal in the prevention of infection. The general public, through health education, are more inclined to use the services provided by the local authority, and in this way the health standards have improved.

CHAPTER 29

Infectious Diseases

The purpose of this chapter is to stress the early signs and symptoms of infectious diseases which are likely to attack children in this country, so that *all precautionary measures* can be taken from the very beginning of the illness. The chief of these is to obtain medical advice, and if in any doubt to isolate until a diagnosis is made. Such symptoms as a rise of temperature, sore throat, headache, or diarrhoea must be treated with suspicion. It is too late to wait until a rash is visible, as the patient is infectious when the first symptoms appear. Therefore delay in isolating may result in many more cases which might have been prevented by prompt action.

In the latter part of the nineteenth century an Infectious Diseases Notification Act was passed making it compulsory to notify infectious diseases to the Medical Officer of Health for the area in which the illness occurred. Notification enables the local health authority to make investigations as to the cause of the outbreak and to take measures to prevent the development of further cases or severe epidemics. The Medical Officer of Health may ask his local authority to extend the Notification Act to include a disease not on the list of notifiable diseases and this must receive the approval of the Minister of Health. It must be remembered that contact with a mild case may cause a serious attack in another child.

Provision is made by the local authority for the reception of infectious diseases in special hospitals and for an ambulance service. The doctor in attendance advises either home nursing or removal to hospital, according to the facilities available in the home and the patient's condition.

It is the duty of the local health authority to provide a *disinfecting* and *cleansing station* (see Chapter 31) where bedding, clothing or other materials may be taken for disinfection, after removal of the patient to hospital or, if nursed at home, after the recovery of the child. Facilities are also provided for fumigating the home or any infected premises. The work of the cleansing station include the treatment of *scabies* and all *verminous conditions* (see Chapter 31).

Measles (morbilli)

This disease is transmitted from one child to another by *direct contact*, through sneezing or coughing (*droplet infection*), and in a few cases infected clothing or toys may be responsible for the spread of infection.

Children are seldom affected before six months, the most usual period being between 18 months and seven years.

Measles affecting the young child under two years is more likely to be serious than in an older child, and the disease is most fatal in areas, where nutrition and housing conditions are bad. It is very infectious in the catarrhal stage.

Incubation period is ten to fourteen days.

Quarantine is for about fifteen days; this applies to nurseries and nursery schools or to anyone who has been in contact with the infection.

Isolation is necessary for two weeks after the appearance of the rash.

Symptoms

The earliest symptoms are those of a very bad cold, with sneezing, coughing and watering eyes with a tendency to conjunctivitis. There is a loss of appetite, with slight headache, sore throat, a rise in temperature, and the child is miserable and irritable. The catarrhal conditions increase until the rash appears on the fourth day, when the temperature may rise to 104° F to 105° F (40° C–40.6° C).

Koplik's spots may be seen on the second day, inside the cheek at a level with the lower teeth in about 75 per cent of patients. These are small, bluish grey spots with a slightly raised red margin and they are very helpful in diagnosing true measles, but these are often missed because they may very quickly disappear.

The rash appears about the fourth day first on the face and behind the ears as small, deep pink spots and spreads rapidly over the body. The spots are small to begin with, becoming larger and causing a blotchy appearance. After three to four days the rash gradually subsides and there is a very slight peeling of the skin. The temperature falls with the disappearance of the rash and the child continues to improve. The eyelids may be swollen and the child unable to tolerate any direct light upon his eyes, which can make him very miserable.

Complications

Laryngitis may occur during the disease, and conjunctivitis is fairly common and may damage the sight and possibly cause blindness. Inflammation of the middle ear (otitis media), ulceration of the mouth (stomatitis), convulsions and diarrhoea and vomiting may appear. Respiratory conditions such as bronchial catarrh may lead to bronchitis or pneumonia, which may possibly prove fatal.

Immunisation against measles, see Chapter 28.

Special care must be taken to avoid eye strain. The child must not face strong light or look at books or any play materials which may strain his eyes.

For care of the sick child, see Chapter 23.

German measles (rubella)

This disease is spread through *direct contact* by *droplet infection*. It is more common in older children and adolescents. In children it usually takes a mild form and there are seldom any complications.

Incubation period is fourteen to twenty-one days.

Quarantine for those who have been in contact with the disease is twenty-one days but contacts are not now excluded from school.

Isolation is necessary for one week after the appearance of the rash.

Symptoms

These are usually of a very slight nature, possibly sickness, rise in temperature, catarrh, sore throat, enlarged glands particularly noticeable in the lymphatic glands at the back of the neck, but the rash which should appear on the second day may be the first indication of any illness. The rash first appears on the face and neck, spreading to the trunk and extremities, or it may show all over the body at once. It consists of pink spots which gradually fade on about the third day. The rash may be accompanied by a marked rise in temperature, but the child does not seem very ill, and a quick recovery to normal is usual.

Complications

The chief complication of german measles is the effect it may have on the foetus if an expectant mother contracts the disease during the first three months of pregnancy. The baby may be born with mild or serious abnormalities affecting his sight or hearing, his internal organs, brain or indeed any part of him. Therefore expectant mothers should take precautions to avoid the disease as far as they possibly can.

Scarlet fever and tonsillitis

The germ causing scarlet fever is often identical with that causing tonsillitis. These diseases are commonly spread by *droplet infection*, any discharge from the nose, ear, mouth or throat are highly infectious and the convalescent patient may be a carrier. The infections can also be spread by *indirect contact* such as infected milk, clothing, flies, or by a person neglecting to take the necessary precautions after attending to a patient. The disease is more common after five years of age and very unusual under one year. Scarlet fever in the majority of cases appears in a milder form than it did some years ago.

Incubation period is two to seven days.

Quarantine for contacts is seven to ten days.

Isolation. The patient is infectious until all discharges containing the germ cease, but an uncomplicated case of scarlet fever is usually free from infection at the end of four to six weeks. The convalescent patient with recurrent discharges may be a *carrier* of the organism (see p. 318). As a precautionary measure cases discharged from hospital should not sleep with young children for two or three weeks and any discharges must be treated as infectious.

Symptoms of scarlet fever

The onset is usually sudden and acute with shivering, headache, sore throat, flushed face and a hot dry skin. There is a rise in temperature with a comparatively rapid pulse. The rash of scarlet fever appears on the second day and looks like bright red spots on a paler flushed background. It appears first on the neck and chest, missing the face, then spreads over the trunk and limbs. The cheeks are flushed with a marked pallor round the nose and mouth. The temperature rises to 102° F to 104° F (38.9° C–40° C), with the rash and gradually falls when the rash starts to fade about the third day. The tongue is coated by a white fur, with the swollen red papillae on the tongue showing through. After a few days the white coating peels off leaving a clean red tongue similar in appearance to a strawberry – hence the typical strawberry tongue of scarlet fever.

The tonsils are usually swollen and bright red spots can be seen on the palate.

As the temperature becomes normal about the eighth day, the acute symptoms gradually disappear and the patient recovers.

Complications

Inflammation of the middle ear caused by the infection spreading along the Eustachian tubes. Purulent nasal discharge is common and can be very persistent. Nephritis, or inflammation of the kidney, and rheumatism with heart complications occasionally follow scarlet fever. Septic glands in the neck may require surgical treatment.

Symptoms of tonsillitis

These are similar to scarlet fever – but there is no rash. The temperature may be high and the patient extremely ill and infectious.

Complications

These may include respiratory conditions, middle ear infection, and sometimes rheumatism is associated with tonsillitis.

Pus accumulated in the crevices of the tonsil may form an abscess (quinsy).

Whooping cough (pertussis)

This disease is more common before school age and very dangerous in young babies. It is spread by *direct droplet infection*, and it is most infectious during the catarrhal stage. Articles such as feeding utensils, handkerchiefs, and pencils may be responsible for the spread of this infection. It is possible for babies to have whooping cough at the same time as pneumonia or bronchitis which may prevent the true diagnosis being made.

Immunisation does not give 100 per cent protection although it reduces the severity of the attack, and it must be remembered that a child can get whooping cough even if immunised. He may not have the whoop but he will be infectious and a danger in a nursery.

Incubation period is seven to eighteen days.

Quarantine for all who have been in contact with infection is twenty-one days.

Isolation. Diagnosis may be difficult before the whoop appears. The patient is infectious during the catarrhal stage and is usually considered infectious for four weeks or until a pharyngeal swab is negative, proving that there are no germs present. Children with a normal temperature should be out in the fresh air as much as possible during this time, but kept away from others. After some weeks, a fresh cold may cause a return of the whoop, but this may not be infectious.

Symptoms

The disease first appears as a common cold and is infectious in the early stages. Gradually the symptoms become more severe, with a rise in temperature and a harsh, dry cough which is troublesome at night. After a few days the spasms of coughing become more severe and more frequent. The child gives a number of short, sharp expiratory coughs, the face turns red or purple, eyes bulge, then suddenly an inspiration is taken which causes the characteristic whoop. These paroxysms of coughing vary in their intensity, often leaving the young child very exhausted. The maximum amount of fresh air is valuable to all children with whooping cough. Over-excitement or emotional upsets may stimulate the spasms of coughing. Vomiting occurs frequently after the cough and may prove a great difficulty in feeding the child. As soon as the child has rested after an attack of coughing he should have a little light nourishing food of a smooth texture to avoid any irritation. Infants may require a predigested feed but it is most important to maintain adequate nourishment, which is a great problem when vomiting is present.

The temperature usually becomes normal in about ten days from the onset, and after two to three weeks the paroxysms gradually become less severe. Toddlers, except in very severe cases, are not affected so much by the cough and between the spasms they seem quite normal and comparatively well.

Complications

Bronchopneumonia may develop at any stage of whooping cough and this combination proves one of the most dangerous to young children, causing a very high death rate. Infection of the middle ear and convulsions are not uncommon. Catarrh may be the forerunner of enteritis. Haemorrhage is common from the nose and very occasionally in the brain, causing a squint to appear.

Immunisation against whooping cough (see Chapter 28).

Mumps

Mumps is caused by a virus and usually affects the school child and is seldom seen in a child under three years. It is nearly always transmitted by *direct contact* through secretions from the nose and mouth (droplet) and very rarely by *indirect contact* through clothing or people.

Incubation period is eighteen to twenty-eight days.

Quarantine for those who have been in contact with the infection is twenty-eight days. Contacts are not excluded from school.

Isolation is necessary for three weeks after the onset of the disease or for one week after the swelling of the glands has subsided.

Symptoms

In some cases the earliest symptom is pain and swelling of the gland (parotid) situated under the jaw and under the ear, on one or both sides of the neck, but with others there may be a rise in temperature, headache and sore throat for one or two days, before the swelling of the gland is obvious. There is pain and tenderness over the region of the swelling and in severe cases there is great difficulty in feeding. The flow of saliva may be increased or diminished. All the glands of the neck may become swollen and very painful, but this is only in severe cases. Sometimes only the glands on one side of the neck are affected at the onset, but when these have recovered the other side may be painful.

The swelling takes about a week to subside. By this time the temperature has become normal and the general condition of the patient improves.

Complications

These are rare in young children but occasionally the testes of the older boy and the ovaries of the girl may be affected. These glands become inflamed, swollen and painful. This may occur after the first week. It is thought this may cause sterility in some instances.

Diphtheria

This condition is commonly caused by *direct infection* through sneezing, coughing, and even talking (droplet), but it can be caused by *indirect* methods such as contaminated milk, clothing or utensils. Diphtheria carriers may also be responsible for the spread of the disease. Convalescent patients may remain infectious for some time and thus be termed carriers.

Diphtheria usually affects children between the ages of two and ten years, and the mortality rate is highest in young children.

Incubation period is from two to six days.

Quarantine for all contacts is twelve days.

Isolation. The patient is considered infectious until three negative swabs have been taken. Swabs are specially prepared sterilised pieces of cotton wool attached to thin sticks, enclosed in a sterile test tube and sealed. They are provided by the local authority. The doctor uses the cotton wool on the stick to brush over the infected area to absorb a specimen of the germs. Immediately afterwards the swab is returned to the tube and sent for examination (see p. 358). In diphtheria the period of infection varies considerably.

Symptoms

The onset of the disease may be sudden or it may be rather slow with no very marked symptoms. It may even go unnoticed in the early stages unless the child is thoroughly examined by a doctor. The disease usually affects one of the following areas:
  (a) *The throat*, when the symptoms are loss of appetite, vomiting, headache, swollen glands, rise in temperature and a slight degree of sore throat. White, greyish patches can be seen over the tonsils which may spread quickly right over the throat.
  (b) *The larynx*, which is commonly affected in young children, produces the characteristic symptoms of a harsh cough with noisy and difficult breathing. In severe cases this is an extremely dangerous condition. Sometimes an operation has to be performed, making an opening into the trachea, to avoid asphyxia.
  (c) *The nasal passages* are frequently affected with either of the two former types mentioned, and a nasal discharge and slight bleeding result.

Complications

These are of a very serious and lasting nature, the chief being *paralysis* affecting different parts of the body, for example:
  (a) the palate, which complicates feeding,
  (b) the muscles of the neck, trunk, diaphragm and the limbs.

Pneumonia may result from the paralysis. The toxins or poisons affect the heart and may cause sudden heart failure in any stage of the disease.

The importance of the *prevention* of diphtheria by immunisation has already been discussed in the previous chapter.

Poliomyelitis (infantile paralysis)

This disease can be caused by three different viruses. The virus is excreted in the stools and the disease can be spread by the infectious faeces of a carrier. It may also be spread by contact (droplet). Several members of a family may be carrying the virus, and possibly spreading the infection, but only one of them may develop paralytic poliomyelitis. The motor nerve cells are attacked by the viruses, causing paralysis. Cases of poliomyelitis may occur throughout the year but are more common in the autumn.

Incubation period. This is not definitely known, but it may be from three days to as much as thirty-five days.

Quarantine for contacts is twenty-one days.

Isolation – twenty-one days.

Symptoms

There may be a general feeling of pain and nausea with headache and stiffness of the neck and back, with a rise in temperature. The illness can easily be mistaken for influenza, and it may pass off in a few days. There are many more cases of this non-paralytic type than is often realised and these are very infectious. In the paralytic type the first symptoms may be similar, but more severe, with paralysis developing in a few days.

In children the growth of the affected muscles will be considerably retarded. Much can now be done to reduce the degree of resulting paralysis by skilful treatment, but the patient must have specialised care from the earliest stages.

All secretions from the nose and throat, and all stools must be disinfected before disposal.

For the prevention of poliomyelitis by vaccination, see the table on page 323.

The common cold

This is an infection affecting the respiratory passages which lasts from about three days to two or three weeks. It may be simply a cold, or it may be a symptom of some other disease. It is spread through secretions, by coughing, sneezing or even talking (*droplet infection*).

Incubation period is not known. A person with a slight cold may be highly infectious, causing a severe cold in other people. Much depends on the individual's ability to resist infection.

Complications

Catarrh may occur, middle ear infection (otitis media), bronchitis or pneumonia.

Anyone with a cold should wear a mask when attending to young babies.

Influenza

Influenza is a name which is often very loosely applied to any conditions resembling the common cold. This is an infectious disease in which one attack does not provide immunity to other attacks. It is spread by *direct droplet infection*. It affects people of any age and frequently epidemics affect the whole country.

Incubation period is one to three days.

Isolation. Influenza is considered infectious until after the fever has passed. Catarrh excretions must be treated as infectious.

Symptoms

The onset of this disease is sudden. The general symptoms are headache, shivering with aching in the limbs, vomiting and a rise in temperature. This disease if more severe may have *complications* which can develop in the following ways – for example:

(a) Catarrh may cause respiratory conditions, such as bronchitis or pneumonia.
(b) Gastro-enteritis may occur with severe vomiting and diarrhoea (common in young children).
(c) The nervous system may become involved, leading to convulsions.
(d) Jaundice.
(e) Anaemia.

In a mild form influenza is not serious, but it leaves a marked lassitude and depression which is rather difficult to cope with in children. It is important to realise that influenza is a very infectious condition and must be taken seriously to prevent complications. Immunisation against certain types of influenza is available.

Catarrhal jaundice (infective hepatitis)

This condition is common in older children and is frequently referred to as epidemic jaundice. It is due to a virus which causes inflammation of the liver and is spread by direct contact, infected milk, water and contaminated food, and inadequate precautions when emptying infectious stools.

Incubation period is two to four weeks.

Symptoms

The condition develops gradually with headache, loss of appetite, rise in temperature, vomiting, and loose stools, which are infectious in the early stages. Milk is often disliked and all forms of fat. After a few days the white of the eyes become yellow; then the skin changes to a deep yellow colour, the urine is dark and the stools pale in colour. The temperature slowly returns to normal and the jaundice fades by the end of two to three weeks.

Diet. Fat must be restricted.

Complications

In a few instances serious liver disorders may develop, but other complications are rare.

Care must be taken to *disinfect all stools* and *wash hands* after attending to the patient (see Chapter 23).

Infectious enteritis or diarrhoea

This is a highly infectious disease which mainly attacks the child under eighteen months. It was frequently referred to as summer diarrhoea in the past, as it was more prevalent in the hot weather. It is now more common in the late winter months and found especially in densely populated districts with bad housing conditions.

It is *caused by contaminated milk*, dirt, flies, or by careless handling of the infant's feeds. The boiling of all milk and the use of strict hygiene do much to prevent diarrhoea, which is less commonly found in breast-fed babies. It is possible that certain bacilli in the intestine of a normal healthy child may prove to be harmful to other young babies.

Incubation period is two to five days.

Isolate until a few days after the stools have become normal. All stools must be disinfected before emptying and napkins should be first disinfected, then washed and boiled (see Chapter 23).

Symptoms

The onset of the disease is usually rather sudden, vomiting, colic, screaming, undigested loose stools, with a rapid pulse and a rise in temperature. The stools then become more frequent, green and watery. The baby's condition quickly changes, the tissues become dehydrated, the fontanelle is depressed, the infant loses weight and appears very pale and ill. Gradually the condition improves except in very severe cases when the child collapses and the disease proves fatal.

When any symptoms of infectious diarrhoea are present, medical advice must be obtained immediately, and the child must be isolated and should be treated as highly infectious. In the meantime he must be kept warm, given only boiled water until seen by the doctor, who usually prescribes half-strength saline with or without glucose. No milk should be given until ordered by the doctor, which is usually in about two or three days, when a weak dilution of milk may be prescribed.

Complications

The child is very liable to develop respiratory conditions such as bronchitis or pneumonia.

Dysentery

This is a type of gastro-enteritis which affects children and adults, but it is extremely dangerous in young children. Stools with blood and mucus are characteristic of the disease. One variety of the disease is frequently spoken of as *Sonne dysentery* because it is caused by a germ called *Shigella sonnei*. It is spread by contaminated milk or water, by carriers, or by carelessness after attending to the napkins or stools of an infected person. Flies can be a very real source of danger.

Incubation period is two to six days.

Isolation is necessary for about one week after the stools have become normal. Chronic cases of dysentery which recur at intervals should have the stools examined to determine if they are *carriers* of this particular germ. Good general hygiene with special care of napkins and stools and *thorough hand washing* will do much to prevent the spread of this infection. All cases should be isolated and medical advice must be obtained at once. Adults with any suspicious symptoms should report these at once. In nurseries it is essential for rectal swabs of everyone to be sent for investigation to enable any carriers to be treated.

Symptoms

In the majority of cases the onset is sudden and the symptoms are usually very severe. There is vomiting, fever, colic and very loose green and watery stools with blood and mucus, and there is a good deal of straining when passing the stool. Infants very soon become dehydrated and may collapse.

It is important that the child should be kept warm and have medical care at once. *All milk must be stopped immediately.* Drinks of boiled water or half-strength saline with or without glucose are essential to replace the fluid loss.

Enteric fevers

Enteric fevers is a term which is now used to include three separate, but closely allied diseases, namely: (1) typhoid, (2) paratyphoid A, (3) paratyphoid B.

Typhoid fever is characterised by a prolonged high temperature, which is usually rather higher at night than in the morning. This disease may occur at any age but children are less liable to serious attacks. The germs gain access to the system through the mouth by contaminated milk, water, food or by the hands of someone who is either a carrier or who has failed to disinfect and wash their hands after attending to an infectious patient. Epidemics may be caused by watercress or oysters from stagnant waters and by carriers who may be working with food.

Incubation period is fourteen to eighteen days.

Isolation is necessary until the urine and the stools are free from the bacilli causing the disease. To prove this, tests are made which must be negative for three successive weeks. All stools, urine, and vomit must be disinfected before being emptied into the lavatory (see Chapter 23). The hands must be well washed with soap and water, using a nail brush, and disinfected after touching any infected article or the patient.

Symptoms

The onset of the disease is gradual with loss of appetite, tiredness, headache, loose stools, nose bleeding, and in severe cases abdominal pain and vomiting. The temperature continues to rise for about a week and remains high for two to three weeks, then slowly falling to normal. The abdomen is distended and tender. The rash, consisting of small, rose-coloured spots spreading over the abdomen and the chest, appears in the second week and fades after a few days.

In infants and children the disease may take a milder form, with a much shorter period of pyrexia (rise in temperature). There may be acute abdominal pain, sometimes at first thought to be appendicitis.

Constipation or diarrhoea may be present.

M

Complications

Haemorrhage and perforation of the intestine may occur from the third week onwards, and will prove fatal unless surgical treatment is given immediately. Heart failure may be caused by any slight exertion of the patient. Abscesses and inflammation of the long bones (osteomyelitis) or of the spine may occur after five weeks and infection may spread to the kidney.

Bronchopneumonia and meningitis may occur, but they are not common.

For typhoid immunisation, see Chapter 28.

Chickenpox (Varicella)

This is caused by *direct contact* with the infection or *indirectly* by clothing and toys or by a third party. The condition is highly infectious. There appears to be a relationship between shingles and chickenpox, because a child in contact with shingles may develop chickenpox, or vice versa, but an immunity to chickenpox will not prevent shingles.

Incubation period is twelve to twenty-one days.

Quarantine for all contacts is twenty-one days.

Isolation. The disease is most infectious during the first two weeks, but for safety it should be considered necessary to isolate until all the scabs have dropped off.

Symptoms

In mild cases the rash will be the first indication, but in more severe cases for one or two days the child may have a slight rise of temperature and not feel very well. The rash takes the form of spots which are small and round. They quickly fill with a clear fluid, which by the third day appears to have turned to pus. Gradually a crust is formed which dries and the scab drops off in a few days. The rash commonly starts on the body, then spreads to the face or scalp and finally to the limbs. Single spots or groups of spots appear according to the severity of the condition. The eruption can be very irritating.

By three weeks the scabs should have all cleared.

Complications

In the majority of cases complications are unusual. Occasionally there may be a secondary infection due to scratching.

It is usual to make *chickenpox* notifiable if there happen to be cases of *smallpox* in the area, to ensure that no mild smallpox cases are missed.

Smallpox

Smallpox is a very infectious disease. Fortunately vaccination has greatly reduced the occurrence of this condition, but there are still cases occurring in Britain. The disease may occur at any age if the person has not been recently vaccinated. It is caused by *direct contact* with an infected person or *indirectly* by contacts, clothing or infected articles and may be airborne from a considerable distance. The germs have the power to remain active on clothing or articles for a fairly long time. Smallpox patients are always nursed in an Isolation Hospital.

This disease causes a high death rate among unvaccinated persons of any age (see Chapter 30).

Incubation period is twelve to fourteen days.

Quarantine should be seventeen days and contacts are excluded from school for twenty-one days, unless recently vaccinated.

Isolation is necessary until all scabs have fallen off. Throughout the illness all scabs and discharges must be considered as highly infectious. All contacts in the home who have not been recently vaccinated should be done immediately.

Symptoms

The onset is sudden with shivering, headache, backache, marked rise in temperature, abdominal pain and vomiting. There is a similarity in the early symptoms to those of influenza. The temperature falls and the symptoms become less when the rash appears on the third day. This is in the form of small red spots, which grow in size and form a raised bleb containing clear fluid which turns to pus in about six days. Inflammation is present in the surrounding area of the pustules. Gradually scabs form which later drop off, the whole process taking about four weeks. If the rash is severe the temperature may rise again until the rash subsides.

The rash is first seen on the face and wrists, gradually spreading to the trunk and the limbs. The palate and pharynx are also attacked. The pustules in smallpox take much longer to develop and they are more numerous than those already described in chickenpox.

The rash causes a great deal of irritation and after the scab drops off there is a pitting in the surface of the skin, and a permanent scar where each pustule has been.

Complications
Inflammatory conditions of the eye, ear and throat may occur before or after the scabs have dropped off. Bronchitis and pneumonia may occur after a severe attack of smallpox.

Tetanus
The germ causing tetanus is chiefly found in dirt, manure, animal faeces and in cultivated soil. It is highly resistant to extremes of heat and cold, and can remain active over a long period. Entrance to the body is through a cut or wound. Tetanus affects the central nervous system.
Incubation – seven to fourteen days.

Symptoms
These may appear very rapidly or some time after the infection. Rigidity of the neck and jaw muscles, giving rise to the term 'lockjaw' appears and gradually painful muscular spasms develop and increase in severity. The longer the incubation period the less likelihood of any serious results.
For tetanus immunisation, see Chapter 28.

Venereal Disease

Syphilis
This is a highly contagious disease which is usually transmitted by sexual intercourse but the microorganism can pass through any damaged area of skin or mucous membranes, e.g. by kissing.
Congenital syphilis is inherited from the parents. If the mother is syphilitic, and untreated, the baby becomes infected through the mother's blood when in the uterus; where the condition is only slight the child may appear perfectly healthy at birth, but develops positive symptoms later on. The *early symptoms* in infants are 'snuffles' of varying degrees accompanied by a hoarse dry cry, and a copper-coloured rash may appear some weeks after birth. This usually affects the face, genital organs, buttocks, palms of the hands and soles of the feet. Gradually more definite symptoms appear, such as wasting, restlessness and skin irritations. Common *symptoms in the older child* with inherited syphilis are anaemia, with debility and stunted growth.

The true diagnosis of syphilis is made by testing the blood of the mother and the baby (Wassermann test).

Curative treatment can be given to anyone infected with syphilis. The infected expectant mother should be treated early in pregnancy to ensure that the baby is born free from syphilis. Advice can be obtained at any public health department or infant welfare centre and from the doctor. All discussions are treated as highly confidential and anyone with any suspicions of having the condition must never hesitate to seek advice and treatment.

Gonorrhoea

This is also a highly contagious disease.

Mothers with a vaginal infection can infect the child at birth, causing an inflammation of the eyes (*ophthalmia neonatorum*) which appears within forty-eight hours and may result in total blindness. Gonorrhoea is usually acquired by sexual intercourse with an infected male or through the skin or membranes if they are damaged and get contaminated by gonorrhoeal pus. The condition can be spread by contaminated towels, lavatories, or the dirty hands of an infected person. Any discharge from the eyes of an infant must be under medical care and treated as infectious.

Incubation period three to ten days.

Advice from the family doctor should be sought and he will explain where treatment can be obtained. Delay in obtaining treatment may result in serious complications in both male and female.

Isolation of the mother is necessary, and the nurse must pay strict attention to all infected articles and to the disinfection and scrubbing of the hands after touching the patient. This must be continued until any alteration is sanctioned by the doctor.

Vaginitis in the child

This may be caused by accidental means or by gonorrhoeal infection. Already mentioned in Chapter 22.

Signs and symptoms

There is frequency in passing urine, much irritation in and around the vulva caused by a purulent discharge which can also be offensive. To diagnose it, a swab of the vaginal discharge is taken for examination. If it is positive, the child must be isolated and will have to receive medical treatment.

Small girls can get a similar condition through crawling on floors if they are not properly cared for and do not wear a nappy or pants, but this is not likely to be of gonorrhoeal origin.

Any one with a gonorrhoeal infection, or vulvo-vaginitis in the woman and urethritis in the male, should seek advice at the public health department or from the family doctor (see Chapter 31).

PART EIGHT
Social and Welfare Services

CHAPTER 30

History and Development

From the very earliest times interest has been shown in the health of the mother and her baby and in the second century A.D. Soranus of Ephesus wrote a treatise dealing with pregnancy and labour and the care of the child in infancy. In France much was done even in early days to encourage and improve the care of the infant, for example, homes were established for orphans and in 1070 an Order was founded which was dedicated to the care of sick and abandoned infants. In England the Foundling Hospital was opened in London in 1739 and was the first hospital for sick children in the country. Thirty years later a dispensary for the relief of poor children was founded in Red Lion Square, London; this was the earliest type of infant welfare work in this country but around the turn of the century it had to be closed due to lack of funds. A new dispensary was opened in 1816, advised by Dr. Brunnel Davis, who favoured the idea of visiting children in their own homes.

Before the second half of the nineteenth century doctors and scientists chiefly studied the methods of curing disease, because up to that period there was little scientific knowledge available to enable them to study preventive medicine, or positive health as it is known today. Severe epidemics of diarrhoea, measles, scarlet fever, diphtheria typhoid and smallpox took a heavy toll of life throughout the country each year, but little was known about bacteriology and it was difficult to prevent the occurrence and spread of such diseases. Later research work produced some very valuable facts relating to bacteria (see Chapter 28), which gave quite a new aspect to infectious diseases and to public health work in general.

About the middle of the nineteenth century, health pioneers began to realise that bad hygiene and poor living conditions were largely responsible for illness and loss of life through infection. In

1848 the first Public Health Act was passed, which concentrated chiefly on sanitation and general hygiene. Great efforts were made to provide better housing conditions, with good drainage and sanitary arrangements, a pure water supply, with improved food inspection and good storage provision in the home. Sanitary Inspectors (now known as Public Health Inspectors) visited the homes of the people to advise on essential additions or alterations.

The interest of voluntary and pioneer workers was stimulated, and the enthusiasm of these people developed in many towns. As far back as 1862 the Manchester and Salford Sanitary Association started a scheme to provide workers who went into the homes to guide and advise on hygiene in an effort to prevent sickness and to promote a higher standard of living conditions. Gradually this idea was developed in London, Bristol, Liverpool, Manchester, Birmingham, Glasgow, Sheffield and many other progressive towns. These local organisations worked from a unit which was commonly called "The School for Mothers" and proved to be the beginning of infant welfare work as it is known today. In many of these areas milk depots were set up in an endeavour to help to give a clean milk supply to children and thus ensure better nutrition.

The first public social service to be established in this country was the Poor Law in the reign of Queen Elizabeth I, which provided for those who had no means of support. Until then it had been the duty of the Church to help such people from voluntary subscriptions. The National Assistance Act, 1948, now provides help for poor people by the National Assistance Board and local authorities.

In 1847 the first Medical Officer of Health in England and Wales was appointed to Liverpool and a year later the City of London appointed a Medical Officer of Health. In 1872 every local authority was required to appoint a Medical Officer of Health for its area.

Medical Officers of Health in the latter part of the nineteenth century showed grave concern about the high mortality rate of children under five years and the still higher death rate of children during the first year of life. Diarrhoea was causing the greatest number of deaths during the first year of life, chiefly amongst artificially fed babies, and breast feeding was encouraged as a means of preventing this scourge. Leaflets were distributed on the subject but with little result, and because many people could not read it was felt to be more valuable to visit the mother in her own home to try to advise her on the general principles of hygiene.

By this time a few progressive local authorities were appointing paid health visitors to visit systematically all young children in their own homes and to report results to the Medical Officer of Health. The idea of preventing disease instead of trying to cure it was gaining ground, and on the great work done through Medical Officers of Health and pioneer bodies such as 'The School for Mothers' were built the foundations of the Maternity and Child Welfare Services.

When the development of the social services is studied, it will be noted that new ideas have been tried out by voluntary organisations and, when proved successful, have been taken over and administered by the government department directly concerned. This may be partly due to the fact that it is felt to be unwise to use rate-payers' money on any scheme which has not been tried out and found successful.

Much effort was made in the eighteenth and nineteenth centuries to encourage better *maternity services*. In 1881 the Midwives Institute was founded but it was not until 1902, when the first Midwives Act became law, that real progress was made. Up to this time any untrained woman could act as a midwife. The Central Midwives Board was created as a governing body to regulate the training and the practice of midwives.

In 1870, the Education Act was passed which provided free education for every child between the ages of five years and fourteen years. This has now been extended to sixteen years, with further education up to eighteen years. Previously the education of children had been done by private or voluntary bodies, resulting in many parents sending young children of ten or twelve years to work rather than pay for their education. Compulsory education did much to improve general conditions in the country. The ability to read gave people wider opportunities to gain knowledge, and thus the desire developed for better living conditions. Once the average young person could read he had a basic framework on which further teaching could be based, and also more appreciation of what was essential to life.

In 1907 the School Medical Service (now known as the School Health Service) came into being. This scheme arranged for doctors and nurses to visit the schools and to examine the children at regular intervals. Bad hygiene was responsible for many infectious diseases, poor health and verminous conditions. The nurses did much follow-up work in the homes after the medical examinations, trying to encourage and teach a higher standard of cleanliness both to the children and to the parents and to see that any prescribed treatment had been carried out. Then school clinics were opened to enable treatment ordered by the doctor to be given as often as was necessary.

Gradually younger children were allowed to attend school, and it was quickly realised that children under five years wanted rather different management and occupation from those over five years. To meet this requirement teachers were specially trained in the care and needs of children from two to five years, and they became known as *Nursery School Teachers* in charge of nursery schools.

The importance of good feeding grew to be appreciated, and voluntary efforts were made to provide breakfasts or other meals for school children. One of the first experiments was made in Brighton. Gradually, as the value of such work was proved beyond doubt, free school meals were provided by the local authorities.

From observations made by the school medical service it became obvious that the health of the child when he entered school at five years was far from perfect. It was clear that provision should be made to improve the health of children before school age by preventing the development of physical defects and deficiency diseases. Rheumatism and heart conditions were also fairly common. It was realised that physical and mental defects or illness would hinder the true development and education of the children.

Since the beginning of the twentieth century many Acts of Parliament have been passed which have had a direct bearing on the health of mothers and children. The following are a few of the principal ones:

The Infectious Diseases Notification Act, 1889 (notification was made compulsory ten years later). This act made it compulsory for doctors to notify cases of infectious diseases to the Medical Officer of Health, which proved of great value in controlling these diseases. This information enabled the Medical Officer of Health to investigate the cause of the infection and in this way prevent further epidemics.

The Midwives Act, 1902. This Act did much to promote better treatment and conditions for pregnant and nursing mothers. It forbade any woman to call herself a midwife unless she was specially trained and certified by examination.

The Notification of Births Act, 1907. This Act made it compulsory for all births to be notified in writing to the Medical Officer of Health within thirty-six hours of the birth. This is quite apart from the *Registration of Births* for which purpose notification of every birth is sent to the Registrar within forty-two days of its occurrence.

The Children Acts, passed in 1907 and 1915, made it compulsory for anyone who received payment for nursing or caring for a child up to seven years of age in her own home to notify the local authority within two days of taking the child. This law did not apply to children who were relatives. Inspection of the home was carried out by a Local Health Authority Official at any time, and no objection or refusal could be made by the occupants to this procedure. The purpose of this law was to safeguard the child.

In 1912 **Tuberculosis Regulations** made it compulsory to notify all forms of tuberculosis. Some years later, anyone suffering from tuberculosis was prohibited from working in any capacity on a farm or in a dairy. Legislation in 1930 made it compulsory for the Medical Officer of Health to keep a confidential register of all notifications, to investigate the source of infection, and to prevent the spread of the infection.

The Maternity and Child Welfare Act, 1918, made it compulsory for all local authorities to make provision for the health of mothers and young children. It empowered them to set up *Infant Welfare Centres* subject to the approval of the Ministry of Health, the Medical Officer of Health being responsible for the working of the Act under his Maternity and Child Welfare Committee.

Children and Young Persons Act, 1933. The Act seeks to protect a child under fourteen years of age who is neglected or cruelly treated – a young person is one between fourteen and seventeen years of age. Action can be taken against the parents or those responsible, by the local authority or the N.S.P.C.C.

The Public Health Act, 1936, makes local authorities responsible for (*a*) safe water supply, (*b*) good sanitation, (*c*) notification of infectious diseases, (*d*) disinfection, (*e*) registration of Nursing Homes, etc.

The Food and Drugs Act, 1938 and 1955, demand that all food sold for human consumption shall be clean and in good condition. The local authority has power to examine any food, and to inspect the premises used for the manufacture of food.

The Education Act, 1944. Under the provisions of this Act, the local education authority must make special provision for children under five years by means of *Nursery Schools* or *Nursery Classes*. Special schools or classes must be provided for *handicapped children*, for example, blind, deaf, crippled, educationally subnormal, diabetic, epileptic, and maladjusted. Residence must be provided when necessary. Medical inspection and treatment (including dental care) must be arranged for all children of school age. Cleanliness examinations may be carried out by a doctor or nurse, and the child cleansed by the local authority if the parents fail to do so.

It is the duty of the local education authority to provide milk and meals for the pupils in the school.

The Family Allowances Act, 1945 to 1959, provides for the payment of a weekly allowance to the mother for each child in the family, with the exception of the first born, until the child reaches school leaving age.

The National Insurance Acts, 1946 to 1957, provides for the payment of unemployment, sickness, maternity and widows' benefit, for guardians' allowance, retirement pension and death grants.

The National Health Services Act, 1946, came into operation in 1948. The Act covers all the health services provided by the local authority, home nursing, medical and dental treatment, medicines, ophthalmic and hospital services (see Chapter 31).

National Assistance Act, 1948, replaces the old Poor Law Act. The *National Assistance Board* is responsible for giving financial aid to people in need. The local health authorities must provide (*a*) residential accommodation for people in need, (*b*) maintain a register of handicapped people, and (*c*) give information and guidance to handicapped people.

The Milk and Dairy Regulations, 1949, require all dairy farms to be registered. All milk must be protected from contamination and any infectious disease among the workers on the farm or in the dairy must immediately be notified to the Medical Officer of Health.

The Milk Regulations, 1949. These apply to the production of milk under special gradings (see Chapter 10).

The Children Act, 1948, defines the deprived child as one who, for any reason, is either temporarily or permanently deprived of home life. It is the duty of the local authority to appoint a *Children's Committee* to deal with all matters relating to deprived children in the area. A *Children's Officer* must be appointed who will be responsible to the Children's Committee for the care of all deprived children in the district. The local authority is responsible for the well-being of the child until he is eighteen years of age. He may be placed in a residential home, which according to the Act must be registered, or with a foster parent who can provide a good home life for the child. The Children's Officer is responsible for the supervision of foster homes. An Advisory Council on Child Care is appointed for the purpose of advising the Secretary of State on matters connected with the Act. The local authority is responsible to the Secretary of State.

The Adoption Act, 1949–1950. The purpose of this Act is to safeguard the child. It regulates the management of adoption societies and demands that they be registered. Profit making is prohibited. Arrangements for adoption may be made between the parent and the adopter, or by the adoption society and the adopter. The final stage must always be by application to the court for an adoption order to be made. The Act demands that a register shall be maintained of all adopted children (see Chapter 31).

Mental Health Act, 1959, repeals previous mental health legislation. Mental Health Tribunals are established which have absorbed the functions of the Board of Control. Part II of the act empowers local authorities with greater freedom to organise services for the mentally handicapped within their general health, welfare and child care services. Training centres to be established for children unsuitable for education in school.

Acts of Parliament

Suggestions for new legislation usually originate in the House of Commons or the House of Lords. Proposals relating to any aspect of health or of local government are introduced into the House of Commons by means of a 'white paper'. A Committee of experts may then be appointed to study the proposals. Finally, when a bill is approved by both Houses, it is given the Royal Assent then termed as an Act, and becomes law.

Central administration

The Ministry of Health, now the Department of Health and Social Security, came into being in 1919, when this Department took over the work of the Local Government Board. The main function of the Department of Health and Social Security is to supervise and direct the comprehensive National Health Service of 1946, which is designed to promote improvement in the physical and mental health of the population and to deal with the prevention, diagnosis and treatment of disease. The Minister of Health, who may be a member of the Cabinet, presides over the Department. He has a permanent secretary and a staff of permanent civil servants.

The Chief Medical Officer of the Department of Health and Social Security is also the Chief Medical Officer of the Department of Education and Science and of the Home Office. There are Assistant Medical Officers and a Nursing Division with a Chief Nursing Officer, and Regional Nursing Officers.

The Welsh Board of Health carries out many duties for the Ministry of Health in Wales. The Scottish Home and Health Department performs similar duties in Scotland.

The Department of Education and Science (formerly the Ministry of Education)

This department is responsible for the provision of education for all adults, for children from the age of two years and for all handicapped children. In addition, school medical officers make routine examinations, and if they find any defect in a child he is immediately referred for treatment. School meals are available for a minimum charge with the idea of promoting good nutrition. Child guidance clinics with trained staff are available in many areas in order to give aid in the case of problem children. The Minister of Education and Science is responsible for directing this service.

The Home Office

This provides for the care and supervision of deprived children. Inspectors visit children's homes and give guidance, where necessary, to the Children's Committees. The Secretary of State for Home Affairs directs the work of the Home Office which also has many other functions.

Local government

The Parish Council

This was the oldest governing body for local affairs, but in 1888 the *Local Government Act* created the present arrangements for local administrative matters.

County Boroughs

Towns with populations of 50,000 and over are county boroughs.

In future, however, towns wishing to attain this status will be required to have populations of over 100,000. A county borough, although situated within a county, is a self-contained unit and performs all the functions of local government; it is directly responsible to the central government.

County Councils

These are areas similar to those of geographical counties, but some large counties are split into two or three administrative units, e.g. Yorkshire is divided into three independent areas and Sussex into two. The responsibilities of the county council are similar to those of the county borough, but some of the work may be delegated to the local Urban District Council and Rural District Council within the county concerned. The county council is directly responsible to the central government. The London boroughs combine the functions of county boroughs and county councils.

Urban District Councils are usually smaller towns within the county and are responsible to the county council for any work delegated to them, e.g. water supply, sanitation, disposal of refuse, control of infectious diseases and inspection of food. Health education and the provision of statistical data may also be included amongst their functions.

Rural District Councils are usually country areas containing many small villages. They are responsible to their county councils for work very similar to that done by Urban District Councils.

The Redcliffe-Maud Report of 1969 proposes considerable changes in local government. It recommends that towns should be united with their surrounding country rather than administered separately, and that in the majority of areas a single authority should be responsible for all services which are now divided between county and borough councils. It is now doubtful whether the recommendations of this report will become law. However, considerable changes in local government organization are likely in the next few years.

Local authorities

The inhabitants of an area elect the members of the local council, and at the first council meeting following an election a chairman is elected. In a county borough he is known as the Mayor or the Lord Mayor. The council then proceeds to form committees from amongst their members. They have power to appoint a person to serve who is not a member of the council but possesses special knowledge which will benefit the work (co-opted members). Most authorities have committees to deal with health (all aspects), child care, welfare, mental health, education, inspection of foods, water, sewage and finance. The larger authorities require also sub-committees to supervise such matters as maternity and child welfare, ambulance services and for any others to meet the needs of the area.

The law requires that the local authority must appoint a medical officer of health to advise on all health matters, to have executive control over his department and to prepare an annual report for the Minister of Health and Social Security.

Vital statistics

Vital statistics are compiled facts, which have been classified and relate to the health and well-being of the community. These figures are of great value in providing accurate information in relation to the general health and conditions prevailing in the country. For example:

(a) They give information about the prevalence of any disease, where it occurs and its effect on the different age groups of the people.

(b) The incidence of ill health can be ascertained, showing improvement or otherwise in the health of the nation.

(c) They are a valuable guide in building up preventive measures.

(d) They give facts relating to the health of workers in industry, showing the effect of different work on individual people.

Statistics are available on many different aspects of children's health. Valuable information has been collected on the effect of breast feeding, which proves beyond all doubt the value of breast feeding to the health of the baby. Another striking example is the evidence showing the marked reduction in the number of cases of diphtheria due to the immunisation of young children. All such information is most useful in preventive medicine.

Statistics commonly considered are those relating to births, marriage, deaths, but there are many other records kept which cover both health and disease throughout the country. These are published quarterly and can be obtained from Her Majesty's Stationery Office.

Death rates may apply to the community as a whole, to individual groups in certain areas, to different age groups of children, or in fact to any particular category desired.

Generally the death rate means the number of deaths annually per thousand of the population, and to find the death rate the number of deaths during a period of one year is multiplied by 1,000 and then divided by the population.

For example if a town had fifty thousand inhabitants and one hundred people died during the year 1960 the result would be:

$$\frac{100 \text{ deaths} \times 1,000}{50,000 \text{ population}} = 2.0 \text{ death rate for 1960.}$$

The common death rates used in relation to children are:

The infant mortality rate is the proportion of deaths of children under one year to every thousand live births each year. This rate fluctuates amongst the different classes and in the variously populated areas. When studying the statistics it can be seen that the death rate is higher in the neo-natal period (the first month of life) than in the following months. Respiratory conditions such as bronchial pneumonia cause the greatest number of deaths in children under one year, with enteritis following closely behind. Whooping cough has been responsible for many deaths during this period, but immunisation of older babies means that very young babies are much less likely to come into contact with the disease. On examination of the fatal cases it is interesting to note that approximately 80 per cent were artificially fed babies; 18 per cent were partially breast fed babies; whilst only 2 per cent were entirely breast fed.

The death rate in England and Wales of children under one year was:

111 in 1913			
70.0	1927	23.1	1957
49.1	1943	21.6	1961
46.0	1945	20.9	1962
41.4	1947	20.6	1964
33.9	1948	19.6	1965
29.8	1950	18.8	1967
25.0	1954	18.7	1968
24.0	1956	18.0	1969

Illegitimate babies and premature babies have a higher death rate in the early months of life. This death rate varies in different countries, some higher and some lower.

The *childhood mortality rate* applies to children from one year to school leaving age. Here again the death rate is higher in the youngest age groups and gradually decreases as the child reaches school age.

The chief causes in the second year of life are respiratory diseases, measles, tuberculosis, whooping cough and enteritis. In the third year pneumonia still takes a heavy toll of life, closely followed by tuberculosis and measles. From three to five years there is a slightly reduced number of deaths from respiratory conditions and tuberculosis.

In comparing the present death rates with those of fifty years ago it can be seen that very great progress has been made in preventing the loss of child life. The increased maternity and child welfare services, including home visiting by the health visitor, a wider understanding of nutrition and a greater knowledge of preventive work have done much to achieve such results, but the influence of environment on the nation must always be considered and improved. Still greater efforts will be necessary if progress is to be maintained. According to existing scientific knowledge many of the fatal cases of infectious diseases could still be prevented, if the public would only make the fullest use of all the public health services available to everyone.

CHAPTER 31

Health and Social Services

The National Health Service Act of 1946 introduced a comprehensive scheme for the provision of free health services for the whole population. Its purpose is to deal with the prevention, diagnosis and treatment of disease and so to improve the physical and mental health of the people. The Department of Health and Social Security is the official governing body, but other ministries, e.g. the Home Office, the Department of Education and Science and the Ministry of Housing and Local Government, are also concerned.

For the convenience of study this Act will be considered in three sections, (1) hospital and special services; (2) general medical and dental services; (3) health services provided by local health authorities.

1. Hospital and specialist services

(a) *Teaching hospitals* are associated with the universities and are responsible for providing medical education and post-graduate courses in all specialised fields of medicine. They are directed by a Board of Governors directly responsible to the Department of Health and Social Security, and usually have a group of small hospitals attached to them.

(b) *All other hospitals* in the fifteen regions of England and Wales are governed by the Regional Hospital Boards who are responsible for their administration, including the maintenance of premises and equipment and the provision of specialist services within the area. The regional Boards appoint Hospital Management Committees to administer the individual hospitals under their control.

(c) *Specialists* or *Consultants* are available for in-patients and out-patients at hospitals and also for patients at home. They may also be called in to local authority health centres.

(d) *Radiographic units*, also directed by the Regional Hospital Boards, are available, within the regions. Some of the units may be mobile and some are provided in hospitals and chest clinics.

(e) *National blood transfusion services* are the responsibility of Regional Hospital Boards. The blood banks have medical directors.

The Regional Nursing Officer is a trained nurse with good administrative experience in public health and nursing. His or her duties consist of liaison between the ministries in all nursing matters, the Hospital Management Boards and the voluntary organisations, and in this way he coordinates the nursing services in the area.

2. General medical and dental services (*including pharmaceutical and ophthalmic services*)

These are administered by an Executive Council within each county or county borough. This council must see that the undermentioned facilities are available.

(a) *Medical and dental practitioners* must be adequately distributed within the area so that the needs of the population can be met. Doctors are paid according to the number of patients on their list. Fees are paid for immunisations and for midwifery if the doctor is on the local list of obstetricians.

(b) *Dental services* are controlled in a similar way. The local authority provides dental care for young children, school children and expectant mothers. This is necessary because there is a shortage of dental practitioners.

(c) *Pharmaceutical services.* It is the responsibility of the Executive Council to supply adequate drugs and appliances under medical or dental prescription. A small charge is made for each article.

(d) *Ophthalmic services* function under the Executive Councils, who are responsible for providing qualified doctors, ophthalmic opticians and dispensing opticians to undertake this work. Optical appliances must also be supplied.

3. Health services provided by local authorities

Local authority health services are provided by county councils and borough councils. They have the following purposes:

(*a*) To provide and equip health centres at which facilities are provided for all local health services, together with medical, dental, pharmaceutical and specialist services.

(*b*) To supervise the provisions of the Midwives' Acts and to provide adequate midwifery services e.g. ante-natal, post-natal and infant welfare centres as well as facilities for hospital and home confinements.

(c) To ensure that there is adequate home visiting by health visitors encouraging good mental and physical health.

(d) To provide a home nursing service.

(e) To arrange facilities for vaccination and immunisation.

(f) To provide an ambulance service to take mentally and physically sick persons, and expectant mothers to hospitals or clinics.

(g) To provide care or after-care for the mentally ill.

(h) To provide a home help service for expectant or lying-in mothers, in cases of illness in the home and for aged persons and, in some instances, for the mentally subnormal or for handicapped persons.

(i) To provide a cleansing station and disinfecting services.

(j) To ensure good environmental conditions.

(k) To investigate epidemics of infectious diseases within the area.

The health and social services of any area are available for everyone living in the district and they are organised for the express purpose of promoting health and preventing disease. This is not a charity or voluntary organisation, but a provision made compulsory by Act of Parliament, which is financed jointly by the national insurance contributions and by the exchequer. These services should be used to the fullest extent by all members of the community.

Officers and services in the public health field

The Medical Officer of Health

This is the chief administrative officer of the local health department. He is a doctor with a special qualification in public health work. The function of the Medical Officer is to promote health within his area. He must be aware of social and environmental conditions in the district which may cause illness.

He is responsible for advising his Council on all matters relating to health and he compiles a detailed annual report to be presented to the Minister of Health and Social Security which includes all vital statistics. According to the size and population of the district he may have a deputy medical officer and possibly in larger areas several assistants all possessing similar qualifications.

Superintendent health visitor

In large towns a supervising health visitor is appointed to administer and direct the work of the health visitors department and she is directly responsible to the Medical Officer of Health.

The health visitor

A health visitor is a State Registered Nurse, a certificated midwife, or holds Part I of the Midwifery Certificate, and she has had special training in social and public health work and has gained the Certificate of the Royal Society of Health. The Notification of Births Act has made it compulsory for all births to be notified to the Medical Officer of Health within 36 hours. The local health authority, by good co-operation with maternity hospitals and domiciliary midwives, is able to ensure that a health visitor calls on the mother without delay to advise and guide her regarding the care of her baby. Follow-up visits will depend partly on circumstances found within the home and partly on whether or not the mother attends the child welfare centre.

The health visitor acts as a health teacher in the home and also at maternity and child welfare centres under the direction of the Medical Officer of Health. Her work is to guide and advise mothers in order to build up good mental and physical health and to prevent disease. The health visitor is usually well known in her district and mothers are at liberty to call her in if they wish to discuss their difficulties. She works in close association with the family doctor and knows what facilities are available for special problems she may encounter in the course of her duties. The health and welfare of the aged, the physically handicapped, the chronically sick and those mentally ill are also her concern, and in some rural areas she may combine her duties with school nursing, home nursing and midwifery. In towns she seldom does any actual nursing herself.

The health visitor can be of great assistance to the matrons of day nurseries because she knows the backgrounds of the children admitted to nurseries and can often explain the reason for difficult behaviour. In the same way, her records may be very useful to the Children's Committees when children have to be taken into care. Anyone can contact the health visitor at the local Health Department.

The domiciliary midwife

She is a trained midwife capable of conducting normal confinements in the homes of her patients. She must adhere to the rules laid down by the Central Midwives Board, e.g. she can give the patient an inhalation analgesic only if she has had instruction and proved herself to be efficient. She must take a refresher course in midwifery if she has been out of practice for five years or more.

Most local health authorities have a domiciliary midwifery scheme, of which they are the supervising body. The midwife must give ante-natal care to the expectant mother in the home if she is to be respon-sible for the delivery, or she must ensure that the mother to be attends an antenatal clinic. In any emergency she must call a general practitioner or arrange for an ambulance to take the patient to hospital.

The birth of a baby must be notified to the Medical Officer of Health within 36 hours, and the midwife must notify the existence of any abnormal condition that may have developed in the baby or mother. On the completion of her duties she will notify the Medical Officer of Health and then the health visitor will visit the mother within a few days.

As more and more women are having their babies in hospital, but often staying in for only two or three days, the domiciliary midwives attend these patients up to the tenth day after delivery.

In large counties or county boroughs a superintendent home nurse is employed in order to organise and direct the service.

The home nurse

Previously known as a district nurse, the home nurse is, as a rule, a State Registered Nurse, but some authorities employ State Enrolled Assistant Nurses. The home nurse is employed by the local health authority, and her services are free to everyone; her work in the home is carried out on the instructions of the family doctor. Her patients may include those who are ill but not in need of hospitalisation, the chronic sick, the aged and people who have been discharged from hospitals. If she is directed to do so by the doctor, she gives injections and carries out any necessary surgical dressings. Medical appliances and equipment may be lent to her by the local health authority or the Red Cross. In some areas male nurses are employed and night nurses are available.

In rural areas home nursing, health visiting and midwifery may be undertaken by one suitably qualified person (see p. 359).

Tuberculosis advice

Usually a health visitor is employed by the local health autho-rity, and attached to a chest clinic, who is responsible for the pre-vention of the disease and the care of patients with tuberculosis and those in contact with them. She can give advice about the personal and financial problems that a long illness like tuberculosis may bring. Tuberculosis is a notifiable disease and the visitor must report all cases to the Medical Officer of Health. She may also be responsible for people who suffer from other chest conditions, such as chronic bronchitis.

Mobile mass radiography units have in the past played an important part in the detection of the early stages of tuberculosis, but with the dramatic decline in the incidence of this condition, they are gradually being phased out, the chest clinics now providing adequate services.

BCG vaccine is given to all tuberculosis contacts and is also available to school children.

Home help service

This is provided by the local health authority. A charge is made to cover the cost but in some circumstances, e.g. in the case of a poor home, a reduction may be made and, occasionally, the service is given free.

The home help does the cooking and domestic work, but undertakes no nursing duties. Her services may be necessary for the sick, aged or infirm who are living alone, or to help families if the mother is ill or in hospital, or where there is a mentally sick child in the home. Sometimes expectant mothers may need domestic help both before and after confinement.

A few local authorities have night attendants who may be sent to care for the chronic sick. Applications for any of these helpers must be made to the local authority direct.

The medical social worker

She is a trained social worker usually in a hospital. Although not employed by the local authority her work brings her into close contact with officers concerned with preventive medicine. Her duties are to investigate the background and social needs of patients and to maintain a liaison with all other social workers. She may make arrangements for convalescence and, in some circumstances, she may be able to arrange financial aid for parents to visit a child in hospital.

The public health inspector

This official was formerly known as a sanitary inspector. He holds the certificate of the Royal Society of Health. In large towns he may have several trained assistants, to whom he can allocate responsibility for certain sections of the work. He deals with a wide variety of matters, e.g. water, housing defects, atmosphere pollution, inspection of food, pet shops, factories and slaughter houses. He must also supervise the control of rats and other vermin, the removal of refuse, the ensuring of satisfactory sanitation, and the provision of disinfection services for premises, bedding and clothing following infection. His work plays a very important part in preventing outbreaks of food poisoning or other serious infections. The Chief Inspector is responsible to the local Medical Officer of Health, to whom he must make an annual report to be included in the Medical Officer's annual report to the Ministry of Health.

Disinfection unit

This is often called the cleansing station and it provides a service controlled by the local health authority; the public health inspector is in charge of it. After infection has existed in a home or nursery, bedding, toys, books, and clothing are collected in covered vans (free of charge) and taken to the unit where they are thoroughly disinfected.

The disinfection unit also treats verminous conditions in both children and adults.

Although the treatment may be done in a thorough and systematic manner it is better to clean the verminous head of a young child in the home or in the nursery rather than run the risk of making him feel guilty of an offence quite out of his control. Parents are advised if the school child has vermin and given directions as to how to treat the hair. If the child is not treated at home, then the local authority has power to do it (see p. 358).

Public baths and wash-houses

Public baths are the responsibility of the local health authority. The water in the swimming pool must be chlorinated and changed regularly. Bathrooms are available for anyone who wishes to have a hot bath.

The wash-house service is of great value to families living in rooms with few facilities for washing. It is fully equipped with all the essentials for laundry work, including ironing and airing.

Ambulance service

Ambulances and hospital cars are provided by the local health authority to take unfit people from place to place when necessary.

This generally means from home to hospital or clinic and back again. The service is free, but except in emergencies can only be ordered by the family doctor or hospital.

Health centres

Although health centres were recommended in the National Health Service Act these have been very slow in getting under way largely because of the cost. However, they are gradually coming into being particularly in the new towns and ideally should consist of the following units:

(a) Central lecture hall, which should be fitted and equipped for lectures, film shows and demonstrations. To assist health teaching, gas and electric cookers should be provided.

(b) Infant welfare unit, consisting of waiting room, weighing room, doctor's room, and store room.

(c) Immunisation and vaccination clinics.

(d) Dental unit, consisting of waiting room, surgery and recovery room.

(e) Waiting rooms and treatment rooms would be provided for services provided by the local authority, e.g. sunlight, chiropody, etc.

(f) Waiting rooms and consultants' rooms for special clinics, e.g. eyes, ear, nose and throat, orthopaedic, etc.

(g) Waiting rooms and consulting rooms for general practitioners.

(h) Antenatal rooms, consisting of a waiting room fitted with dressing cubicles, from which the patient can go straight into the doctor's consulting room. Also used for post-natal work.

(i) Department for the sale of dried milks, vitamins or any other articles prescribed by the child welfare centre doctor.

(j) Staff rooms.

(k) Lavatory accommodation for mothers, children and staff.

(l) Covered pram shed.

(m) Toddlers' play room.

(n) School clinic.

If suitable accommodation is available several clinics may be functioning at the same time, which encourages good coordination between the specialists in charge of the various departments and with general practitioners.

Child welfare centres

Although eventually all child welfare work should be carried out in the health centres, at present it is done very largely in child welfare centres. These may be in buildings specially built for the purpose but they are often in improvised premises such as church halls.

The general organisation of the work is done by the centre superintendent, with health visitor experience. Local health visitors attend the infants' and toddlers' clinics on certain days when they meet the mothers from their own districts, and are able to discuss any special problems of a child or his family *with the mother and the centre doctor.*

Clerks are employed in many centres to handle the investigation and sale or distribution of dried milk, vitamin supplements, etc., and voluntary workers give valuable assistance in some centres by doing all sorts of jobs during the sessions. The right type of voluntary worker is essential; she must be really interested in the cause, appreciate the importance of the work and, above all, be regular in her attendance. Good help of this kind frees the trained worker to devote her time to advising the mothers.

In rural districts the child welfare centre services are usually limited to consultation sessions once a week. Accommodation is mostly provided in the local hall, which means that all equipment must be stored away after each session. The local health visitor and a doctor are in attendance. Excellent health education can be given, although mothers may have to travel considerable distances if children require special treatments.

All child welfare centres usually display a board giving the dates and times of sessions. All mothers are welcome to bring their children to these consultations.

Consultations and weighing sessions for children under two years of age. The young baby is weighed without clothes by the health visitor, who observes the child's condition and discusses any problems that may be raised by the mother. At the first visit the doctor will examine the baby and give any necessary advice. The mother will be encouraged to attend the centre at regular intervals, which are planned in accordance with the child's needs.

If the doctor's findings make this desirable, the child may be investigated by a specialist in regard to his hearing, sight, mental condition, physical state (e.g. deformity), or for any suspected defect. All prematurely born babies should be observed with particular care. Young, inexperienced mothers are taught the general principles of child care.

Breast feeding is encouraged and test weighing is done in difficult cases. Failing the establishment of natural feeding, the doctor prescribes the artificial feed, and if a dried milk is used the mother can purchase this at the welfare centre at cost price, together with the cod liver oil and orange juice, but in some areas there may be other arrangements for obtaining these.

Directions are often written out for feeding and the health visitor will teach the mother how to make up the feed stressing the importance of cleanliness.

Records of each visit to the centre are accurately kept, with the health visitor's details of her visits to the home.

The child aged two to five years

Any child who has been delicate and slow in his physical and mental growth should attend for examination at least once a month. After the age of two the healthy child need not attend so frequently. In many areas it is now the practice to have toddler's sessions where the children from two to five years attend by appointment, at intervals of three to six months, when they have a full medical examination, including physical and mental aspects and, if necessary, treatment is advised. When the child is five years old and he becomes the responsibility of the local education authority, the records of the child's medical progress are then transferred to this authority.

Special sessions

Vaccination and immunisation clinics

Mothers can have their children protected against smallpox, tuberculosis, whooping cough, tetanus, measles, diphtheria, poliomyelitis, and typhoid if required.

Mothers are given a special card on which a record is made each time the child is immunised or vaccinated, and the card is transferred to the school medical service when the child reaches the age of five years. It is therefore necessary to take care of the card, so that it can be produced when required. The protection can be given by the family doctor if the mother prefers this. Directives on vaccination and immunisation are given by the Department of Health and Social Security in England to the local health authorities and by the Scottish Home and Health Department to Scottish local authorities. These are revised when necessary.

Dental care

This can be provided in large child welfare centres and is a valuable preventive service. If the child has previously attended the same clinic he will know the centre and will be happier about his treatment here than he would be in strange surroundings. Early dental care promotes healthier permanent teeth and therefore better general health.

Deafness

Provision should be made for the investigation of any signs of defective hearing in the very young child, and he should be taught in his earliest months to accept a hearing aid if this is necessary.

The Orthopaedic Clinic

This is extremely valuable in providing for the correction of defects and in the early recognition of serious conditions which, untreated, could lead to severe handicap in later life (see Chapter 25).

The Ophthalmic Clinic

This performs a valuable service in the early diagnosis of eye defects. Mothers often worry about the slightest sign of squint in a young baby and often it is difficult to convince them that this may right itself and is, in any case, amenable to treatment.

The existence of all these special clinics in or near the welfare centre has many advantages to both mother and child. They tend to accept the services offered because they know the centre and the staff, which is a great help in dealing with young children.

Health education (physical and mental)

These subjects should occupy much of the health visitor's time. Adequate demonstration materials should be available. Mothers particularly enjoy seeing films. The great majority of the women who attend these are practical rather than theoretical, a fact that should be borne in mind during teaching sessions. On such occasions it is a great help to both mothers and the teacher if the children are cared for by a voluntary helper in a separate room.

Behaviour problems

These, in children, can be a source of great anxiety to parents. They should be advised to attend a child guidance clinic with a note from the doctor. Sometimes, in the case of problem families, the family doctor may have good understanding of the difficulties within the home and be able to cooperate with the child guidance clinic.

Practical classes

These are given for mothers in such subjects as cookery, needlework and handicrafts, all of which are useful in the home. When such classes are being given, the children must be occupied and supervised in another room. When mothers see the play materials provided at the welfare centre, they gain ideas as to what to buy in the way of toys for use at home.

Clubs for mothers or parents

These provide a variety of interests for all concerned, including discussion groups, lectures and social gatherings. Broadening of the parents' general interests is something that indirectly reflects upon the children to the general benefit of the family.

Convalescence

Convalescent care is an essential part of any health scheme for children and mothers. Convalescent homes may be administered by voluntary societies, who receive recognition in the form of a grant from the Department of Health and Social Security, by hospital Boards or local health authorities. The patients are usually recommended for vacancies through the local authorities.

Antenatal care

This is essential to every pregnant woman (*a*) to insure good health during pregnancy, a normal delivery and a speedy return to full health; (*b*) to have a healthy full term baby; (*c*) to ensure a good physical and mental relationship between mother and child.

The mother will be guided by the doctor and health visitor or midwife as to the best arrangement to make for her confinement.

When a midwife is to deliver the baby at home, she will visit the home to guide and help the mother in preparing for the confinement and will usually advise her to attend the antenatal clinic at the child welfare centre for a medical examination when the midwife would be present. The midwife must give antenatal care, or know that the mother is having this care. Maternity hospitals or maternity wards usually have an antenatal clinic for all booked patients. Nursing homes may or may not give antenatal care, but the person engaged for the confinement would be responsible for ensuring that the mother was under supervision during this period.

Antenatal clinics provided by the local health authority are usually held at the maternity and child welfare centres and anyone may attend. There is a doctor in attendance who has specialised in this work and a trained visitor or midwife. During these sessions courses of instruction are given on hygiene, general nutrition, relaxation, breast feeding and the care of the infant. Dental treatment is available for all patients. Mothers should attend each month until they are six months pregnant, then at fortnightly intervals or as advised by the doctor. In most clinics relaxation classes are held each week, with a physiotherapist in charge.

Any complications arising in pregnancy are immediately referred to hospital for further advice or treatment.

Postnatal care

It is recommended that all mothers should have a postnatal examination about five weeks after the baby is born. This should take place whatever antenatal care has been given. In some child welfare centres special days are set aside for this work but in most areas it is combined with the antenatal work.

Maternity benefit. The mother receives a grant of money to help cover any costs incurred at this time whether she is confined at home or in the hospital.

Child minders receive children into their own homes during the daytime in exchange for payment. If more than two children are taken the minder must register with the local health authority and the house is then regularly inspected. A satisfactory standard of hygiene and child care and good nutrition are demanded. The registration may be cancelled at any time if the care of the children is poor or the conditions in any way unsatisfactory.

The local health authority may inspect any premises if there is reason to believe that children are being received there for payment.

This provision was made when many day nurseries were being closed because local authorities considered them to be too costly.

Nursery Provision

This is a wide term and includes day nurseries, short stay nurseries, residential nurseries, nursery schools, and nursery classes. These will be discussed separately because they are the responsibility of different departments.

Day nurseries

Late in the nineteenth century the first nursery movement was started in France to enable mothers to work in industry. The nursery was then spoken of as a crèche. Britain opened several such places in towns where women were employed in industry. These were run by voluntary bodies and the mothers usually paid about ten shillings a week, the remainder of the cost being paid from voluntary contributions. During the 1939–45 war the then Ministry of Health permitted local authorities in consultation with the Ministry of Labour to open nurseries wherever necessary in order to free mothers to enter industry. In areas where nurseries had never existed it took a little time before the mothers had confidence to leave their children, although they very much appreciated the benefits which the children derived from the care given in the day nurseries.

Under the Nurseries and Child Minders Regulations Act of 1948, it is the duty of the local health authority to register all day nurseries and to ensure that each is a suitable place to accommodate children in the day-time. The day nursery is run by the local health authority, who is responsible to the Department of Health and Social Security. Children are admitted from the age of one month to five years, although in many areas the Medical Officer of Health will not allow children under six months into the day nursery, because it is felt that the proper place for any baby is in his own home in the care of his own mother. Some local authorities make exceptions and accept an illegitimate baby when the mother is anxious to work but wants to keep her baby and make a home for him. Other instances of economic difficulties caused by illness of the husband or widowhood are also sympathetically considered.

The Department of Health and Social Security makes regulations about the qualifications of the staff and the ratio of staff to children according to age, with domestic helpers in addition. Regulations also govern the number of children to be admitted to each age group in the nursery and the minimum floor space required for each child according to his age. The local authority's weekly charges vary according to the family income.

The Department of Health and Social Security and the Department of Education and Science make regular routine inspections of the day nurseries which are training nursery students.

Day nurseries are invaluable to the unmarried mother who is working and is anxious to keep her baby herself. If she is young and inexperienced she can benefit through her contact with the nursery staff, who will always discuss any of her problems with understanding and sympathy. There is no doubt too, that day nurseries can be a really valuable social service in relation to problem families. Many such homes may be due to ignorance of the parents, to the low mentality or poor health of the mother or possibly to poor living accommodation. Placing the child in the nursery for a time may relieve the mother and give her a chance to improve in health and thus be able to maintain a better home for her family in the future and prevent the breaking up of the home. Children living in flats can benefit by having a few hours in a day nursery where they can have more varied and interesting occupations with complete freedom. The 'only' child will find companions of his own age, so essential for him.

Nurseries must be considered as an extension of the home and not as a separate provision. Parents' clubs, giving a good opportunity for health teaching, should be encouraged. Mothers and fathers can contribute largely to the successful running of a nursery by helping in all sorts of ways, and thus, instead of the parents having less responsibility, they are encouraged to take an even keener interest in the nursery life of their children. Usually the child who has been in a good happy day nursery will adjust himself more easily to school life.

Care of deprived children

Deprived children are the concern of the local authority and there is a children's officer in every local authority area who is responsible for them.

The Children Act, 1958: Child Protection

A foster child is a child below the school leaving age who, for a financial return, is maintained for a period of over one month in the home of a person who is not a relative. The local authority must ensure that all foster children in their area are visited and that the visiting officer is satisfied that such children are well cared for. The officer submits a report on all visits that he makes.

A child is *not* a foster child while he is in the care of a local authority or voluntary organisation, or boarded out by an education authority, or is in a hospital or approved school, or if a parent, relative or guardian is living in the same house.

Inspections are made of all premises in which foster children are living or in which it is proposed that they shall live. The local authority controls the number of foster children that may be placed in one home.

Boarding-out regulations

These apply in the case of children boarded with foster parents by the local authority or by *Voluntary Societies*. Each child must have a medical examination and the doctor reports on his physical and mental health and indicates whether or not he is fit to be boarded out. Regular visits are made to the home and reports are submitted on the child's health, conduct and progress. Children in the care of local authorities, and children in institutions run by voluntary societies may be orphans, children whose parents are unable to care for them and are therefore taken temporarily into care. Children and young persons guilty of delinquent acts and in need of care.

Residential nurseries

These may be run by the local authority or by voluntary societies such as Dr. Barnardo's, or the National Children's Home or the Church of England's Children's Society. All homes are regularly inspected by officers from the Home Office and the Department of Education and Science.

The children in residential nurseries may be orphans or illegitimate children, or their own home conditions may be harmful. When two or more children are admitted from one family every effort is made to keep them together in the same group. The children may be resident for long periods and it is essential for such provision to be made to meet all emergencies. Later it may be possible to place the children in suitable private homes with *foster parents*.

As these children are without the security of their parents, it is very important for the staff of a residential nursery to be prepared to give the children the best environment and care in order to ensure happiness and true development. The matron is usually a trained nurse who has had experience with normal healthy children, and if there are children between the ages of two and five years, there should be a nursery school teacher or a warden to be responsible for this age group during school hours.

The ideal plan for all residential nurseries is to arrange the children in small groups of not more than ten, with ages ranging from one year to seven years, and in some nurseries they remain and go to the local school until about eleven years old. With such an arrangement there can at least be a resemblance to family life, as each group should have

N

one person (the house mother) responsible for their care (see Fig. 73). In this way the children are given stability and a sense of security by having at least one adult who understands them and to whom they can always go when they require her help. In normal home life a

FIG. 73. Home conditions that children should experience in residential care.

child acquires his own possessions which are very precious to him, and in a residential nursery facilities should be provided to allow each child to keep his own personal things to which he attaches great value and which are possibly a contact with home.

Meals should be served to the individual units, except perhaps on very special occasions such as parties, when the greater numbers would be appreciated by all. Much of the point of family life is lost if all the groups unite each day for all meals. The older children will naturally go to their nursery school room during school hours under the nursery school teacher's supervision, when the toddlers in each group will meet one another. After nursery school the child returning to his own family group will take part in their activities, and will possibly relate his day's experiences to his group mother. Preparations for bedtime are much more homelike in a small group than in a larger group of children all the same age.

In all such homes one great difficulty is to provide some male element to replace the lack of their normal home life. Children enjoy contact with men and they benefit by it. Therefore it is important to

FIG. 74. Matron's dog is good company –
some children enjoy a pet.

arrange some contacts with men with whom the children can talk and play through the actual working of the home. Men who work in the nursery or in the garden can be a very great value to the children.

The person responsible for running such nurseries must ensure that the children have opportunities to learn something about the world outside, just as a normal child at home would do, otherwise they cannot gain a true picture of life and may find it hard to adjust themselves in later years. The children are most interested to hear about the home or parents of any members of the staff and are delighted if they can actually go on a visit and meet these people.

Foster parents

No matter how good a residential nursery is, it cannot give as good a background to the child as a normal home can do. Therefore, the children's officer, assisted by boarding-out officers, tries to find suitable foster parents with whom the child can live as a member of their family, and about half the children under local authority care are with foster parents. Great care is taken in selecting these homes, because it is essential for the child and the foster parents to be able to adjust themselves to one another. The child must be allowed time to get fond of the foster parents, and some children are slow in making friends, but this process must never be rushed. If the home proves to be suitable then the child will live there until his education is completed. When eighteen years old, he will no longer be the responsibility of the local authority. Foster parents sometimes adopt the child.

In some cases the child may remain with his foster parents, as he considers this to be his home even after he is eighteen years old, which is a very satisfactory position.

Short-stay nurseries

These are administered and maintained in the same way as residential nurseries, the children being termed 'deprived' children during their stay in the nursery.

They provide full residence for children up to five years of age when emergencies arise in the home, for example, when a mother is confined or ill.

Adoption of children

Any person adopting a child must be at least *twenty-five years of age*, and twenty-one years older than the child to be adopted. Arrangements for adoption may be made through a local authority, a registered adoption society, or by agreement between the parent and the adopter, but the final stage must always be by an application to the court for an adoption order to be made.

The Adoption Act states that there shall be a probationary period of at least three months, and during this time the child lives in the home of his adopters and cannot be moved unless by a court order. The local authority is notified of the pending adoption and the children's officer in the area of the adopter is responsible for the supervision of the child during the probationary period. Before an order is made, the court must be satisfied that the order will be for the benefit of the child, that all necessary consents have been obtained and that the adoption is not being made for payment. It is clear to the parents that they are giving up all parental rights. Any unsatisfactory reports will prevent the adoption order being granted. When the order has been made, the adoption is registered at Somerset House and the child is given a new birth certificate. The person who adopts the child assumes the parents' responsibilities and by law becomes the child's legal guardian and the child in turn is heir to his adoptive parents.

Medical aspects of adoption. It is advisable in all cases of adoption that the health of the child and his parents be investigated and also that of the adopters. This is done by local authorities and adoption societies to ensure that defects are known and that their importance for the future can be considered.

Illegitimate children

Although unmarried mothers and their children have lost most of the stigma formerly attached to them, there are still many problems which they have to face. The support of family or friends during pregnancy plays a vital part in the girl's general well-being. After the baby is born she will still need help and friendship, whether she decides to keep the baby and face the financial problems this will entail, or whether she arranges to have it adopted and submit to the acute psychological stress this is bound to bring.

There are *Mother and Baby Homes*, run by the local health authority and in some instances by voluntary societies, where the girl can go before her baby is born and during her residence there she can be given instruction on baby care, nutrition, hygiene and relaxation. If she has her baby in hospital she will return to the home after the birth for a few weeks. If it is at all possible the mother must not be separated from her baby. Some find domestic work where they can have the baby with them, and some are able to place the infant in a day nursery, do daily work and have the child at night and at weekends.

In many instances, where day nursery provision is not available, illegitimate children are placed in residential nurseries, which usually means that the mother has little opportunity of visiting and really knowing her baby. The child may be placed with foster parents, and quite frequently, in despair, the unmarried mother agrees to have the infant adopted. Such a step needs much consideration, as she may very much regret it later on.

The mother must register the birth, but the father's name does not appear on the certificate unless requested by the father and the mother. Much good work is done by social and welfare workers in assisting mothers to obtain an affiliation order on the father of the child, which means that the father would be ordered to pay a sum of money (not exceeding £2.50) each week to the mother for the maintenance of the child.

The infant mortality rate of illegitimate children is much higher than that of legitimate children.

Family planning

Most local authorities run family planning clinics usually in conjunction with the Family Planning Association. Advice on planning families and on the use of contraceptives is given free of charge, though a charge is normally made for the supplying of contraceptive devices. This service is doing much to reduce the numbers of unwanted children and thus to cut down on the numbers of problem families and of children who might have to come under local authority care of one sort or another.

Nursery schools and nursery classes

Rachel and Margaret Macmillan were successful pioneers of nursery school work. The nursery schools take children from two years to five years.

The average number accommodated is usually forty. One of the earliest kindergartens was founded in 1873. This was free to children from two to six years, giving them meals, baths, and general care including play, rest and sleep. Nursery schools open during school hours and usually they are closed during school holidays. The nursery school is under the supervision of a *nursery school teacher*, who may have trained and untrained assistants. In some areas nursery nurse students take part of their training in the nursery school and part in a day nursery, or a residential nursery.

Nursery schools, as opposed to day nurseries, are run by the local education authority under the Department of Education and Science. Although the Education Act of 1944 empowered local authorities to provide nursery schools, very few were established because of a shortage of money, and in the 1950's the Government prevented the establishment of any more believing that all available resources should be spent on older children. However the *Plowden Report of 1967* underlined the vital importance of nursery education particularly in underprivileged areas, and so gradually some of the restrictions are being removed.

The premises must be spacious, to meet regulation standards, well ventilated, with good heating arrangements. A good garden and playground are essential for providing the necessary outdoor activities. Washing facilities and toddlers' lavatories are provided according to the regulations and standards for schools. A good midday meal is provided and a morning drink is given in many nursery schools. The parents pay for meals but the milk is free. The children have a large selection of play materials and the opportunity for play with companionship, combined with the necessary routine, in which good food, rest, sleep, exercise, fresh air and a happy atmosphere play a large part. There is no doubt that children benefit from attending a nursery school, and particularly those from poor homes, the only child, or the difficult child.

Regular medical inspection is arranged and in some schools the health visitor pays a daily or weekly visit. The good nursery school can regard itself as an extension to the home, and by cooperation with the parents the good work done in the nursery school can be continued in the home. Many nursery school superintendents run *Parents' Clubs* which stimulate the interest of the parents and in this way promote better child care.

Part-time nursery schools have been tried in some areas with reasonable success. The children come for the morning or for the afternoon, thus enabling a greater number of children to benefit. This service is now expanding because of the acute shortage of nursery schools.

Nursery school classes have been developed and are increasing in some areas where there is a lack of nursery schools. These classes are usually attached to the infant school and are run by a nursery school teacher, who has young assistants who are under the guidance of the head teacher. The class consists of twenty to twenty-five children from three to five years. The room is equipped with suitable furniture and all necessary play materials, and cloakroom and lavatory accommodation is provided. As in the nursery school a morning drink of milk is provided and a good midday dinner.

Voluntary associations sometimes run playgroups or play centres in densely populated areas, where it is recognised that many children, especially those living in high blocks of flats, need companionship and the opportunity to play in safety. Inadequate staffing and lack of suitable accommodation means there are not nearly enough of these centres, and those that do exist are usually only open for two or three days a week. Women with experience in the care of children are in charge and there is usually a small payment. The establishment has to be approved by the local authority.

The School Medical Service

The *Local Education Authority* is responsible for the medical and dental supervision and treatment of all school children and of all children attending nursery schools and nursery classes.

Treatments which may be provided free at a School Clinic are:

(a) *Dental* treatment.
(b) *Minor ailment* treatment (including skin diseases).
(c) *Ear*, *nose* and *throat* treatment.
(d) *Remedial exercises* for physical defects, such as knock knees, bow legs, and many other conditions.
(e) *Speech therapy* for speech difficulties.
(f) Treatment for *nutritional disorders* or *malnutrition*.
(g) *Child guidance* clinics.

Specialists are consulted at the clinic or in hospitals, and they report to the school medical officers, and advise on any essential treatment. The school medical officer should notify the family doctor of all conditions being treated.

The scheme for vaccination and immunisation continues throughout the child's period at school.

The school medical service also includes the provision of medical care of all handicapped children (see p. 380).

Much is done in the schools to prevent and control the spread of infection. The law requires that there must be good sanitation, lavatories in sufficient numbers for the children accommodated at the school and an adequate number of wash hand basins. Suitable cloak rooms and facilities for recreation are further essentials.

The *school medical officer* is appointed by the local health authority and is responsible for school medical inspections. Each child has

FIG. 75. A seven year old with his own special friend.

three medical examinations during his school years, but the parents or teacher may ask to have a child examined more frequently. Parents are invited to attend all medical inspections. Records are kept of each child's general condition and of all medical or dental treatment. If any defect is found in a child, he will be examined more often and sent for special treatment.

The *school nurse* attends all school medical inspections and visits the schools and homes in instances when the parents are not taking the child for treatment advised by the school medical officer. The *school clinic* is open daily, when a school nurse is in attendance. It is now considered desirable for the school nurse to have health visitor qualifications. It is important that there should be good liaison between the school health service and the *family doctor* as the child is, in fact, his patient, as long as he is registered with him.

Verminous conditions

The school nurse is responsible for examining the children for any unclean conditions. If a child is found to be verminous, his mother is advised on what treatment to give, but if the condition does not improve the child can be excluded from school. In persistent cases the child can be taken to the cleansing station for disinfestation (see p. 362).

Accidents at schools

Accidents usually happen in the playground at recreation periods. A certain amount of adult supervision is therefore absolutely necessary. The playground should have a safe surface and be of a suitable size. Infants and older children should not be mixed, overcrowding should be avoided. *First aid equipment* must be available and at least some members of the staff should have a knowledge of first aid. *School crossing patrols* should, if possible, be provided and these have saved many road accidents.

The handicapped child

The local education authority must make provision for children who, because of a *physical* or *mental* disability, are unable to be educated in an ordinary school.

Special schools are provided for the:
(a) Blind and partially blind child.
(b) Deaf and partially deaf child.
(c) Crippled child.
(d) Epileptic child.
(e) Child with defective speech.
(f) Diabetic child.
(g) Delicate child.
(h) Educationally subnormal child, (mentally handicapped, but not severely subnormal).
(i) Maladjusted child.

In some instances, when the child's disability is not very severe, it may be possible for him to have tuition specially adapted to his needs in an ordinary school. The full-time education of handicapped children continues until they are eighteen years old and every effort is made to fit them to be able to earn their own living by including training in several trades. *Residential schools* are necessary because these children come from wide areas. Some cater for only one defect, e.g. deafness or blindness, but some schools cater for multiple handi-caps. The principal of such a school encourages good cooperation with the parents. Staff in these schools are specially trained and the children receive constant medical and dental care throughout their school life.

Mental Health Act, 1959

Mental Health Review Tribunals have been set up to undertake the responsibility for administering the provisions of this Act.

Prevention of mental ill-health

Early recognition of emotional disturbances in young children, which are often caused by the ignorance of parents or of those in charge of children, is essential if worse trouble is to be avoided later. The family doctor can educate the family to appreciate the need for mental hygiene, and the health visitor can do much to guide the mother in respect of behaviour problems.

Maladjusted children provide many behaviour problems which can be classed into various groups, e.g. behaviour disorders, habit disorders and emotional disturbances. Many behaviour difficulties can be traced back to infancy. They may be due to health conditions or handicaps, mental or physical, and all such children need careful, often prolonged, observation before a definite diagnosis can be made.

Child guidance services

These are provided by the Regional Hospital Boards at out-patient departments, by education authorities, or by voluntary associations.

Child guidance clinics

The purposes of these clinics are (*a*) to assess the behaviour of the child and to try to prevent maladjustment; (*b*) to cooperate with other services or individuals who may be able to help a maladjusted child; and (*c*) to encourage good mental health education.

Child guidance clinics must be run in close cooperation with family doctors, paediatricians and the local health and education services. The staff usually consists of a consultant child psychiatrist, an educational psychologist and psychiatric social workers. To co-ordinate the work, other authorities, e.g. the school medical officer, health visitors and speech therapists, may attend from time to time when their advice is required, as their knowledge of the child's background may be helpful and thus enable a true assessment of the child's behaviour to be made and in this way the right treatment can be given to the child.

The atmosphere of a child guidance clinic must be friendly and the clinic should be furnished in a home-like way. It is best for this unit to be situated quite apart from other services.

The mentally handicapped child

Mental subnormality may exist in varying degrees, ranging from the child who can be taught simple things to those who appear to be unteachable. The child may have been born subnormal or the condition may have developed from many causes, including cerebral injury at birth, metabolic disorders, e.g. cretinism, phenylketonuria and glactosaemia (see Chapter 27), or for many other reasons. The child's mental condition may be first recognised by his parents, by a health visitor, or by his teacher at school.

The education of the handicapped child. This will naturally be influenced by the degree of the defect. The child may attend a nursery school where he may be slow to learn certain procedures, although he may well gain by his attendance there. By five years of age, he will not have reached the normal mental age of five years. Provision is made by the education authority for a child who will not benefit by class teaching to attend an occupational centre, where he will be given simple instruction in drawing, music, singing and speech, thus developing his interests and giving him a certain pleasure in any progress of which he may be capable. The parents must report to the school medical officer if they do not send the child for this training.

Home teaching. This is more often practised in rural areas where a centre is not available. The child will usually benefit from this teaching, but he will lack the incentives provided by group teaching in the centre scheme.

Home teaching is provided for any child who cannot benefit from the occupation centre.

Treatment centres for venereal diseases

It is the responsibility of the regional boards to establish treatment centres; they are usually in hospitals, and the Medical Officer of Health deals mostly with the social and welfare side of the work. Times and places for V.D. treatment are published locally or can be obtained from any public health department, child welfare centre or from the family doctor. Anyone who may be in doubt or worried about any symptoms they may have, can be thoroughly examined and if necessary be treated. All treatment is confidential and free of charge.

Voluntary societies

The development and expansion of the officially organised health, education and social services in the last fifty years has to a great extent been due to pioneer efforts made by voluntary societies. In several instances these societies have received financial aid, without losing their voluntary status, in recognition of their valuable work. Many of these voluntary societies in conjunction with the official social services are doing excellent work at the present time. Being voluntary they have certain advantages in their methods of approach, as they are freer to act than local authorities controlled by the various ministries. In the present health service the number of professional social workers has grown enormously, but the voluntary social worker is still used on quite a large scale throughout the country. During recent years these activities have been slightly restricted because of other duties, but nevertheless they play an important part in the social services of the country.

The Seebohm Report 1968

The Seebohm Report proposes a complete reorganisation of the social services in order to provide a much more coordinated service which sees people less as individual units but as members of families and as parts of the whole local community. To this end it proposes the setting up of a new Social Service Department which will include:

(a) The present services provided by the children's departments.

(b) The welfare services provided under the National Assistance Act 1948.

(c) Educational services and child guidance health services.

(d) The home help service, mental health social work services, adult training centres, other social work services and day nurseries, provided by local health departments.

(e) Certain social welfare work currently undertaken by some housing departments.

This new department would work in close cooperation with the health and education departments.

The Redcliffe-Maud Report 1969

This report is concerned with the reorganisation of local government and so will have a direct bearing on the social services. It recommends that England (excluding London) should be divided into 61 new local government areas each including town and country. In all but three a single authority should be responsible for all services, and in the three larger ones around Birmingham, Liverpool, and Manchester, responsibility should be divided between a metropolitan authority, and a number of metropolitan district authorities; the latter would be concerned with the social services education, health and housing. This is a somewhat similar arrangement to the division of responsibility between the Greater London Council and the London boroughs. At the time of writing it seems unlikely that this report will be implemented in the near future.

The social and health services and education services have grown up in a somewhat haphazard way over the years and the most important factor in both these recent reports is the emphasis they place on coordination. In the past families with problems have found themselves involved with endless different departments and people, and it is hoped that in the future there will be much closer cooperation between departments and the help that they are able to give will be that much more valuable as well as being much more easily obtainable.

CONVERSION TABLES

TABLE XII

Body weight
(approximate equivalents)

Ounces (oz)	Grams (g)	Pounds (lb)	Kilograms (kg)
½	14·2	1	0·45
1	28·4	2	0·91
2	56·7	3	1·36
3	85·1	4	1·81
4	113·4	5	2·27
5	141·8	6	2·72
6	170·1	7	3·18
7	198·5	8	3·63
8	226·8	9	4·08
9	255·2	10	4·54
10	283·5	11	4·99
11	311·9	12	5·44
12	340·2	13	5·90
13	368·6		
14	396·9		
15	425·3		

TABLE XIII

Dosage volume
(approximate equivalents)

Minims (min)	Millilitres (ml)	Fluid ounces (fl oz)	Millilitres (ml)
1½	0·1	½	15
3	0·2	1	30
4	0·25	3½	100
5	0·3	10 (½ pint)	300
8	0·5	17	500
10	0·6	20 (1 pint)	600
12	0·8	35	1000
15	1	40 (1 quart)	1200
30	2		
45	3		
60	4		

1 fluid ounce = approx. 30 ml
1 fluid drachm = approx. 4 ml = 1 tsp.
15 minims = approx. 1 ml

TABLE XIV

Fahrenheit and centigrade scales

To convert Fahrenheit to Centigrade:
Subtract 32 and multiply by $\frac{5}{9}$

Example

Convert 104° Fahrenheit to Centigrade
$$104 - 32 = 72$$
$$72 \times \tfrac{5}{9} = 40$$
$$104°F = 40°C$$

To convert Centigrade to Fahrenheit:
Multiply by $\frac{9}{5}$ and add 32.

Example

Convert 37·5° Centigrade to Fahrenheit
$$37·5 \times \tfrac{9}{5} = 67·5$$
$$67·5 + 32 = 99·5$$
$$37·5° C = 99·5° F$$

Fahrenheit (°F)	Centigrade (°C)	Fahrenheit (°F)	Centigrade (°C)
95·0	35·0	103·0	39·4
95·5	35·3	103·5	39·7
96·0	35·6	104·0	40·0
96·5	35·8	104·5	40·3
97·0	36·1	105·0	40·6
97·5	36·4	105·5	40·8
98·0	36·7	106·0	41·1
98·5	36·9	106·5	41·4
99·0	37·2	107·0	41·7
99·5	37·5	107·5	41·9
100·0	37·8	108·0	42·2
100·5	38·1	108·5	42·5
101·0	38·3	109·0	42·8
101·5	38·6	109·5	43·1
102·0	38·9	110·0	43·3
102·5	39·2		

FURTHER READING

Child Development

How a Baby Grows (in pictures) by A. Gasell (Hamish Hamilton)
Introduction to Development Assessment in the First Year by R. S. Illingworth & Sheridan (Heinemann)
Life Before Birth by Ashley Montague (Four Square Books)
The First Five Years of Life by A. Gesell (Methuen)
The Normal School Child by R. S. Illingworth (Churchill)
The First Nine Months of Life by L. Flanagan (Heinemann)
The New Born Baby by D. Villiamy (Churchill)
Social Development in Young Children by S. Isaacs (Routledge & Kegan Paul)
Babies and Young Children by R. S. & C. M. Illingworth (Churchill)
Language and Mental Development of Children by F. Watts (Harrap)
How Children Learn to Speak: Infant Speech by N. M. Lewis (Harrap)
The Rights of Infants by M. A. Ribble (Columbia University Press)
Human Growth and the Development of Personality by J. H. Kahn (Pergamon Press)
Creative and Mental Growth by V. Lowenseld & W. L. Brittain (Collier-Macmillan)
Patterns of Infant Care by J. & R. Newsome (Penguin Books)
The Children We Teach by S. Isaacs (Routledge & Kegan Paul)
Children with Special Needs in Infant Schools by Lesley Webb (Fontana Books)
Speech and the Development of Mental Processes in the Child. The First Years in School (4-7). Symposium of the Institute of Education (Harrap)
Education through Experience in Infant School Years by E. Mellor (Blackwell)
Education of Young Children by D. E. M. Gardner (Methuen)
Inside the Primary School by J. Blackie (H.M.S.O.)
Working with Children by J. Llewellyn Owens (Bodley Head)
The Lore and Language of School Children by I. & P. Opie (Oxford University Press)
Children in Search of Meaning by Violet Madge (S. C. M. Press)
Life in the Nursery School by Lilian de Lissa (Longmans)
The Nursery Years by S. Isaacs (Routledge & Kegan Paul)
Intellectual Development of Young Children by S. Isaacs (Routledge & Kegan Paul)
Art in the Primary School by Kay Melsi (Blackwell)
Creative play in the Infant School by D. Simpson & D. N. Alderson (Pitman)
Understanding and Guiding Young Children by K. Read Baker & X. F. Fane (Prentice-Hall)

Planning for Play by Lady Allen of Hurtwood (Thames & Hudson)
Play in the Infant School by E. R. Boyce (Methuen)
The First Year in School by E. R. Boyce (Nisbet)
Play in Childhood by M. Lowerfield (Portway Press)
Play with a Purpose for the Under Sevens by E. Matterson (Penguin Books)
All Our Children by Simon Yudkin (Max Reinhardt)
The Communities Children by J. Parfit (Longmans)
√The Child's World by P. Hostler (Pelican)
 Children of Today by S. E. Pococke (Longmans)
√ Literature and the Young Child by J. Cass (Longmans)
 Parents are Welcome by P. McGeeney (Longmans)
The Complete Book of Childrens Play by Hartley and Golderson (Cromwell
    Textbooks Inc.)
Children as Artists by R. R. Tomlinson (Penguin Books)
Learning begins at Home by M. Young & P. McGeeney (Routledge & Kegan
    Paul)
Education through Art by H. Read (Faber)
Creative Crafts for Children by M. Early (Batsford)
The Formative Years (B.B.C. Publications)

Health and Hygiene

Children's Health and Happiness by Marg Brady (Health for All Publishing)
Let's have Healthy Children by Adele Davies (Allen & Unwin)
Everyday Health by Eira Grewer (Pergamon Press)
Health Education edited by B. Edsall (B. Edsall & Co Ltd)
Health of the School Child (H.M.S.O.)
A Handbook of Health Education (H.M.S.O.)
Health in Education (H.M.S.O.)
Child Health and Development by W. B. Ellis (Churchill)
Health and Hygiene by A. L. Banks & J. A. Hislop (University Tutorial Press)
Health Personal and Communal by John Gibson (Faber)
Care of Young Babies by John Gibbens (Churchill)
Care of Children, 1–5 Years by John Gibbens (Churchill)
The Care of Your Feet by Foot Health Education Bureau (Livingstone)
Man Against Disease by Lapage (Abelard-Schuman)
Your Child's Teeth by E. Bacon (Heinemann)
Preventive Medicine Community Health and Social Services by F. D.
    Meredith-Davies (Baillière, Tindall & Cassell)

Nutrition and Infant Feeding

Second Book of Food and Nutrition by Wendy Mathews (Home Economics &
    Domestic Review)
Teach Yourself Nutrition by N. Pyke (English Universities Press)
The Womanly Art of Breast Feeding by the Laleche League (Souvenir
    Press)
A Time for Joy by Martha Blount (A. Wingate)
Your Diet and Your Health by Kenneth Hutchin (Longmans)

First Aid

Accidents to Children by Maurice Ellis (Evans Bros)
First Aid Emergency by E. Yates (Seymour Press)
Preliminary First Aid (St John's Ambulance Association)

Care of the Sick Child

Hospitals and Children by James Robertson (Victor Gollancz)
Play and the Sick Child by E. Noble (Faber)
The Medical Care of Children by S. D. M. Court (Oxford University Press)
Helping Your Child to get Well by L. Challoner (Allen & Unwin)
Play for Convalescent Children by A. M. Smith (Thames & Hudson)

Books which may be Helpful for Students

Golden Treasury of Poetry by L. Untermayer (Collins)
Children's Games by I. P. Opie (Oxford University Press)
Something to do by Septima (Collins)
Collage by M. Connor (Batsford)
Oxford Dictionary of Nursery Rhymes by I. & P. Opie (Oxford University Press)
The Book of a Thousand Poems edited by M. Murray McBain (Evans Bros.)
The Jumbles and Other Nonsense Verse by Edward Lear (Frederick Warne)
Fireside Book of Folksongs by M. Boni & N. Lloyd (Simon & Schuster New York)
The Childrens Song Book by E. Poston (Bodley Head)
Mother Goose Nursery Rhymes (collected edition) by Esme Eve (Blackie)
Mother Goose Nursery Rhymes by Esme Eve (Blackie)
Children's Singing Games by Alice Comme (Dover Publications)
There's Music in Children by E. D. Sheehy (Henry Holt New York)
Ditties for the Nursery by I. & P. Opie (Oxford University Press)
Faber Book of Carols and Xmas Songs by E. Roseberry (Faber)
Dolls—Pleasures and Treasures by A. Fraser (Weidenfeld & Nicolson)
Childrens Toys throughout the Ages by L. Darken (Spring Books)
Make Your Own Dolls by I. Strobl-Wohlshlager (Batsford)
Dolls Houses by J. Latham (A. & C. Black)
Growing with Children through Art by A. C. Snow (Reinhold Publishing Co.)
Paint all Kinds of Pictures by A. Spika (Blackie)
The Tale of Beatrix Potter by M. Lane (Frederick Warne)

Children with Difficulties

The Mentally Retarded Children by Abraham Levinson (Allen & Unwin)
The Young Handicapped Child by A. H. Bowley & L. Gardner (Livingstone)
Children in Care: Disturbed Children by Robert Todd (Longmans)
The Family and the Handicapped Child by Sheila Hewitt in collaboration with J. & E. Newsome (Allen & Unwin)
The Education of Slow Learning Children by R. Gulliford & A. E. Tansley (Oxford University Press)
Residential Child Care Facts and Fallacies by M. Kellmer Pringle (Longmans)
New Backgrounds: the Immigrant Child at Home and School by R. Oakley (Oxford University Press)
Adoption Facts and Fallacies by M. Keller Pringle (Longmans)
Foster Home Care by M. Keller Pringle & R. Dinnage (Longmans)
Poverty and the Fatherless Family by D. Marsden (Allen Lane at the Penguin Press)
Our Deaf Children by F. Bloom (Heinemann)

Speech Difficulties in Childhood by Rhona Williams (Harrap)
Street Children by B. S. Johnson & Marg Mead (Hodder & Stoughton)
Families by Marg Mead (Macmillan)
Family Advice Services by Aryeh Leissner (Longmans)
The Community's Children by J. Parfitt (Longmans)
Investment in Children by K. L. M. Pringle (Longmans)
Four Years Old in an Urban Community by Y. & E. Newsome (Allen & Unwin)
Play Activities for the Retarded Child by B. W. Carlson & D. R. Ginglend (Baillière, Tindall & Cassell)

Index